RADARS: New Concepts

RADARS:
New Concepts

Michel H. Carpentier

*Ecole Nationale Supérieure
de l'Aéronautique, Paris
Ecole Supérieure d'Electricité, Paris
Institut Supérieur d'Electronique, Paris
Radar Technical Manager, Compagnie Française
Thomson-Houston-Hotchkiss-Brandt*

Preface by

Général F. Penin

*Head of Service Technique des
Télécommunications de l'Air*

GORDON AND BREACH Science Publishers

NEW YORK   LONDON   PARIS

PREFACE

It is about thirty years since the electronics men of the era started to think that electromagnetic waves might be used to detect and localise material obstacles in space. From the beginning they tried various ways to arrive at this sought-after result. But rapidly, as it often happens, technology very soon overtook the principles. The magnetron, the only tube for many years capable of furnishing high power, oriented radar towards its classical form, utilising high instantaneous power and short pulses but inside which it remained almost impossible to control the h.f. oscillation frequency.

If the great efforts accomplished during the Second World War brought these radars to a high degree of perfection, it none-the-less remains true that the transmitters used were quite comparable to those with one-stage auto-oscillators of the first generation of transmission in which the engineers, often trying to stabilise the working, rarely attempted to impose on it a more subtle law to follow.

It was necessary that on the side of tubes we felt the approach of the limit with regard to the possibilities of the magnetrons, to encourage research workers to develop tubes on quite different principles and arrive finally at tubes which could be piloted. Simultaneously, the close examination of the conditions of functioning of classical radars and their results led to criticisms of certain well established ideas, such as that connecting the notion of precise and direct measurement of distance to the use of short pulses.

The fact that the useful signal at the receiver input is constantly fluctuating and, this cannot be distinguished, in the limit, from the disturbing signal which is the noise, itself fluctuating, led to the re-examination of the theory of radars from the viewpoint of probabilities.

The technical progress, associated with the progress in the understanding of the phenomena in question, permit to conceive radars based on new principles, which for certain particular applications allow us to hope for performances that were practically inaccessible for classical radars.

This new philosophy of radars has become fundamental. As always, it has appeared only progressively and is found disseminated in a great number of articles in specialised journals, each article being devoted to an aspect of a certain particular problem.

Hence it is with great satisfaction that we welcome today a publication like this, which is the synthesis of these recent ideas.

During the few years, very short in my opinion, that Michel Carpentier has spent in the Service Technique des Télécommunications de l'Air, the head of a team of brilliant engineers, he has set out with great renewed faith to clarify these new concepts, to discuss them with the best of the engineers in the industry, to confirm them by good work both in theoretical as well as in practical aspects.

As professor of radars in many engineering schools, he initially introduced these new notions to his students in a textbook of limited objective but the depth of the work cannot escape the reader.

For the sake of those students who could not always be extremely familiar with all the aspects of calculus of probabilities and analysis, he had to limit the mathematical parts to the essential, so that he could stress the concrete and physical aspects of the phenomena.

A didactic treatise on the one hand, the book of Michel Carpentier presents a great interest to all active engineers, since neglecting voluntarily all that is known about the classical radars, it gives them the principle of specialised articles with all the clarifications resulting from his own researches.

This book is bound to appeal to a large number of people and its success, of which we are convinced, will contribute to encourage further progress, not visualised a few years ago, in this technique that is radar.

F. PENIN

FOREWORD

The present treatise constitutes the second edition of *Radars: Modern Theories* published in 1963. It differs from it, however, in a significant manner because of the following two principle reasons:

(*a*) firstly, the courses given on the basis of the first edition brought to light a number of errors, imprecisions, and certain faults in the logic of the presentation; and

(*b*) secondly, the rapid evolution of conceptions in the subject matter of radars and the declassification of several studies now permit a better treatment of some points, which could only be touched upon in the first edition.

In a more precise manner: the notions in random functions have been completed and regrouped in the first chapter as a preliminary; the considerations over the ambiguity and the pulse compression are developed; considerations on the constant false alarm rate reception and on certain new aspects of the theory of angular measurement have been introduced; and a few problems have been set for the reader.

Many a mistake has been corrected; new errors have certainly been made. We hope that on the whole the outcome is positive.

M. CARPENTIER

CONTENTS

CHAPTER I

INTRODUCTION TO RANDOM FUNCTIONS

1.0 PRELIMINARY REMARKS

This chapter introduces the fundamental properties of random functions. A knowledge of these will help the reader to follow developments in later chapters.

It is not at all our intention to introduce mathematics just for its intrinsic beauty. From this point of view, the treatment will rarely be rigorous. The author realises this, and does not regret it, if this attitude could render random functions less forbidding.

However, this chapter (and therefore the whole book) can appear only because there have been mathematicians, attached to essentially rigorous definitions and proofs, who have approved of the "massacre of mathematics" that follows.

1.1 GENERAL. NOTION OF STATIONARITY

Generally, we understand the notion of a random function by the notion of *noise*. How can we define noise? One definition—among many others—could be the following:

Noise is a random and obstructive phenomenon which accompanies and distorts useful information.

This definition implies that the notion of noise is subjective, i.e. that which is a noise for one person need not be a noise for another. For example, a lecture given by a professor could be recorded by means of a microphone in the form of an electric tension as a function of time

$$V = f(t)$$

Thus, the curve $V = f(t)$, corresponding to this lecture, would seem quite random. However, when it is transformed by an amplifier and a loudspeaker and heard by the speaker, the curve becomes a much less random phenomenon.

For the English-speaking student, the lecture would be less random than for a student who does not know the language. The same phenomenon cannot be a random one for everyone. Similarly, a disturbance could be random for the person or instrument disturbed, but it could also be not random for the source of the disturbance.

In the same way (often as a corollary) a phenomenon could be a hindrance for some and not for others: the professor's lecture would not be a hindrance to the interested students, while it could be to those who are engaged in conversation between themselves. And similarly this conversation of the few students during the lecture

— is not random for those engaged in it;
— is random for those who listen to it (otherwise it is not an interesting conversation);
— is a hindrance to the speaker;
— is not a hindrance to those students who listen to it and not to the lecture.

The nature of randomness (and this is logical, since we have seen that a certain phenomenon was more or less random) does not mean that the phenomenon follows the laws of chance like a number that is drawn at roulette, but that it is at least not exactly predictable.

As an example, let us take D to be the variable distance between an individual and his apartment. This distance is a random phenomenon as a function of time. However, this phenomenon has certain properties:

(a) First, D is always positive: the probability that D shall be negative is zero, by definition. Or again, if we consider the probability that at a given time in the future, D will be between 1,000 and 1,001 km, then this probability is less than the probability that D lies between 0 and 1 km. And the probability that D lies between 50,000 and 50,001 km is, in general, very low, if not zero. This indication of the degree of variation of D, expressed in mathematical terms, is called the *distribution of amplitude* of D.

(b) If we know that at a given time $t = 0$, $D = 15$ km, the probability that at a time $t = 1$ sec D would lie between 14·9 and 15 km is generally greater than the probability that D would lie between ($t = 1$ sec) 15·5 and 15·7 km (assuming that the individual concerned is not a jet pilot), and the probability that D would lie between (at $t = 1$) 30·0 and 30·2 km would almost be zero. Or again, the value of D diminishes to zero once (or twice) regularly every day. These characteristics (b) which indicate the speed with which D varies, when expressed in mathematical terms, give what we call the *frequency distribution* of D, or, in other words, the spectral density of D (connected in a $1-1$ manner with the *autocorrelation function* of D).

We see, therefore, that if the variation of D, as a function of time, is random (at this stage we cannot foresee the exact value of D), then this random phenomenon is subject to the laws of statistics. Here these laws depend on the individual's profession, character, and age. They are well defined in a short interval of time (for example, a month), during which the phenomenon is said to be *stationary*.

But they are less well defined over a long period (for example, over 10 years, since the individual may change his profession, or move elsewhere). This notion of random phenomenon being stationary is better understood by means of examples.

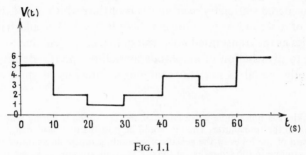

FIG. 1.1

(1) Let us consider a random function obtained in the following way: a normally perfect dice is thrown every 10 sec and the number, V, on the uppermost face is noted. We thus obtain a function discontinuous with respect to time, as shown in fig. 1.1. The distribution of amplitude here is simple. It is expressed by saying that all the integers from 1 to 6 have an equal probability of being on the uppermost face and that every other value of V has zero probability.

The spectral density of $V(t)$ is not calculated in a simple way, but we know that if we replace the interval of 10 sec by an interval of 1 sec, then the distribution of amplitude would remain unchanged while the spectral density would indicate an increased rapidity in the ratio of $1:10$.

As long as the dice is normal, the casting of it impartial, and the clock keeps good time, the function $V(t)$ is stationary. But if over a period of time, for some reason or other, the centre of gravity of the dice is moved towards one of the faces, say 6, then the probability of 6 appearing becomes less and less, and we could no longer consider $V(t)$ to be stationary. Similarly, if the clock regularly loses we could no longer consider the phenomenon to be stationary. However, if the displacement of the centre of gravity is gradual with respect to the interval of 10 sec (i.e. it takes a day for the probability of 6 to pass from 1/6 to $1\cdot05/6$ or it takes a day for the interval to pass from 10 sec to $10\cdot5$ sec), we could admit that over an interval of 1 hour the phenomenon is sufficiently stationary.

(2) Let us consider a directional aerial (for example, an aerial of a panoramic radar), constantly rotating round a vertical axis at a speed of 6 revolutions per minute near a transmitter sending out a perfectly stationary noise from a certain

distance. It is clear that the gain of the aerial in the direction of the transmitter varies as a function of time: in particular, when the radar beam passes over the transmitter the average power received by the aerial will be high, while it will be very low when the radar beam is turned in the opposite direction. More precisely, if the radar beam has a width of 1° (in azimuth), the diagram of the aerial will resemble leaves with lobes of similar width such that the mean power received will be almost constant during a time similar to that which the aerial takes to turn through 1°, i.e. about 30 ms. Thus the noise received by the aerial could be considered stationary over intervals of time which are of the order of a thousandth of a second or less: during these intervals it would have the same characteristics as the transmitted noise (modulo a coefficient due to attenuation) with regard to distribution of amplitude as well as spectral density. The noise received by the aerial is not stationary over intervals of time of the order of 0·1 sec.

But the problem is not simple if we consider the few seconds during which the aerial is turned away from the transmitter. Then it would be possible to consider in certain instances that the diagram of the lobes of the aerial corresponding to the direction of the transmitter (side lobes) is random in the sense that, if the (difficult) measurements giving it have not been made, we do not know them *a priori* as it depends both on the antenna and its environment, although we know statistically the characteristics concerning these lobes (amplitude and spectrum distribution) for such antennae in such positions. So during a period of the order of a few seconds, and for want of better evaluation, the noise shall be considered in the computations as being stationary, but with a distribution of amplitude and spectral density taking into account that of the transmitted noise and of the side lobes.

If now we average the noise received during 1 sec (filtering the signal in a narrow band receiver, with a width of the order of 1 Hz), we obtain a practically periodic signal with a period of 10 sec, which is no longer random: this is obvious.

All these useful considerations being made, the following sections only treat stationary random functions, i.e. those whose statistical properties are invariant with respect to any change of origin of time[1].

1.2 NOTION OF DISTRIBUTION OF AMPLITUDE

1.2.1 General

1.2.1.1 Let us consider a random function $D(t)$. By

$$p(D_0)\, dD$$

we define the probability that at any given instant the value of $D(t)$ lies between

---

[1] In fact we admit the ergodic hypothesis, which assumes that the means in the time measured over a sample of the random function are the same as the means of the set of different possible realisations of the random function.

D_0 and $D_0 + \mathrm{d}D$. $p(D)$, which is a density probability, characterises the distribution of the amplitude of D. It would be useful to recall certain mathematical properties connected with these facts.

1.2.1.2 First, we have by definition

$$\int_{-\infty}^{+\infty} p(D)\,\mathrm{d}D = 1$$

1.2.1.3 It is convenient for the purpose of calculations to associate to $p(D)$ a function called a "characteristic function" $\varphi(u)$ such that $\varphi(-2\pi f)$ is the Fourier transform of $p(D)$, and we know that the characteristic function of a sum of two independent variables is the product of the characteristic functions of each of these variables. We also note that generally $\varphi(u)$ has no simple physical interpretation.

1.2.1.4 We define the moments of the order 1, 2, etc., as being the mean values of D, D^2, etc., as follows:

$$\text{Moment of order 1} = \int_{-\infty}^{+\infty} Dp(D)\,\mathrm{d}D,$$

$$\text{Moment of order 2} = \int_{-\infty}^{+\infty} D^2 p(D)\,\mathrm{d}D,$$

etc.

In the particular case in which the moment of order 1 is zero, the moment of order 2 is called the "mean quadratic value" whose square root is the root mean square; and in electronics we usually call the moment of order 2 of a random function whose mean value is zero the "power" of the function (the square of the r.m.s.). And in the case of a gaussian variable of mean value zero, the mean quadratic value (power) is called the variance, and the root mean square, the standard deviation.

1.2.1.5 It can be easily shown that if we denote by M_1, M_0, ... the moments of order 1, 2, ... respectively, the characteristic function $\varphi(u)$ can be written as

$$\varphi(u) = 1 + \mathrm{j}M_1 u + (\mathrm{j})^2 M_2 \frac{u^2}{2!} + (\mathrm{j})^3 M_3 \frac{u^3}{3!} + \ldots$$

1.2.1.6 It follows that when we add two independent variables, the moment of order 1 of the sum is the sum of the moments of order 1 of each of the variables.

If, on the other hand, the moment of order 1 of one of the variables is zero, then the moment of order 2 of the sum is the sum of the moments of order 2.

1.2.1.7 If we consider the variable $Y = kD$, it is evident that we have

$$p_1(Y)\, dY = p(D)\, dD,$$

where we denote the density probability of Y by $p_1(Y)$. Hence,

$$p_1(Y) = \frac{1}{k}p(D)$$

$$p_1(Y) = \frac{1}{k}p\left(\frac{Y}{k}\right)$$

It follows that the characteristic function of Y is $\varphi(ku)$.

1.2.1.8 It is also useful to recall, for the purpose of calculations, that if $p(D)$ is symmetrical about $D = 0$, and since $p(D)$ tends to zero as D tends to infinity, $\varphi(u)$ is obtained by taking the Laplace transform of $p(D)u(D)$ (where $u(D)$ is the unit step), by replacing there the Laplace operator by $(-ju)$ and by taking twice the real part of the expression obtained, thus obtaining a function $\varphi(u)$ symmetrical about $u = 0$.

Once these properties have been recalled the notion of distribution of amplitude will be better understood through numerical examples.

1.2.2 First example

Let us consider a random function $V(t)$ defined in the following way:

(*a*) $V(t)$ is constant for values of t lying between $t = 0$ and $t = 1$,

between $t = 1$ and $t = 2$,

etc.

(*b*) In each of these intervals, $V(t)$ has a 50 per cent chance of being equal to 3, and a 50 per cent chance of being equal to 1.

(*c*) The drawing of lots which give the values of V in each of these intervals are independent (see fig. 1.2).

We could show the distribution of amplitude by simply saying that V has

a probability of 0·5 to be equal to 3,

a probability of 0·5 to be equal to 1,

a probability of zero to be different from 3 or 1,

and we write

$$p(V) = \tfrac{1}{2}[\delta(V-1)+\delta(V-3)],$$

where $\delta(t)$ is the Dirac pulse.

The mean value of $V(t)$ being equal to 2, it is convenient to write $V(t)$ in the form

$$V(t) = 2 + v(t)$$

where $v(t)$ is a random variable of zero mean value, symmetrical about zero (the moments of odd order being zero), whose power (mean quadratic value) is equal to

$$\tfrac{1}{2}(1+1) = 1$$

and whose moment of order 4 is equal to 1 (i.e. the square of the power) and all the moments of even order are all equal to 1.

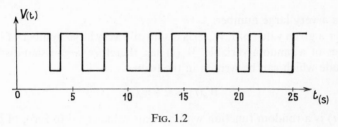

FIG. 1.2

We also find directly that the characteristic function of $v(t)$ is of the form

$$\varphi(u) = \tfrac{1}{2}[\exp(-ju) + \exp(+ju)]$$

because the probability of $v(t)$ is written in the form

$$\tfrac{1}{2}[\delta(v+1) + \delta(v-1)],$$

i.e. we have

$$\varphi(u) = \cos u = 1 - \frac{u^2}{2!} + \frac{u^4}{4!} + \ldots,$$

which confirms (if need be) that all the moments of even order are equal to 1.

If we now study the random function $W_1(t)$ defined by

$$2W_1(t) = V(t) + V(t-1),$$

we could write it in the form

$$2W_1(t) = 4 + v(t) + v(t-1),$$

in which $v(t)$ and $v(t-1)$ are two independent variables having the same density probability, i.e. $W_1(t) = 2 + w_1(t)$, where $w_1(t)$ is a random function of mean value zero, and whose characteristic function is equal to

$$\cos\frac{u}{2} \times \cos\frac{u}{2} = \left[\cos\left(\frac{u}{2}\right)\right]^2 \qquad \text{(from sub-sections 1.2.13 and 1.2.17)}$$

i.e.

$$\frac{1+\cos u}{2} = 1 - \frac{u^2}{4} + \frac{u^4}{2 \cdot 4!} - \dots$$

The power (mean quadratic value) of $w_1(t)$ is therefore equal to 0·5, which we obtained directly because it is twice the power of $v(t)/2$.

The moment of order 4 of $w_1(t)$ is also equal to 0·5, i.e. twice the square of the power, and all the moments of even order are also equal to 0·5.

Finally, let us study the random function $W_n(t)$ defined by

$$nW_n(t) = V(t) + V(t-1) + \dots V(t-n)$$

where n is a very large number.

Here, for a given value of t, $W_n(t)$ is a sum of a very large number of independent values of a random variable. $W_n(t)$ has, therefore, a gaussian distribution of amplitude which can be written in the form

$$W_n(t) = 2 + w_n(t)$$

where $w_n(t)$ is a random function with a mean value equal to zero, of gaussian distribution, and whose variance is n times that of $v(t)/n$, i.e.

$$n\left(\frac{1}{n^2}\right) = \frac{1}{n}.$$

The distribution of amplitude of $w_n(t)$ is represented by

$$p(w_n) = \frac{n^{\frac{1}{2}}}{\sqrt{2\pi}} \exp\left(-\frac{nw_n^2}{2}\right)$$

In other words, during 70 per cent of the time $W_n(t)$ is between $(2 - 1/\sqrt{n})$ and $(2 + 1/\sqrt{n})$.

The moment of order 4 of $w_n(t)$ is known to be equal to three times the square of the variance of $w_n(t)$.

1.2.3 Second example

Let us now consider the random function $x(t)$ defined in the following way:

$$x(t) = \sin[\varphi(t)]$$

where

$\varphi(t)$ is constant between 0 and 1 sec and between 1 and 2 sec, etc.

The values of $\varphi(t)$ in each of these intervals are independent.

And finally, $\varphi(t)$ could assume all values between 0 and 2π with the same probability.

For a value of x there corresponds two values of $\varphi(t)$ lying between 0 and 2π such that the probability that x lies between x_0 and $x_0 + dx$ is equal to the probability that φ lies between $\varphi_0 = $ Arc sin x_0 and $\varphi_0 + d\varphi$ plus the probability that φ lies between $\pi - \varphi_0$ and $\pi - \varphi_0 - d\varphi$. (Arc sin x is the principal value of arc sin x.)

Therefore,

$$p_2(x_0)\, dx = 2p_1(\varphi_0)\, d\varphi,$$

φ_0 being between $-\pi/2$ and $+\pi/2$, with

$$\int_0^{2\pi} p_1(\varphi)\, d\varphi = 1; \quad p_1(\varphi) = \frac{1}{2\pi},$$

and

$$dx = \cos\varphi\, d\varphi = d\varphi\sqrt{1-x^2},$$

$p_2(x)$ being the distribution of amplitude of x, and $p_1(\varphi)$ being that of φ.

Thus,

$$\boxed{p_2(x) = \frac{1}{\pi\sqrt{1-x^2}}}$$

$|x|$ not exceeding 1.

As an indispensable verification we calculate

$$\int_{-1}^{+1} p_2(x)\, dx = \frac{2}{\pi}\int_0^1 \frac{1}{\sqrt{1-x^2}}\, dx = 1.$$

I.2.4   Third example

Let us now consider a random function

$$Y(t) = y^2(t)$$

where $y(t)$ is a gaussian random function with a mean value equal to zero, and with a variance equal to 1 [$Y(t)$ is the output of a quadratic detector which receives a gaussian noise].

The mean value of $Y(t)$ is evidently 1, so that we can write

$$Y(t) = 1 + \mathcal{Y}(t)$$

where $\mathcal{Y}(t)$ is a random variable of mean value equal to 0.

The distribution of amplitude of $\mathcal{Y}(t)$ could be shown by the moments of order 2, 3, 4, etc. The moment of order 2 is written as:

$$\text{mean value of } (y^2(t)-1)^2 = \overline{(y^2-1)^2}$$
$$= \overline{y^4}-\overline{2y^2}+1.$$

The moment of order $2r$ of y (a gaussian variable of mean value zero) is equal to 1, 3, . . . $(2r-1)$ times the rth power of the moment of order 2. The moment of order 2 is therefore equal to 2.

The moment of order 3 is

$$\overline{(y^2-1)^3} = \overline{y^6}-\overline{3y^4}+\overline{3y^2}-1$$
$$= 15-9+3-1 = 8.$$

The moment of order 4 is

$$\overline{(y^2-1)^4} = \overline{y^8}-\overline{4y^6}+\overline{6y^4}-\overline{4y^2}+1$$
$$= 105-60+18-4+1 = 60.$$

Thus the characteristic function associated with $\mathcal{Y}(t)$ is written in the form

$$\varphi(u) = 1-u^2-\mathrm{j}\,\frac{4u^3}{3}+\frac{5u^4}{2}+ \ldots$$

1.2.5 Important remark

A random function is often found to be the sum of a known function and a random function of mean value 0. This decomposition very often enables us to simplify the calculations. Thus in particular we can always write—and this is often useful—a random function as being equal to the sum of a constant, equal to its mean value, and of a random function of mean value 0.

In the sections that follow *we shall consider only random functions with a mean value equal to* 0.

1.3 NOTION OF SPECTRAL DISTRIBUTION $A^2(f)$

1.3.1 Let us assume a random function to last as long as we could imagine (for an infinite time, t), conserving all its statistical properties (since it is stationary), and let us assume, for simplicity, that its mean value is 0 (and it is known from previous observations that there is no loss of generality here).

More precisely, let us consider the function $v(t)$ defined in sub-section 1.2.2 and shown in fig. 1.2 (which in fact shows $v(t)+2$).

We could consider the function which is equal to $v(t)$ for $0 < t < 3$ and zero for t to be outside the interval of time $0-3$. It can be written in the form

$$[u(t)-u(t-3)],$$

where $u(t)$ is the unit step, and we could calculate

$$\int_0^3 v(t)\, dt = 3,$$

$$\frac{1}{T}\int_0^T v(t)\, dt \qquad \text{for} \qquad T = 3,$$

the expression being equal to 1: this is the mean value of $v(t)$ in the interval 0, T.
We could also calculate

$$\frac{1}{T}\int_0^T v^2(t)\, dt \qquad \text{for} \qquad T = 3,$$

an expression being equal to 1. This is the mean value of the power of $v(t)$ in the interval 0, T. We could also calculate the Fourier transform of the sample of duration T thus defined of $v(t)$, which can be written as

$$A_{T=3}(f) = \int_0^{T=3} v(t)\exp(-2\pi jft)\, dt = \frac{1}{2\pi jf}[1-\exp(-3\times 2\pi jf)],$$

$$A_T(f) = \frac{(1-\cos 6\pi f)+j\sin 6\pi f}{2\pi jf}.$$

We find that $A_T(f) = A_T^*(-f)$, the asterisk indicating that the function A_T^* is the complex conjugate of A_T, and that

$$A_T(f)\cdot A_T(-f) = |A_T^2(f)| = \text{even function of } f,$$

$$\boxed{A_3^2(f) = \frac{\sin^2 (3\pi f)}{\pi^2 f^2}}$$

and finally, we define

$$\frac{A_T^2(f)}{T} = \frac{\sin^2 (3\pi f)}{3\pi^2 f^2} \qquad \text{for} \qquad T = 3.$$

In order to clarify matters, let us assume that $v(t)$ is expressed in volts:

$A_T(f)$ will be expressed in (volt · sec),

$|A_T(f)|^2$ will be expressed in (volt · sec)^2,

$\dfrac{|A_T^2(f)|}{T}$ will be expressed in (volts)^2 · sec or in (volts)^2/Hz.

It is also clear that

$$A_T(0) = \int_0^T v(t)\, dt$$

and that

$$\frac{A_T(0)}{T} = \frac{1}{T} \int_0^T v(t)\, dt,$$

and we verify this here because

$$A_3(0) = 3, \qquad \frac{A_3(0)}{3} = 1.$$

And by Parseval's theorem we have

$$\int_0^T v^2(t)\, dt = \int_{-\infty}^{+\infty} |A_T(f)|^2\, df,$$

i.e.

$$\frac{1}{T} \int_0^T v^2(t)\, dt = \int_{-\infty}^{+\infty} \frac{|A_T(f)|^2}{T}\, df = 1,$$

and this is verified for $T = 3$.

Figure 1.3 shows the variations of $|A_T(f)|^2/T$ for $T = 3$.

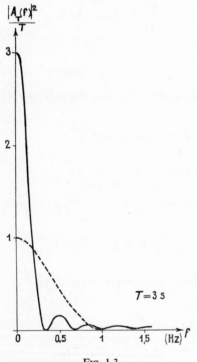

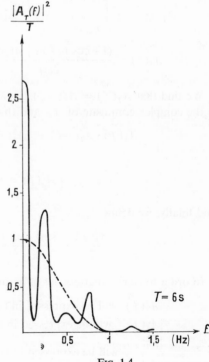

Fig. 1.3   Fig. 1.4

1.3.2 If we consider a sample of the same function $v(t)$ but longer, say, with length $T = 6$, then we obtain

$$u(t) - 2u(t-3) + 2u(t-4) - u(t-6),$$

$$\frac{1}{6} \int_0^6 v(t) \, dt = \frac{2}{3} = \frac{A_6(0)}{6},$$

$$A_6(0) = |A_6(0)| = 4; \qquad \frac{|A_6^2(0)|}{6} = \frac{16}{6} = 2.7$$

$$\frac{1}{6} \int_0^6 v^2(t) \, dt = 1 = \int_{-\infty}^{+\infty} \frac{|A_6(f)|^2}{6} \, df.$$

Figure 1.4 shows the variations of $|A_T(f)|^2/T$ for $T = 6$.

1.3.3 The sample of $v(t)$ lying between 0 and $T = 12$ (see fig. 1.2) gives

$$\frac{1}{12} \int_0^{12} v(t) \, dt = \frac{1}{6} = \frac{A_{12}(0)}{12}, \qquad A_{12}(0) = 2,$$

$$\frac{|A_{12}(0)|^2}{12} = \frac{4}{12} = 0.33,$$

$$\frac{1}{12} \int_0^{12} v^2(t) \, dt = 1 = \int_{-\infty}^{+\infty} \frac{|A_{12}(f)|^2}{12} \, df.$$

Figure 1.5 shows the variations of $|A_T(f)|^2/T$ for $T = 12$.

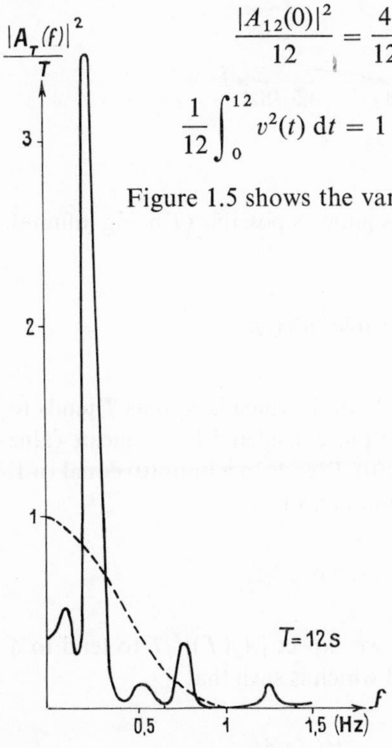

FIG. 1.5

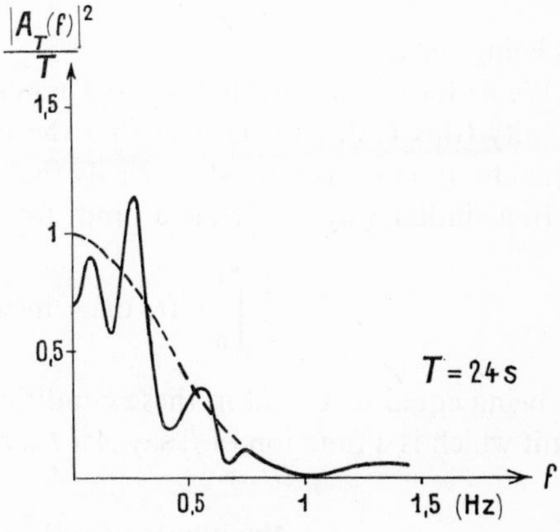

FIG. 1.6

1.3.4   The sample of $v(t)$ lying between 0 and $T = 24$ (see fig. 1.2) gives

$$\frac{1}{24}\int_0^{24} v(t)\ dt = \frac{4}{24} = \frac{1}{6} = \frac{A_2(0)}{24}, \quad A_{24}(0) = 4,$$

$$\frac{|A_{24}(0)|^2}{24} = \frac{16}{24} = 0\cdot 67,$$

$$\frac{1}{24}\int_0^{24} v^2(t)\ dt = 1 = \int_{-\infty}^{+\infty} \frac{|A_{24}(f)|^2}{24}\ df.$$

Figure 1.6 shows the variations of $A_T(f)^2/T$ for $T = 24$.

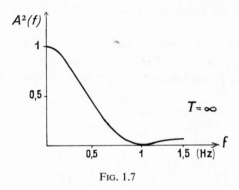

Fig. 1.7

1.3.5   By generalising this process for T as large as possible (T being infinite), we define a limit, for T infinite, of

$$\frac{1}{T}\int_0^T v(t)\ dt = \text{mean value of } v(t),$$

as being zero.

We deduce from this that $A_T(0)/T$ tends to a limit which is zero as T tends to infinity (this is due to the fact that the function considered has a mean value equal to 0). However, we show easily that $A_T^2(0)/T$ tends to a limit (0) equal to 1.

In a similar way we define a limit, for T infinite, of

$$\frac{1}{T}\int_0^T v^2(t)\ dt = \text{mean value of } v^2(t),$$

as being equal to 1, and in these conditions we expect $|A_T(f)|^2/T$ to tend to a limit which is a function of f, say $A^2(f)$, and which is such that

$$\text{the power of } v(t) = \int_{-\infty}^{+\infty} A^2(f)\ df.$$

In the example chosen, the function $A^2(f)$ is shown by the curve in fig. 1.7 (the method for obtaining this curve will be described in section 1.6).

The above mentioned relation explains why we call $A^2(f)$ the spectral density (of power) of the random function $v(t)$.

If $v(t)$ is expressed in volts, then $A^2(f)$ will be expressed in (volts)^2 per Hz.

Since $|A_T(f)|^2/T$ is an even function of f, its limit $A^2(f)$ is also the same, so that we could write

$$\text{the power of } v = \int_0^\infty 2A^2(f) \, df,$$

and thus $2A^2(f)$ represents the density of $v(t)$ when we restrict ourselves to positive frequencies, which is often convenient for purposes of calculations.

1.3.6 Generalisation

By considering only random functions of a mean value zero, we see that we are led to define a spectral density $A^2(f)$ which represents the value, for T sufficiently large (in the sense of the law of large numbers), of the square of the modulus of the Fourier transform of a sample of duration T of the random function, divided by the duration T of the sample.

The function $A^2(f)$, which has the dimensions of a power density (with respect to the frequency f), is a real function of the frequency f, and an even function whose integral over all frequencies is equal to the power of the random function.

Also the function $A^2(f)$, which characterises the spectral distribution of the random function, has a physical meaning because if the random function considered shows the variations of the voltage of an electrical current as a function of time we obtain the diagram experimentally, with the help of an apparatus called a spectral analyser.

1.3.7 Definition

When $A^2(f)$ is constant in a certain frequency band (between f_1 and f_2, for example) we say that the random phenomenon is white in this frequency band.

1.4 PASSAGE IN A LINEAR FILTER

1.4.1 Theorem

Let us consider a random function $x(t)$ fed through a linear filter which is characterised by its transfer function $F(p)$. If $A_e^2(f)$ is the spectral density of $x(t)$, then what is the spectral density of $y(t)$ at the exit of the filter (see fig. 1.8)?

Consider a sample of duration T of the function $x(t)$ whose Fourier transform is $A_{Te}(f)$. We know that the sample of $y(t)$ would have

$$A_{Ts}(f) = A_{Te}(f) \cdot F(2\pi j f)$$

as the Fourier transform. Thus we have

$$\frac{|A_{Ts}^2(f)|}{T} = \frac{|A_{Te}^2(f)|}{T} \times |F(2\pi j f)|^2$$

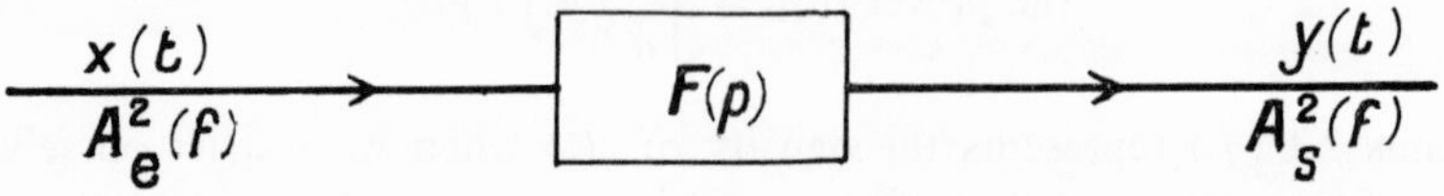

FIG. 1.8

and by passing to the limit as T tends to infinity,

$$A_s^2(f) = A_e^2(f) \cdot |F(2\pi j f|^2$$

REMARK

We shall note that just as section 1.3 does not rigorously justify the right to define $A^2(f)$, similarly the above reasoning cannot in any circumstances be taken for a proof. At most, it could be taken as an explanation. Any person with an alert mathematical mind would easily discover that the above reasoning in fact proves nothing at all. All the same, in the physical sense (particularly for use in electronics) it is very satisfactory; and, it is always reassuring to know that the formula has been proved rigorously (cf. section 9.2 of *Complements de Mathematiques à l'usage des Ingénieurs de l'électronique et des télécommunications* (A. Blanc-Lapierre), by General A. Angot, Editions de la Revue d'optique). Henceforward wherever insufficient proofs are supplied the reader must refer to authors who are more rigorous in their treatment, especially to Angot.

1.4.2 Example

Let us reconsider the example given in sub-section 1.2.2. It was seen that $v(t)$ had a spectral density represented by fig. 1.7 which could be written (see section 1.6) as

$$A^2(f) = \left(\frac{\sin \pi f}{\pi f}\right)^2$$

Our aim is to determine the spectral density of the random function

$$w_1(t) = \tfrac{1}{2}[v(t) + v(t-1)].$$

We obtain it easily by assuming $w_1(t)$ to be obtained from $v(t)$, as shown in fig. 1.9, and the transfer function of w_1/v to be equal to

$$F(p) = \frac{1 + \exp(-p)}{2}.$$

Thus the spectral density of $w_1(t)$ can be written as

$$\left[\frac{\sin \pi f}{\pi f}\right]^2 \times \frac{1}{4} \times |1 + \exp(-2\pi j f)|^2,$$

$$\left[\frac{\sin \pi f}{\pi f}\right]^2 \times \cos^2 \pi f = \left[\frac{\sin 2\pi f}{2\pi f}\right]^2.$$

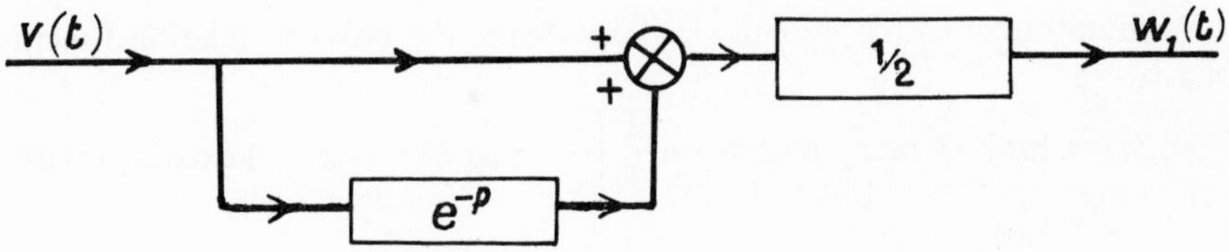

FIG. 1.9

1.5 APPLICATIONS OF THE THEOREM OF CONVOLUTION AUTOCORRELATION FUNCTION $\rho(\tau)$

1.5.1 Theorem of convolution

Let $X(t)$ and $Y(t)$ be two functions whose Fourier transforms are $\Phi_X(f)$ and $\Phi_Y(f)$ respectively. We can prove the following relation, which is useful in many fields:

$$\int_{-\infty}^{+\infty} X(t) \cdot Y(t - t_0)\, dt = \int_{-\infty}^{+\infty} \Phi_X(f) \cdot \Phi_Y(-f) \exp(2\pi j f t_0)\, df.$$

By writing $Y(t) = X(t)$ and $t_0 = 0$, we return to the Parseval theorem already used in 1.3.1, because the relation becomes

$$\int_{-\infty}^{+\infty} X(t)\, dt = \int_{-\infty}^{+\infty} |\Phi_X(f)|^2\, df.$$

1.5.2 Cross-correlation function

Let $x(t)$ and $y(t)$ be two random functions. Consider two samples of duration T (between $t = 0$ and $t = T$) of each of these functions, whose Fourier transforms are $A_{Tx}(f)$ and $A_{Ty}(f)$ respectively. We could then write

$$\frac{1}{T}\int_0^T x(t) \cdot y(t - \tau)\, dt = \frac{1}{T}\int_{-\infty}^{+\infty} A_{Tx}(f) \cdot A_{Ty}(f) \exp(2\pi j f \tau)\, df.$$

c

By making T tend to infinity we see that the mean value of $[x(t) \cdot y(t-\tau)]$, called the function of cross-correlation of x by y,

$$\overline{x(t) \cdot y(t-\tau)} = \rho_{xy}(\tau)$$

has in the limit (as T tends to infinity) its Fourier transform equal to the limit of

$$\frac{A_{Tx}(f) \cdot A_{Ty}(-f)}{T}.$$

Permutating x and y we can similarly define the cross-correlation function of y by x:

$$\rho_{yx}(\tau) = \text{limit}, T \text{ being infinite, of } \frac{1}{T} \int_{-\infty}^{+\infty} A_{Ty}(f) \cdot A_{Tx}(-f) \exp(2\pi j f\tau) \, df$$

$$= \rho_{xy}^*(-\tau).$$

In the particular case discussed in section 1.4, where $y(t)$ is the output from a filter whose transfer function if $F(p)$ receiving $x(t)$

$$A_{Ty}(f) = A_{Tx}(f) \cdot F(2\pi j f),$$

such that $\rho_{xy}(\tau)$ is the limit, as T tends to infinity, of

$$\frac{1}{T} \int_{-\infty}^{+\infty} |A_{Tx}^2(f)| \cdot F(-2\pi j f) \exp(2\pi j f) \, df,$$

$\rho_{xy}(\tau)$ has its Fourier transform equal to

$$A_x^2(f) \cdot F^*(2\pi j f).$$

If x and y were real, $\rho_{xy}(\tau)$ and $\rho_{yx}(\tau)$ are also real, such that

$$\rho_{xy}(-\tau) = \rho_{yx}(\tau)$$

1.5.3 Autocorrelation function. Wiener's theorem

If $y(t) \equiv x(t)$, we could write

$$\frac{1}{T} \int_0^T x(t) \cdot x(t-\tau) \, dt = \frac{1}{T} \int_{-\infty}^{+\infty} A_{Tx}(f) \cdot A_{Tx}(-f) \exp(2\pi j f\tau) \, df.$$

Taking the limit as T becomes infinite, we have

$$\rho_{xy}(\tau) = \overline{x(t) \cdot x(t-\tau)} = \int_{-\infty}^{+\infty} A_x^2(f) \cdot \exp(2\pi j f\tau) \, df.$$

We thus define the autocorrelation function of the random function $x(t)$—denoted by $\rho_{xx}(\tau)$ or, when there is no confusion possible, by $\rho_x(\tau)$ or $\rho(\tau)$—as the mean value of the product of the function $x(t)$ by itself delayed by time τ, $x(t-\tau)$. And we show that this *autocorrelation function* of the function $x(t)$

has its Fourier transform equal to the *spectral density* of the function. Therefore the knowledge of the function $\rho(\tau)$ could replace that of the spectral density for characterising the spectral distribution of the random function.

Mathematically, since $A^2(f)$ is an even function of f, *the function $\rho(\tau)$ presents itself as an even function of* τ, such that

$$\rho(\tau) = \rho(-\tau),$$

$$\rho'(0) = 0,$$

($\rho(\tau)$ is maximal for $\tau = 0$).

The value of $\rho(\tau)$ for $\tau = 0$ represents the mean value of the square of the function $x(t)$.

If, as justified earlier, we consider only those random functions which have their mean value equal to 0, then $\rho(0)$ *represents the power of the random function*.

If, on the other hand, we consider sufficiently large values of τ, it is evident in the physical sense that $x(t)$ and $x(t-\tau)$ will become independent variables, and that the mean of $x(t) \cdot x(t-\tau)$ would be equal to the square of the mean value of $x(t)$. If this is assumed to be zero, as we have admitted, then we can deduce that $\rho(\tau)$ *tends to zero as τ tends to infinity*.

Physically speaking, the fact that $\rho(\tau)$ is very large indicates that there is great resemblance between $x(t)$ and $x(t-\tau)$. If $x(t)$ is large and positive then $x(t)$ and $x(t-\tau)$ have the same sign more often than opposite signs. If $\rho(\tau)$ is large and negative $x(t)$ and $x(t-\tau)$ have opposite signs more often than the same sign.

In other words, if $\rho(\tau)$ tends very slowly to zero, then $x(t)$ changes slowly; but if $\rho(\tau)$ tends very rapidly to zero, then $x(t)$ also changes very rapidly.

We may point out that it could happen that $\rho(\tau) = 0$ without $x(t)$ and $x(t-\tau)$ being independent. This is the case when $x(t) = \sin t$ and $\tau = \pi/2$.

1.5.4 Differentiation of $\rho(\tau)$ when $x(t)$ is real

We write

$$\rho(\tau) = \text{limit}, T \text{ being infinite, of } \frac{1}{T} \int_0^T x(t) \cdot x(t-\tau) \, dt,$$

$$\rho'(\tau) = \text{limit}, T \text{ being infinite, of } -\frac{1}{T} \int_0^T x(t) \cdot x'(t-\tau) \, dt$$

$$= -\rho_{xx'}(\tau) = -\rho_{x'x}(-\tau)$$

$$= \lim_{T \to \infty} \left[-\frac{1}{T} \int_0^T x'(t) \cdot x(t+\tau) \, dt \right]$$

$$\rho''(\tau) = \lim_{T \to \infty} \left[-\frac{1}{T} \int_0^T x'(t) \cdot x'(t+\tau) \, dt \right].$$

The second derivative of the autocorrelation function of $x(t)$ is the same as the autocorrelation function of the first derivative of $x(t)$ except for the change of sign.

1.6 EXAMPLES OF EVALUATION OF $\rho(\tau)$ AND $A^2(f)$ (AUTOCORRELATION FUNCTIONS AND SPECTRAL DENSITIES)

1.6.1 Autocorrelation function associated with a rectangular spectrum

When our considerations are restricted to positive frequencies (cf. the remark at the end of sub-section 1.3.5), the spectral density is zero outside the interval $(f_0 - \Delta f/2, f_0 + \Delta f/2)$ and equal to b inside that interval (the energy of the signal being equal to $b\Delta f$).

In other words, for f positive, we have

$$2A^2(f) = b[u(f - f_0 + \Delta f/2) - u(f - f_0 - \Delta f/2)],$$

$u(t)$ being the unit step.

Using the remark in sub-section 1.2.18 but adapted to the present case, we deduce that $\rho(\tau)$ is equal to twice the real part of

$$\frac{b}{2} \times \frac{1}{2\pi j\tau} \{\exp[-2\pi j\tau(f_0 - \Delta f/2)] - \exp[-2\pi j\tau(f_0 + \Delta f/2)]\}$$

i.e.

$$\rho(\tau) = b\Delta f \cdot \cos(2\pi\tau f_0) \cdot \frac{\sin \pi\tau\Delta f}{\pi\tau\Delta f}$$

It is easily verified that $\rho(0) = b\Delta f$.

1.6.2 Calculation of the autocorrelation function

Let us consider a white noise ($A^2(f)$ being constant in the zone of useful frequencies) after passage through a filter whose transfer function has a circular form in the complex plane. It passes through the origin and is symmetrical about the real axis (see fig. 1.10). The case is

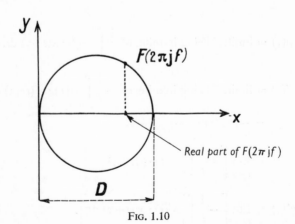

Fig. 1.10

one where the filter is a circuit RC, CR, LR, RL, or an amplifier whose charge is a parallel-tuned circuit.

In this case, the spectral density of the filtered noise is of the form

$$K_1|F(2\pi jf)|^2.$$

If $F(p)$ is the transfer function of the filter, this spectral density is the Fourier transform of the autocorrelation function $\rho(\tau)$ of the filtered noise. The correspondence between $K_1|F(2\pi jf)|^2$ and $\rho(\tau)$ is $1-1$.

On the other hand, if we denote by $G(p)$ the Laplace transform of $\rho(t)u(t)$, the real part of $G(2\pi jf)$ is equal to $K_1|F(2\pi jf)|^2$ (cf. sub-section 1.2.18).

But it is evident that

$$|F(2\pi jf)|^2 = D \times \text{the real part of } F(2\pi jf).$$

As the relation between $\rho(\tau)$ and $\rho(\tau)u(t)$, like that between $\rho(\tau)u(t)$ and $G(p)$, is $1-1$, it follows that it is possible to find only one function $G(p)$ whose real part is equal to $|F(2\pi jf)^2|$ (modulo a factor) and which satisfies the problem (i.e. such that it implies $\rho(\infty) = 0$ or that the limit of $pG(p)$ for $p = 0$ is equal to 0).

If therefore $F(p)$ is such that $pF(p)$ tends to zero as p tends to zero, then $F(p)$ is the required function $G(p)$.

APPLICATION

Calculation of the autocorrelation function of a signal, output of a pentode amplifier when the input is a white noise (see fig. 1.11).

The transfer function $F(p)$ of such a filter is given by

$$\frac{1}{F(p)} = K_2\left[Cp + R + \frac{1}{Lp}\right],$$

$$F(p) = \frac{K_3 p}{(p+\lambda)^2 + \Omega^2}$$

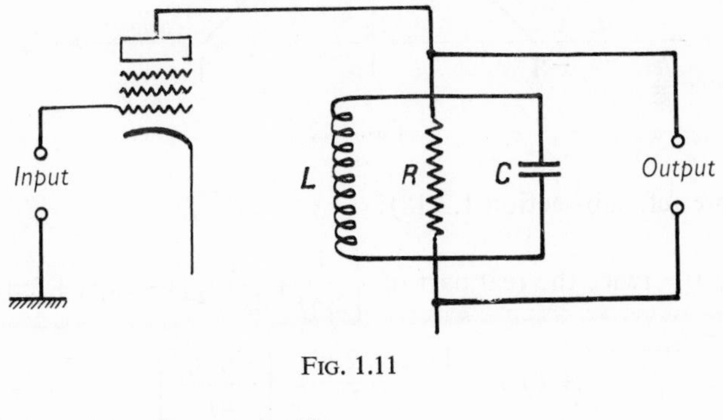

FIG. 1.11

($pF(p)$ tends to zero as p tends to zero) with:

$$\frac{1}{RC} = 2\lambda \ll \omega_0^2,$$

$$LC\omega_0^2 = 1,$$

$$\Omega^2 = \omega_0^2 - \lambda^2 \approx \omega_0^2,$$

(2λ is the pass band at 3 dB in radians per sec.),

We therefore have as the Laplace transform of $\rho(t)u(t)$:

$$F(p) = \frac{p+\lambda}{(p+\lambda)^2+\Omega^2} - \frac{\lambda}{\Omega} \cdot \frac{\Omega}{(p+\lambda)^2+\Omega^2}$$

$$\boxed{\rho(\tau) = \rho(0)\exp(-\lambda|\tau|)\left[\cos\Omega\tau - \frac{\lambda}{\Omega}\sin(\Omega|\tau|)\right]}$$

1.6.3 Calculation of the spectral density of $v(t)$ (see sub-section 1.2.2)

It is clear that the autocorrelation function of $v(t)$ is given by

$$\rho_v(\tau) = 0 \qquad \text{for} \qquad |\tau| \geq 1,$$
$$\rho_v(\tau) = 1 - |\tau| \qquad \text{for} \qquad |\tau| \leq 1 \qquad \text{(see fig. 1.12)}.$$

The Laplace transform of $\rho(t) \cdot u(t)$ is equal to

$$\frac{1}{p} - \frac{1}{p^2}[1 - \exp(-p)]$$

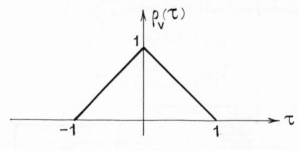

FIG. 1.12

and therefore (cf. sub-section 1.2.18):

$$A^2(f) = \text{twice the real part of } \left\{\frac{1}{2\pi jf} + \frac{1}{4\pi^2 f^2}[1 - \exp(+2\pi jf)]\right\},$$

$$A^2(f) = \frac{1-\cos 2\pi f}{2\pi^2 f^2} = \left[\frac{\sin \pi f}{\pi f}\right]^2$$

1.6.4 Calculation of the autocorrelation function of $w_1(t)$
(see sub-sections 1.2.2 and 1.4.2).

We saw that the spectral density of $w_1(t)$ could be written as

$$\left[\frac{\sin 2\pi f}{2\pi f}\right]^2,$$

which is clearly (see sub-section 1.6.3) the Fourier transform of

$$\rho_{w_1}(\tau) = 0 \qquad \text{for} \qquad |\tau| \geqq 2,$$
$$\rho_{w_1}(\tau) = 0 \cdot 5 - 0 \cdot 25|\tau| \qquad \text{for} \qquad |\tau| \leqq 2 \qquad \text{(see fig. 1.13)}.$$

(We easily verify that the power of w_1 is equal to $0 \cdot 5$.)

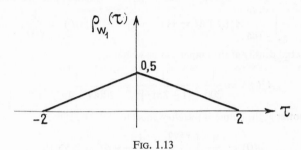

FIG. 1.13

We could also arrive at the same results in a different way by writing:

$$\rho_{w_1}(\tau) = \overline{\{\tfrac{1}{2}[v(t) + v(t-1)]\} \{\tfrac{1}{2}[v(t-\tau) + v(t-\tau-1)]\}}$$
$$4\rho_{w_1}(\tau) = \overline{v(t) \cdot v(t-\tau)} + \overline{v(t-\tau-1) \cdot v(t)} + \overline{v(t-1) \cdot v(t-\tau)}$$
$$\qquad\qquad\qquad\qquad\qquad\qquad + \overline{v(t-1) \cdot v(t-\tau-1)}$$
$$4\rho_{w_1}(\tau) = \rho_v(\tau) + \rho_v(\tau+1) + \rho_v(\tau-1) + \rho_v(\tau).$$

1.6.5 Filtering through a circuit RC

Consider a gaussian noise $v_1(t)$, its mean value being 0 and its root mean square being 1 V. Its spectrum (spectral density) is constant for frequencies less than 100 Hz and is zero for higher frequencies. It passes through a filter RC with $RC = 1$ sec. What is the autocorrelation function of the noise $v_2(t)$ at the output of the filter (see fig. 1.14)?

The transfer function of the filter is given by

$$F(p) = \frac{1}{1+p}$$

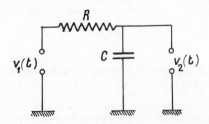

FIG. 1.14

Thus, as a result of sub-section 1.6.2, $1/1+p$ is the Laplace transform (modulo a constant factor) of $\rho(t)u(t)$. We have, therefore,

$$\rho(\tau) = \rho(0) \exp(-|\tau|).$$

In order to determine $\rho(0)$ it is convenient to determine firstly the spectral density $A_e^2(f)$ at the input, between $f = -100$ and $f = 100$ Hz, which is such that

$$\int_{-100}^{+100} A_e^2(f)\,\mathrm{d}f = (1)^2 = 1, \qquad A_e^2(f) = \frac{1}{200}.$$

Thus the spectral density at the output can be written as

$$A_e^2(f) = \frac{1}{200} \times \frac{1}{|1+2\pi\mathrm{j}f|^2} = \frac{1}{200(1+4\pi^2 f^2)},$$

and the noise power at the output is therefore equal to

$$\rho(0) = \frac{1}{200} \int_{-100}^{+100} \frac{1}{1+4\pi^2 f^2}\,\mathrm{d}f = 2{\cdot}5 \cdot 10^{-3},$$

and hence

$$\boxed{\rho(\tau) = 2{\cdot}5 \cdot 10^{-3} \exp(-|\tau|)}$$

1.6.6 Optimisation

In order to measure the vertical velocity of an aerodyne we could either measure its distance from the ground (X) and differentiate it, or measure its vertical acceleration and integrate it. We intend to utilise the two methods to obtain the best possible results.

In fact we measure

— not X but X accompanied by a white noise of spectral density B,
— not $\mathrm{d}^2 X/\mathrm{d}t^2$ but $\mathrm{d}^2 X/\mathrm{d}t^2$ accompanied by a white noise of spectral density C.

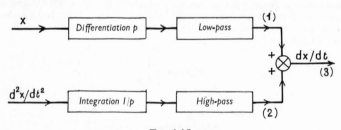

FIG. 1.15

The differentiation of X considerably increases the high frequencies of the accompanying noise and this leads us to send it through a low-pass filter which would eliminate the spectral components above f_0.

The integration of $\mathrm{d}^2 X/\mathrm{d}t^2$ considerably increases the low frequencies of the accompanying noise, and this leads us to send it through a high-pass filter which preserves only those spectral components that are above f_0 (see fig. 1.15).

It is necessary to determine the value f_0 in order to obtain the best result.

The noise power in (1) is written as

$$2\int_0^{f_0} |2\pi jf|^2 B \, df = B\frac{8\pi^2 f_0^3}{3}.$$

The noise power in (2) is written as

$$2\int_{f_0}^{\infty} \frac{C}{|2\pi jf|^2} \, df = \frac{C}{2\pi^2}\times\frac{1}{f_0}.$$

The noise power in (3) is written as

$$\frac{8\pi^2 Bf_0^3}{3}+\frac{C}{2\pi^2 f_0},$$

this quantity must be minimised, and we thus obtain

$$\boxed{(2\pi f_0)^4 = C/B}$$

1.7 SAMPLING THEOREM

1.7.1 Let $F_1(t)$ be any function which is zero for $t < -T/2$ and $t > T/2$. This function generally has a Fourier transform $\Phi_1(f)$, and we have the relation

$$\boxed{\Phi_1(f) = \int_{-T/2}^{+T/2} F_1(t)\exp(-2\pi jft)\,dt}$$

i.e.

$$R[\Phi_1(f)] = \int_{-T/2}^{+T/2} F_1(t)\cos(2\pi ft)\,dt,$$

$$I[\Phi_1(f)] = -\int_{-T/2}^{+T/2} F_1(t)\sin(2\pi ft)\,dt.$$

Let us now consider the periodic function with a period T, which for $-T/2 < t < +T/2$ coincides with $F_1(t)$. Let $f_1(t)$ be this function (see fig. 1.16). Since it is periodic it can be written as

$$f_1(t) = \sum_{-\infty}^{+\infty} A_n \exp(2\pi jnt/T),$$

with n being an integer and A_n being the conjugate of A_{-n}.
By writing

$$A_n = \alpha_n + j\beta_n$$

we have

$$\alpha_n = \frac{1}{T} \int_{-T/2}^{+T/2} F_1(t) \cos 2\pi \frac{nt}{T} \, dt = \frac{1}{T} R\left[\Phi_1\left(\frac{n}{T}\right) \right]$$

$$\beta_n = -\frac{1}{T} \int_{-T/2}^{+T/2} F_1(t) \sin 2\pi \frac{nt}{T} \, dt = \frac{1}{T} I\left[\Phi_1\left(\frac{n}{T}\right) \right]$$

i.e.

$$A_n = \frac{\Phi_1(n/T)}{T}$$

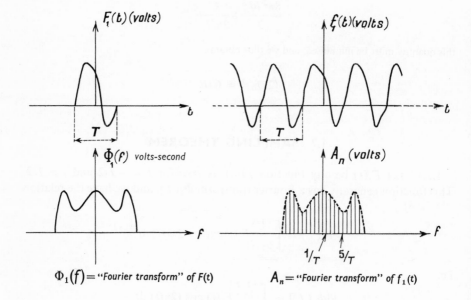

$\Phi_1(f) =$ "Fourier transform" of F(t) $A_n =$ "Fourier transform" of $f_1(t)$

Fig. 1.16

The amplitude of the rays of the spectrum of the periodic function $f_1(t)$ is equal to the amplitude of the spectrum of $F_1(t)$ at the same frequency, modulo a constant coefficient. This is diagrammatically shown in fig. 1.16. (It should not be forgotten that if A_n is expressed in volts, for example, then $\Phi_1(f)$ will be expressed in volts × sec.) Hence, knowing the spectrum of $F_1(t)$, we can immediately find the spectrum of $f_1(t)$.

1.7.2 Let us now suppose that the Fourier transform of $F_1(t)$ is equal to zero for frequencies outside the band $(-\Delta f/2 + \Delta f/2)$. We say that its spectrum is limited to the band $\pm \Delta f/2$.

Strictly speaking, there cannot be a signal of finite duration whose spectrum is of finite width, i.e. we cannot have simultaneously a signal zero strictly for $|t| > T/2$ and the Fourier transform zero strictly for $|f| > \Delta f/2$. On the other hand, we can have a signal strictly zero for $|t| > T/2$ and whose Fourier transform is as weak as is required for $|f| > \Delta f/2$.

It is clear that the expression

$$f_1(t) = \sum_{-\infty}^{+\infty} A_n \exp(2\pi jnt/T)$$

will contain only a finite number of terms, equal to $\Delta f/(1/T) = T\Delta f$.

Since the pair A_n and A_{-n} provide only two items of information (amplitude and phase, for example), we see that $f_1(t)$, and hence $F_1(t)$, depend only on $T\Delta f$ independent parameters, just as we say that a circle in a plane depends only on three parameters or that a straight line in a plane depends on only two parameters.

Since $T\Delta f$ must be an integer, it implies that the spectral width Δf could only be equal to an integer of $1/T$, or—better—that the spectral width Δf could only be defined in terms of $1/T$, and more generally that a frequency during a time T could only be defined in terms of $1/T$.

1.7.3 Let us consider a function of time $F(t)$ such that its duration is T and that its spectrum is limited by the band $\pm \Delta f/2$. In order to know the function completely it is necessary and sufficient to know the values of $T\Delta f$ parameters.

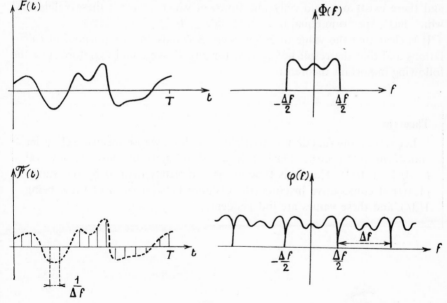

Fig. 1.17

Figure 1.17 shows on the left the function $F(t)$ as a function of time t, and on the right the Fourier transform $\Phi(f)$ of $F(t)$ (in fact, since $\Phi(f)$ is an imaginary function only its diagrammatic representation is of any use).

Let us now consider the function

$$\mathscr{F}(t) = F(0) \cdot \delta(t) + F\left(\frac{1}{\varDelta f}\right) \cdot \delta\left(t - \frac{1}{\varDelta f}\right) + F\left(\frac{2}{\varDelta f}\right) \cdot \delta\left(t - \frac{1}{\varDelta f}\right) + \ldots$$

$$\underbrace{\hspace{8cm}}_{T\varDelta F \text{ terms}}$$

Given the reciprocity of the Fourier transform it is clear that the Fourier transform of $\mathscr{F}(t)$ is a function $\varphi(f)$, of period $1/(1/\varDelta f) = \varDelta f$, and equal to $\Phi(f)$ for f lying between $-\varDelta f/2$ and $+\varDelta f/2$ (see also fig. 1.17).

Knowing $\mathscr{F}(t)$ enables us to know $\varphi(f)$ and hence $\Phi(f)$ and hence $F(t)$.

It is therefore sufficient to know $T\varDelta f$ values of $F(t)$ at the "instants of sampling",

$$0, \quad \frac{1}{\varDelta f}, \quad \frac{2}{\varDelta f}, \quad \frac{3}{\varDelta f}, \ldots$$

in order to know $F(t)$. On the other hand, since we know that $F(t)$ depends on $T\varDelta f$ parameters, these values are independent.

Therefore we could arbitrarily fix these values for the instants of sampling and there exists one and only one function which assumes these values and which has a spectrum equal to zero outside $\pm \varDelta f/2$.

It is clear that the value of T has been used only for the purpose of calculations and that the result holds good for any T. We could therefore state the following important theorem:

Theorem

Let $x(t)$ be any function, in particular random, whose spectrum (Fourier transform or spectral density) is equal to zero outside the interval $(-\varDelta f/2, +\varDelta f/2)$. Then this function is completely defined by the values of $x(t)$ at consecutive instants (the distance between each of these being $1/\varDelta f$), and these values are independent.

I.8 TENDENCY TO THE NORMAL LAW.
GAUSSIAN PHENOMENON. RAYLEIGH'S LAW

I.8.1 Tendency to the normal law

Let us consider a random function $x(t)$ of mean value zero and whose spectral density is zero outside the band $\pm \Delta f/2$. We could deduce the random function $Z(t)$ defined by

$$nZ(t) = x(t) + x\left(t + \frac{1}{\Delta f}\right) + x\left(t + \frac{2}{\Delta f}\right) + \ldots + x\left(t + \frac{n}{\Delta f}\right),$$

where n is very large. $Z(t)$ appears as a sum of n (very large) independent random variables: its distribution is therefore gaussian (or normal or Laplacian).

In practice, $Z(t)$ could be written in the form

$$Z(t) = \frac{\Delta f}{n}\left[x(t) + x\left(t + \frac{1}{\Delta f}\right) + \ldots + x\left(t + \frac{n}{\Delta f}\right)\right]\left(\frac{1}{\Delta f}\right),$$

$$Z(t) = \frac{\Delta f}{n} \int_t^{T + n/\Delta f} x(u)\, du = \frac{1}{T} \int_t^{t + T} x(u)\, du, \qquad \text{with } T = \frac{n}{\Delta f}.$$

Hence whatever be the amplitude distribution of the random function $x(t)$, the random functions

$$\int_t^{t + T} x(u)\, du \qquad \text{and} \qquad \frac{1}{T} \int_t^{t + T} x(u)\, du$$

have, if $T\Delta f$ is very large (integration or taking the mean value over time being much greater than the inverse of the width of the spectrum) a distribution of amplitude that is gaussian.

In reality this has a great significance; let us examine the method of obtaining the mean value (or of integration) of a function $f(t)$:

$$F(t) = \frac{1}{T} \int_t^{t + T} f(u)\, du$$

with

$$f(u) = \int_{-\infty}^{+\infty} \Phi(f) \exp\left(2\pi j f u\right) df,$$

we obtain

$$F(t) = \frac{1}{T} \int_t^{t+T} du \int_{-\infty}^{+\infty} \Phi(f) \exp(2\pi juf) \, df,$$

$$F(t) = \int_{-\infty}^{+\infty} \Phi(f) \left[\frac{\exp(2\pi jfT) - 1}{2\pi jfT} \right] \exp(2\pi jft) \, df.$$

$F(t)$ is obtained by feeding $f(t)$ through a filter of transfer function $G(p)$:

$$G(p) = \frac{\exp(pT) - 1}{pT},$$

i.e. a low-pass filter conserving only those frequencies that are below $1/T$ approximately.

We deduce that all random functions (noise) whose spectrums lie between $-\Delta f/2$ and $+\Delta f/2$, filtered by a low-pass filter cutting off at a level much less than Δf, give at the output of the filter random functions whose distribution amplitude are gaussian.

Similarly, every function whose spectrum lies between $f_0 - \Delta f/2$ and $f_0 + \Delta f/2$ (considering only positive frequencies) gives after filtering through a pass-band filter centred on f_0 and of bandwidth much smaller than Δf, a random function whose distribution is gaussian. This explains why the random functions (noise) that we encounter in electronics are often gaussian.

1.8.2   Representation of gaussian random functions

1.8.2.1   Let us consider a gaussian random function $x(t)$ of mean value zero and whose spectral density (limited to positive frequencies—i.e. $2A^2(f)$)—is equal to b for $f_0 - \Delta f/2 < f < f_0 + \Delta f/2$ and zero for all other values of f (with $f_0 \gg \Delta f$).

We could break down the spectrum of $x(t)$ into a large number, say N, of joint vertical bands of width $\Delta f/N$. In other words, $x(t)$ is considered to be a sum of N independent sinusoidal signals each having a power equal to $b\Delta f/N$

$$x(t) = \sum_{i=0}^{i=N} \sqrt{\frac{2b\Delta f}{N}} \sin(2\pi F_i t + \varphi_i),$$

F_i being the central frequency of one of the bands and φ_i being arbitrary phases independently chosen for each of the bands.

This representation expresses $x(t)$:

— firstly, as a sum of a large number, say N, of independent variables each of a power equal to

$$\frac{1}{2} \frac{2b\Delta f}{N} = \frac{b\Delta f}{N},$$

i.e. as a gaussian variable (of mean value zero) and of power equal to $b\Delta f$;

— and secondly, as having a uniform spectral distribution between $f_0 - \Delta f/2$ and $f_0 + \Delta f/2$.

Application (compare sub-section 1.2.4)

Let us consider a random function $y(t)$ which provides, with the help of a quadratic detector, a random function

$$Y(t) = \overline{y^2(t)} + \mathscr{Y}(t) = b\Delta f + \mathscr{Y}(t).$$

We shall proceed to evaluate the spectral density of $\mathcal{Y}(t)$.

We could write

$$y^2(t) = \left[\sum_0^N \sqrt{\frac{2b\Delta f}{N}} \cos{(2\pi F_i t + \varphi_i)} \right]^2.$$

By developing $y^2(t)$, we find that it is composed of (by the binomial formula):

— N terms of amplitude $b\Delta f/N$ at zero frequency whose sum corresponds to $\overline{y^2(t)}$.

And for $\mathcal{Y}(t)$, strictly speaking,

— $N-1$ terms at the frequency of $\Delta f/N$,
— $N-2$ terms at the frequency of $2\Delta f/N$,
— ....
— 1 term at the frequency of $(N-1)\,\Delta f/N$,

and of terms at frequencies in the neighbourhood of $2f_0$ which in their practical and physical aspects have no interest because they are in general eliminated by a low-pass filter.

The total power of the spectrum at the low frequencies (the only ones considered) is equal to half the power of $\mathcal{Y}(t)$ (the other half corresponding to the frequencies in the neighbourhood of $2f_0$), i.e. (see sub-section 1.2.4) equal to

$$\frac{2b^2\Delta f^2}{2} = b^2\Delta f^2.$$

The form of the useful spectrum (spectral density) of $\mathcal{Y}(t)$ is therefore that which is represented in fig. 1.18 (the area of the triangle being $2b^2\Delta f \cdot \Delta f/2 = b^2\Delta f^2$).

The autocorrelation function of $\mathcal{Y}(t)$ is therefore given by the Fourier transform of $A^2(f)$, i.e. by the real part (see sub-section 1.2.1) of

$$\frac{2b^2\Delta f}{2\pi j\tau} + \frac{2b^2}{4\pi^2\tau^2} [1 - \exp{(2\pi j\tau\Delta f)}],$$

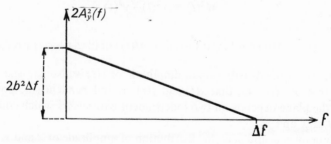

FIG. 1.18

i.e.

$$\rho_{\mathcal{Y}}(\tau) = b^2\Delta f^2 \left(\frac{\sin{\pi\tau\,\Delta f}}{\pi\tau\,\Delta f} \right)^2$$

REMARK

The above reasoning is often applied by physicists but very rarely by mathematicians. The latter arive at the same result in a more exact way by showing that, because $y(t)$ is gaussian, the autocorrelation function of $\mathcal{Y}$ which is $\rho_{\mathcal{Y}}(\tau)$ is equal to twice the square of the autocorrelation function of y (we refer to General Angot's book, already cited, for justification of this):

$$\rho_{\mathcal{Y}}(\tau) = 2\rho_y^2(\tau)$$

Now let (cf. sub-section 1.6.1):

$$\rho_{\mathcal{Y}}(\tau) = 2b^2 \varDelta f^2 \cdot \left(\frac{\sin \pi\tau \, \varDelta f}{\pi\tau \, \varDelta f}\right)^2 \cdot \cos^2 2\pi\tau f_0,$$

$$\rho_{\mathcal{Y}}(\tau) = b^2 \varDelta f^2 \left(\frac{\sin \pi\tau \, \varDelta f}{\pi\tau \, \varDelta f}\right)^2 + b^2 \varDelta f^2 \left(\frac{\sin \pi\tau \, \varDelta f}{\pi\tau \, \varDelta f}\right)^2 \cdot \cos (4\pi\tau f_0).$$

The second term corresponds to frequencies in the neighbourhood of $2f_0$, usually eliminated, and hence strictly *proves* the result shown above.

1.8.2.2 Another representation of the same gaussian random function $x(t)$ (of mean value zero) which derives from the preceding is of the form

$$x(t) = M(t) \sin [2\pi f_0 t + \varphi(t)],$$

where $\varphi(t)$ is a random phase which could, with the same probability, assume all the values lying between 0 and 2π, and $M(t)$ is a positive variable (variable amplitude of the sinusoid randomly modulated in phase) independent of $\varphi(t)$.

In order to obtain simply the distribution of amplitude corresponding to the amplitude $M(t)$, we could write

$$M^2(t) = x^2(t) + y^2(t),$$

with

$$y(t) = M(t) \cos [2\pi f_0 t + \varphi(t)] = M(t) \sin [2\pi f_0 t + \varphi(t) + \pi/2].$$

It is clear that the distribution of amplitude of $y(t)$ is also gaussian and is the same as that of $x(t)$, and that $x(t)$ and $y(t)$ are independent (the position of a point in the plane depends on two independent parameters which could be, say, M and θ or x and y).

Denoting by $p(x)$ and $p(y)$ the distribution of amplitude of x and y, by $p_M(M)$ that of M (which is the vector of a point whose cartesian coordinates are x and y), and by $p_\varphi(\varphi)$ that of φ—the polar angle of the point $p_\varphi(\varphi) = 1/2\pi$—we could write

$$p(x) \cdot p(y) \cdot \mathrm{d}x \, \mathrm{d}y = p_M(M) \cdot p_\varphi(\varphi) \, \mathrm{d}M \, \mathrm{d}\varphi,$$

$$p(x) \cdot p(y) \cdot M \cdot \mathrm{d}M \cdot \mathrm{d}\varphi = p_M(M) \cdot \frac{1}{2\pi} \cdot \mathrm{d}M \, \mathrm{d}\varphi,$$

$$p_M(M) = 2\pi M \cdot p(x) p(y).$$

Therefore, since

$$p(x) = \frac{1}{\sqrt{2\pi b \Delta f}} \exp\left(-\frac{x^2}{2b\Delta f}\right),$$

$$p_M(M) = 2\pi M \frac{1}{2\pi b \Delta f} \exp\left(-\frac{x^2+y^2}{2b\Delta f}\right),$$

$$\boxed{p_M(M) = \frac{M}{b\Delta f} \cdot \exp\left(-\frac{M^2}{2b\Delta f}\right)}$$

A density probability of this type, characterising a variable having a distribution called Rayleighan, is often encountered in characterising the distribution of amplitude of a vector whose coordinates (cartesian) have the same gaussian distribution (of mean value zero).

This result explains why we often (and quite wrongly) say that noise, after filtering through a narrow pass-band, has a Rayleigh distribution. In fact its distribution is gaussian, but it could be considered as a randomly modulated sinusoidal signal (and often slowly) in phase, the amplitude of the sinusoid having a Rayleigh distribution.

We easily find that the mean value of M^2 is twice the power of x, i.e.

$$\int_0^\infty \frac{M^3}{b\Delta f} \cdot \exp\left(-\frac{M^2}{2b\Delta f}\right) dM,$$

i.e., by writing

$$\overline{x^2(t)} = \overline{M^2(t) \cdot \sin^2\left(2\pi f_0 t + \varphi(t)\right)}$$

we get (since $\varphi(t)$ and $M(t)$ are independent)

$$\overline{M^2(t)} = \overline{2x^2(t)} = 2b\Delta f.$$

1.9 IMPERFECTIONS OF PRACTICAL CORRELATIONS

1.9.1 General

In numerous cases of application we are led to use the correlations which are made on two random functions $x(t)$ and $y(t)$ by the evaluation of

$$\rho_{xy}(\tau) = \lim_{T \to \infty} \frac{1}{T} \int_0^T x(t) \cdot y(t-\tau) \, dt.$$

It is evident that this evaluation could be made only for finite T and not for an infinite T, otherwise we have to wait an infinite time for a result, which would have no more than a limited usefulness.

By doing this we do not obtain exactly $\rho_{xy}(\tau)$ but $\rho_{xy}(\tau)$ plus a random term of mean value zero which characterises the error due to the imperfection of the correlation (i.e. of the finite nature of T).

We intend to evaluate this error in this section.

D

1.9.2 Autocorrelation of a gaussian function

Let us consider a random gaussian function $x(t)$ of mean value zero, whose autocorrelation function is $\rho(\tau)$ and whose spectrum has a width Δf. The correlator evaluates

$$C(\tau) = \frac{1}{T} \int_0^T x(t) \cdot x(t-\tau) \, dt,$$

which could be written in the form

$$C(\tau) = \frac{1}{T} \int_0^T \rho(\tau) \, dt + \frac{1}{T} \int_0^T [x(t) \cdot x(t-\tau) - \rho(\tau)] \, dt,$$

$$C(\tau) = \rho(\tau) + C_p(\tau),$$

where the error $C_p(\tau)$ is given by

$$C_p(\tau) = \frac{1}{T} \int_0^T [x(t) \cdot x(t-\tau) - \rho(\tau)] \, dt,$$

$$C_p(\tau) = \underbrace{\frac{1}{T} \left\{ [x(0) \cdot x(-\tau) - \rho(\tau)] + \left[x\left(\frac{1}{\Delta f}\right) \cdot x\left(\frac{1}{\Delta f} - \tau\right) - \rho(\tau) \right] + \ldots \right\} \cdot \frac{1}{\Delta f}}_{T\Delta f \text{ terms}}.$$

Thus $C_p(\tau)$ emerges as a sum of a $T\Delta f$ number (supposed large) of independent variables of mean value zero. It is therefore a gaussian variable of mean value zero, whose variance is given by

$$\overline{[C_p(\tau)]^2} = \frac{1}{T^2 \Delta f^2} \times \text{moment of 2nd order of } [x(t) \cdot x(t-\tau) - \rho(\tau)] \times T\Delta f.$$

But we have

$$\overline{[x(t) \cdot x(t-\tau) - \rho(\tau)]^2} = \overline{x^2(t) \cdot x^2(t-\tau)} - [\rho^2(\tau)].$$

However, we know that (see remark in sub-section 1.8.2.1)

$$\overline{[x^2(t) - \rho(0)] \, [x^2(t-\tau) - \rho(0)]} = 2\rho^2(\tau),$$

$$\overline{x^2(t) \cdot x^2(t-\tau)} - \rho^2(0) = 2\rho^2(\tau),$$

$$\overline{x^2(t) \cdot x^2(t-\tau)} = 2\rho^2(\tau) + \rho^2(0).$$

We have, therefore,

$$\overline{[x(t) \cdot x(t-\tau) - \rho(\tau)]^2} = \rho^2(\tau) + \rho^2(0)$$

and

$$\overline{[C_p(\tau)]^2} = \frac{\rho^2(\tau) + \rho^2(0)}{T\Delta f}.$$

The error of the correlator which measures $\rho(\tau)$ is gaussian if $T\Delta f$ is sufficiently large, of mean value zero and of standard deviation equal to

$$\frac{\sqrt{\rho^2(\tau)+\rho^2(0)}}{\sqrt{T\Delta f}}$$

In the particular case where we measure $\rho(0)$, we commit, if $T\Delta f$ is sufficiently large, a gaussian error of mean value zero and of standard deviation equal to

$$\frac{\rho(0)}{\sqrt{T\Delta f/2}}$$

We again obtain the same result by using the arguments of sub-section 1.8.2, where it is clear that after filtering through a low-pass filter, of cut-out frequency $1/T$, the power of $y^2(t)$, i.e. the power of $[x^2(t)-\rho(0)]$, is equal to $2b^2\Delta f\cdot 1/T$, i.e.

$$\frac{2[b\Delta f]^2}{T\Delta f} = \frac{2\rho^2(0)}{T\Delta f}$$

If, on the contrary, we measure $\rho(\tau)$ for a very large value of τ such that $\rho(\tau) = 0$, instead of finding zero, we shall find a random gaussian term of zero mean value and of standard deviation equal to

$$\frac{\rho(0)}{\sqrt{T\Delta f}}.$$

1.9.3 Autocorrelation of a non-gaussian function for $\tau = 0$

The power of the parasitic term can be written as

$$\frac{1}{T\Delta f}\,\overline{[x^4(t)]-\rho^2(0)]} = \frac{1}{T\Delta f}\,\overline{[x^4-\overline{(x^2)^2}]}.$$

1.9.4 Cross-correlation of two independent variables

If $x(t)$ and $y(t)$ are two independent variables of a spectrum of width Δf, then we find that

$$\rho_{xy}(\tau) = 0,$$

but when we actually evaluate

$$\frac{1}{T}\int_0^T x(t)y(t-\tau)\,\mathrm{d}t,$$

instead of finding it to be zero, we find in a similar way a gaussian parasitic term, if $T\Delta f$ is sufficiently large, whose mean value is zero and whose power is equal to

$$\frac{\overline{x^2(t)\cdot y^2(t-\tau)}}{T\Delta f} = \frac{\overline{x^2(t)}\cdot\overline{y^2(t-\tau)}}{T\Delta f} = \frac{\rho_x(0)\cdot\rho_y(0)}{T\Delta f}$$

1.9.5 Application

We calculate the correlation over a time T of the function $x(t)$ with the function $x(t)+n(t)$, $x(t)$ being a gaussian noise of a spectrum of width Δf and of power $[a\Delta f]$, $n(t)$ being a gaussian noise (parasitic) of a spectrum of width Δf and of power $[A\Delta f]$, with $A \gg a$.

We assume T to be large *vis-à-vis* $1/\Delta f$. We therefore obtain

$$\frac{1}{T}\int_0^T x^2(t)\,\mathrm{d}t + \frac{1}{T}\int_0^T x(t)n(t)\,\mathrm{d}t,$$

i.e. after the observations in sub-sections 1.9.2 and 1.9.4:

— a fixed term called useful, equal to $\rho_x(0)$, i.e. equal to $[a\Delta f]$;

— a first term which is gaussian and parasitic of mean value zero and standard deviation equal to

$$\frac{\sqrt{\rho_x(0)\cdot\rho_n(0)}}{\sqrt{T\Delta f}}, \quad \text{i.e. equal to} \quad \frac{\Delta f\sqrt{aA}}{\sqrt{T\Delta f}};$$

— a second term which is gaussian and parasitic of mean value zero and standard deviation equal to

$$\frac{\rho_x(0)}{\sqrt{T\Delta f/2}}, \quad \text{i.e. equal to} \quad \frac{a\Delta f\sqrt{2}}{\sqrt{T\Delta f}},$$

i.e. negligible *vis-à-vis* the first parasitic term.

We also define the signal-to-noise ratio before correlation by the ratio between the power of $x(t)$ and that of $n(t)$, i.e. by

$$\frac{a\Delta f}{A\Delta f} = \frac{a}{A}.$$

Similarly, we also define after correlation the signal-to-noise ratio by the ratio between the power of the useful term, i.e. $[a\Delta f]^2$ and that of the parasitic term, i.e.

$$\frac{aA\Delta f^2}{T\Delta f}.$$

The signal-to-noise ratio after correlation is therefore equal to

$$\frac{a^2\Delta f^2\cdot T\Delta f}{aA\Delta f^2} = \frac{a}{A}\cdot T\Delta f.$$

"The correlation has multiplied the signal-to-noise ratio (in power) by $T\Delta f$", i.e. by $\Delta f/(1/T)$, say, the ratio between the widths of the bands before and after correlation.

1.10 PROBLEMS

1.10.1 Problem 1

1. The density probability of a variable x is given by fig. 1.19. Find the mean values of

(a) x,

(b) x^2.

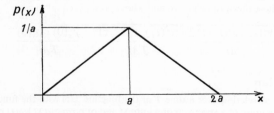

Fig. 1.19

2. A sample of the function $y(t)$ is given by fig. 1.20. Every second the value of $y(t)$ varies by a jump. However, it remains constant for $n < t < n+1$ (n being an integer). The values of y on each side of a jump are independent.

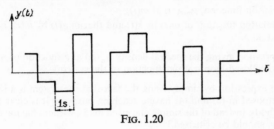

FIG. 1.20

If y_n is the value of $y(t)$ for $n < t < n+1$, the absolute value of y_n being $|y_n|$ has a Poisson distribution, and y_n has as much chance to be positive as it has to be negative; i.e. the probability that $|y_n|$ has non-integer value is zero despite that the probability that $|y_n|$ has an integral value equal to

$$\frac{\lambda^k}{k!}\exp(-\lambda).$$

Give the mean values of $y(t)$, $|y(t)|$, $y^2(\tau)$, and $[y(t)y(t-\tau)]$ for $\tau > 1$ and $\tau < 1$.

1.10.2 Problem 2

We use the feedback system represented by fig. 1.21 to filter a noise $b(t)$ which accompanies the message $m(t)$.

We assume that there is no correlation between $m(t)$ and $b(t)$ and that $m(t)$ and $b(t)$ are random stationary functions of spectral density

$$A_m^2(\omega) = \frac{1}{\pi}\frac{a^2 A^2}{a^2+\omega^2},$$

$$A_b^2(\omega) = \frac{1}{\pi}B^2, \qquad -\infty < \omega < +\infty$$

respectively.

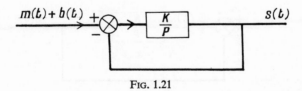

FIG. 1.21

1. Calculate the mean quadratic value, $\overline{m^2}$, of $m(t)$.

2. Assuming that the message lasts for 1 sec, find the signal-to-noise ratio corresponding to R in the input of the system,

$$R \text{ being } \frac{\text{Energy of the message}}{\text{Spectral density of noise}}.$$

3. After defining the error $\varepsilon(t)$ by $\varepsilon(t) = s(t) - m(t)$, give an expression giving the auto-correlation function $\rho_{\varepsilon\varepsilon}(\tau)$ of ε as a function of:

— the autocorrelation function $\rho_{ss}(\tau)$, of $s(t)$,

— the autocorrelation function, $\rho_{mm}(\tau)$, of $m(t)$,

— the cross-correlation function of $m(t)$ by $s(t)$ and that of $s(t)$ by $m(t)$, being respectively $\rho_{ms}(\tau)$ and $\rho_{sm}(\tau)$.

4. Deduce an expression giving the spectral density $A_{\varepsilon}^2(\omega)$ as a function of $A_m^2(\omega)$, $A_b^2(\omega)$ and $H(p)$ ($H(p)$ being the closed-loop transfer function of the system).

5. Find the same expression by simply using the fact that the system is a linear one.

(The methods imposed in (3) and (4) have a teaching purpose. It is clear that an engineer who uses these methods, instead of the simple one given in (5), without having taken the trouble to teach somebody, should be criticised.)

1.10.3 Problem 3

Let us consider a random function $x(t)$ of mean value zero and of power equal to unity. From it we deduce yet another random function $e(t)$, defined as

$$e(t) = x(t) \cdot \sin(\omega_0 t).$$

1. Assuming that the distribution of amplitude of $x(t)$ is gaussian, give a general expression for moments of order n of $e(t)$

— for n odd,

— for n even.

We recall that the mean value of $(\sin t)^{2p}$, where p is an integer, is equal to

$$\frac{1}{2} \cdot \frac{3}{4} \cdot \frac{5}{6} \cdot \frac{7}{8} \cdots \frac{2p-1}{2p}.$$

Under the same conditions, denoting $\rho_x(\tau)$ the autocorrelation function of $x(t)$, give an expression for the autocorrelation function of $y(t) = e^2(t)$.

2. With no more hypothesis on the nature of the distribution of amplitude of $x(t)$ except that $\rho_x(\tau) = Ae^{-\alpha|t|}$, find the value of A.

3. Calculate the autocorrelation function $\rho(\tau)$ of $e(t)$ and trace the graph of that function.

4. Deduce the spectral density of $e(t)$.

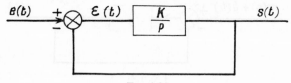

Fig. 1.22

5. The signal $e(t)$ is transmitted into the input of the system represented in fig. 1.22. Calculate the mean quadratic value of the error

$$\overline{\varepsilon^2} = \overline{[e(t) - s(t)]^2}.$$

It will be sufficient to give the result in the form of an integral.

I.10.4 Problem 4

Let us consider a reflector of a panoramic radar, of rectangular form (this form is chosen to simplify the calculations) rotating on a vertical axis in its plane of symmetry.

We assume that this reflector is illuminated by a primary feed situated in its focus just as if we were dealing with a uniformly illuminated reflector (the hypothesis of uniform illumination is also made for the purpose of simplifying the calculations), and all the points of the plane are illuminated in phase with slight faults.

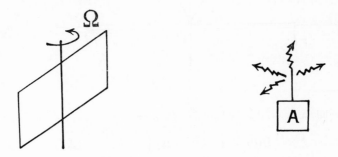

FIG. 1.23

The aerial has a rotation speed Ω (radians per sec) in front of a transmitter A situated at a great distance in the horizontal plane of symmetry of the radar aerial and transmitting a pure CW signal at high frequency (see fig. 1.23).

The signal received by the antenna is directly detected by a quadratic detector, then amplified by a video amplifier such that the output of this receiver is an electrical voltage V_B proportional to the power received by the antenna at a given time. Finally this signal is filtered (see fig. 1.24) to give a signal V_S.

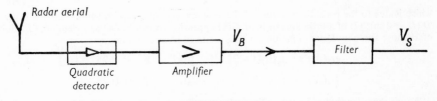

FIG. 1.24

The purpose of this exercise is to study the power of V_S, taking into consideration the nature of the final filter.

1. Consider a trirectangle trihedral rotating with the radar aerial about the vertical axis of the radar $Oxyz$, where O is the centre of the reflector; Ox is a horizontal axis within the plane of the reflector; Oy an axis along the normal to the reflector in the direction of radiation (see fig. 1.25).

Let us denote $\overline{H(\theta)}$ the value of the electrical field at the level of the transmitter as a function of the angle θ between the direction of A (seen from the centre of the reflector) and the direction of the normal to this reflector.

We also assume (to simplify the calculations) that the illumination of any point of the reflector is a function only of x, say $E(x)$.

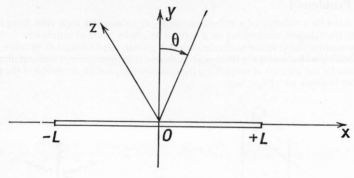

FIG. 1.25

Show, modulo a factor, that we have

$$\bar{H}(\theta) = \int_{-L}^{+L} \bar{E}(x) \exp\left(\frac{2\pi j x \sin\theta}{\lambda}\right) dx$$

where $2L$ is the horizontal opening of the aerial radar ($L = 5$ m) and λ the wavelength considered ($\lambda = 0{\cdot}1$ m).

If $u = (\sin\theta)/\lambda$, what does $H(u)$ represent with respect to $E(x)$, and inversely?

2. The hypothesis that the illumination of the aerial is uniform indicates that $E(x)$ is a complex number of constant modulo A for $-L < x < L$ ($E(x)$ is zero for $x^2 > L^2$).

But the faults in the manufacture of the aerial are such that its phase $\varepsilon(x)$ is non-zero: it is the sum (1) of a periodic fault

$$\varepsilon_2(x) = \varepsilon_0 \sin\frac{2\pi x}{D},$$

which is due to the periodic structure of the antenna, constituted with vertical boards of size D ($D = 2$ m); (2) of a little-known fault $\varepsilon_3(x)$ appearing from this fact as a random function of x whose autocorrelation function $\rho_3(X)$ is assumed to be equal to

$$\rho_3(X) = \rho_3(0)[1-2|X|] \quad \text{for} \quad X^2 < 0{\cdot}25,$$
$$\rho_3(X) = 0 \quad \text{for} \quad X^2 > 0{\cdot}25.$$

We also assume that $\varepsilon_0 = 0{\cdot}1$ radian and that ε_3 is gaussian (of mean value zero) and of standard deviation equal to $0{\cdot}1$ radian.

Show that, by simplifying in a reasonable way, modulo a factor,

$$H(u) = H_1(u) + H_2(u) + H_3(u),$$

with

$$H_1(u) = \int_{-L}^{+L} \exp(2\pi j x u) \, dx,$$

$$H_2(u) = j \int_{-L}^{+L} \varepsilon_2(x) \exp(2\pi j x u) \, dx,$$

$$H_3(u) = j \int_{-L}^{+L} \varepsilon_3(x) \exp(2\pi j x u) \, dx.$$

Also represent $H_1(u)$ as a function of u, for u lying between -10 and $+10$ (u is expressed as $(\text{metre})^{-1}$).

Similarly, represent $H_2(u)$ as a function of u, in the same range of values as u.

Finally, represent (assuming that $2L$ is large with respect to 0.5) $H_3(u)$ as a function of u for the same range of values of u. Let us recall the definition of the spectral density of a random function given in section 1.3.

3. Deduce the curve representing the interfering lobes due to faults in the antenna, i.e. the curve representing $H_2(\theta) + H_3(\theta) = H_D(\theta)$ as a function of θ, θ lying between $+\pi/2$ and $-\pi/2$.

REMARK

The lobes corresponding to $u^2 > 10$ are imaginary ones without any physical existence, at least at a great distance from the antenna.

4. Let us assume that the antenna rotates at a constant speed Ω of 6 rotations per minute, i.e. we assume that

$$\theta = \Omega t.$$

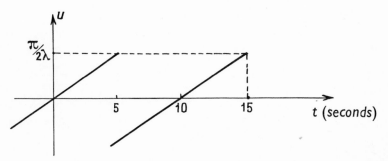

FIG. 1.26

Under these conditions $u = (\sin \Omega t)/\lambda$, but we shall suppose, for simplifying the calculations, that the variations of u in terms of time are represented by the curve shown in fig. 1.26.

Represent, *without making any calculations*, the Fourier transform of V_B.

5. Show the spectral distribution of the *power* of V_B (spectral density). Compare the powers of the output signals $V_s(t)$ according to:

— the final filter allowing past only those frequencies that are between 0.05 Hz and 0.15 Hz;

— the final filter allowing past only those frequencies that are between 0.95 Hz and 1.05 Hz (harmonic tenth);

— the final filter allowing past only those frequencies that are between 4.95 Hz and 5.05 Hz.

CHAPTER 2

SIGNAL AND NOISE
THE IDEAL RECEIVER

2.1 THE RADAR PROBLEM

A radar is, by definition, an instrument of RAdio Detection And Ranging, whose purpose is to indicate: "There is something at such and such a distance".

The very first ideas connected with electromagnetic detection of targets were quite simple (and they are still valid today). A detector consisted of an antenna whose impedance could be modified by an object's proximity and which, in turn, indicated "something abnormal".

However, this information was considered to be insufficient and further research was carried out in this case of abnormal presence to determine the target's position.

But at the same time it was found that there were auto-oscillator tubes (which were later called magnetrons) capable of transmitting high power during brief instants: hence the idea arose of transmitting short but high power signals and of measuring the time between the instant of transmission and that of reception after being sent back by the target, this time being proportional to the distance of the target. Most of the radars manufactured during the last three decades have been based on this principle.

In practice, there are a few problems. Let us consider a transmitter capable of transmitting a short (1 μs) signal consisting of a microwave signal of high power (1 MW). Even if the transmission is concentrated inside a solid angle reduced (this would in addition enable us to have an idea of the target's direction) by means of a large antenna, and even if another large antenna is used at the receiving end, the signal received after reflection by a normal target situated at a reasonable distance (a few hundred miles) will have an energy of the order of 10^{-15} watts.

It will have the same form as the original signal transmitted[1] but will be very weak.

---

[1] We will have an opportunity to deal with this point later.

By itself, the signal's weakness gives no trouble: it would suffice to amplify it as required. But the problem is that this weak signal is unfortunately always accompanied by a background noise resulting from:

— either the atmospheric noise, which one does not know how to suppress entirely;

— or the noise of the receiver, which again one does not know how to suppress entirely;

— or jamming, caused for example, by an enemy (or by a clumsy friend).

Since this background noise obscures the signal, it is better to filter it by diminishing the bandwidth of the receiver. By doing this up to the moment when the bandwidth is almost equal to the inverse of the duration of the signal,

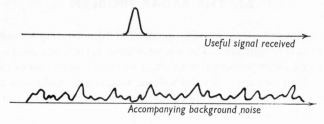

FIG. 2.1

there is an effective gain. And from that moment onwards if the bandwidth is continually reduced then the useful signal is destroyed more quickly than the noise. Hence great care has to be taken while doing this, and the best result is obtained when the bandwidth is almost equal to the inverse of the duration τ of the signal.

Under these conditions the useful signal is no more the good rectangular signal of the transmission, but it is a rounded signal, and the noise is as a sequence of signals having the same appearance. This would mean that we could make a mistake and assume the noise to be a signal (a false alarm), and vice versa (failure to detect) (see fig. 2.1).

What is to be done if we wish to increase the range of a radar? We could certainly increase the transmitted power, but this is a domain in which our resources are limited due to material considerations (e.g. price, flashes in the radar, etc.).

We could reduce the bandwidth of the receiver in order to reduce the noise, but at the same time the duration of the signal transmitted would have to be increased, and this would create two problems (in the case of classical radar):

(1) The longer the signal transmitted, the less precise is the range measurement;

(2) We can distinguish between two targets one behind the other, only if their distance increases as the duration of the signal transmitted.

It is only when the problem has been either to obtain considerable range, or to obtain reasonable range in spite of significant jamming, or even to obtain reasonable ranges together with excellent range accuracy and resolution, that we realised that this was not possible with classical radars.

We then started to take seriously the mathematical considerations of scientists such as Woodward.

We can now say that we have succeeded because the theories of Woodward, once correctly understood and extended, have given birth to a new class of radars which work, and which sometimes have characteristics that classical radars never had (such as speed measurement or clutter rejection).

These theories are based on two mathematical tools, namely

(1) the calculation of probabilities,

(2) the theorem of sampling (see section 1.7).

Starting from the principle that the choice of the signal transmitted from a classical radar was not due to profound philosophical reasons, there is no longer any reason to impose such a limitation on ourselves when there are all types of amplifier tubes available.

We shall therefore assume that a signal which could *a priori* be anything and which lasts for a time T is transmitted. Let it be paired with a Fourier transform $\Phi(f)$ (which will be a transformation of anything).

What do we receive at the end?

In the absence of any target we receive a noise $n(t) = y(t)$.

In the presence of a target we receive

$$y(t) = kS(t - t_{01}) + n(t),$$

where t_{01} measures the distance of the target.

The problem that has to be solved first is the determination of the manoeuvres that have to be carried out in order that there is the minimum possibility of our making a mistake in answering the question:

Does $y(t)$ contain or not contain $kS(t - t_{01})$?

If the answer is in the affirmative, then we proceed to the second question:

What is the most likely value of t_{01}?

Before analysing this problem it would be useful to examine certain simple problems concerning calculation of probabilities.

2.2 *A PRIORI* **AND** *A POSTERIORI* **PROBABILITIES**

2.2.1 Let us consider a game of bridge in which the two pairs of players are X and Y. As a spectator, let us consider a person who is a stranger to the players. What would be his prediction of the outcome of the encounter? He could say that the probability of X winning is $P_1 = 0.5$. This is an *a priori* probability.

As the cards are being dealt, he learns from other spectators that the team X are world champions and that the team Y consists of average players. This additional knowledge enables him to predict the probability of X winning as $P_2 = 0.9$. This, in relation to the earlier situation, is an *a posteriori* probability.

Once the cards are dealt, the spectators learn that the team Y have 37 points (of the 40) between them; our spectator can now predict that the probability of X winning is no more than $P_3 = 0.2$ (especially only if the team Y does not know how to bid a slam).

P_3 is an *a posteriori* probability with respect to P_2 but P_2 is an *a priori* probability with respect to P_3, and so on.

2.2.2 For a simple example let us consider the following game [1].*

Mr. Smith has 5 dice, of which 4 are normal and the fifth has 3 of its faces marked with a "6" and the other 3 marked "1". The game is as follows. Mr. Smith selects a dice at random and asks Mr. Brown if it is true or false, i.e. if $x = A$ (true) or $x = B$ (false).

A priori, the probability that $x = A$ is, of course, equal to 0.8.

$$P_0(A) = 0.8.$$

Before answering, Mr. Brown has the right to throw the dice twice and note the result. He therefore throws the dice and finds that the result is y_1 (see fig. 2.2).

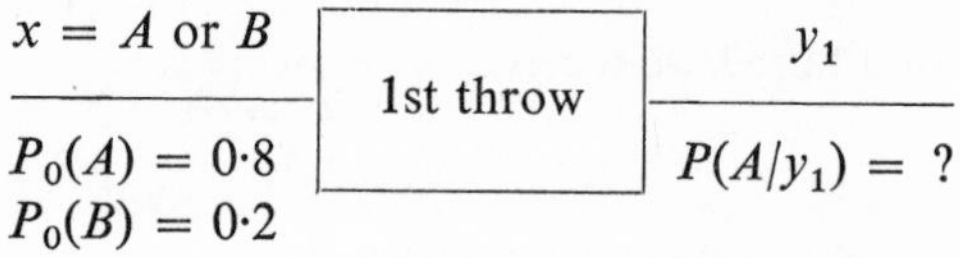

$x = A$ or B	1st throw	y_1
$P_0(A) = 0.8$ $P_0(B) = 0.2$		$P(A/y_1) = ?$

FIG. 2.2

If $y_1 = 2$ or 3 or 4 or 5, Mr. Brown must reply that $x = A$: in other words,

Probability $(x = A) = 1$ if $y = 2$.

$P(A$ if $y_1) = P(A/y_1) = 1$ for $y_1 = 2$ or 3 or 4 or 5 ($P(A/y_1)$ is an *a posteriori* probability with respect to $P_0(A)$).

But if $y_1 = 1$, what is the *a posteriori* probability that $x = A$? The answer is not very difficult.

The probability that simultaneously $x = A$ and $y_1 = 1$, $P(x = A\ y_1 = 1)$, is equal to

(the probability of having $x = A$) × (the probability that $y_1 = 1$ if $x = A$)

which can be written as

$$P(xy_1) = P(x) \times P(y_1/x).$$

* References given in square brackets indicate entries in the Bibliography (page 269).

And we could also write that

$$P(x = A \; y_1 = 1) =$$

(the probability that $y_1 = 1$) $\times$ (the probability that $x = A$ if $y_1 = 1$)

i.e. $P(xy_1) = P(y_1) \times P(x/y_1)$. From this we deduce that

$$P(x) \times P(y_1/x) = P(y_1) \times F(x/y_1).$$

By writing $P(y_1) = 1/k_1$, let

$$P(x/y_1) = k_1 P(x) \times P(y_1/x)$$

$$\left.\begin{array}{l} P_1(A) = k_1 P_0(A) \times P(1/A) \\ P_1(B) = k_1 P_0(B) \times P(1/B) \end{array}\right\} \text{ with } P_1(A) + P_1(B) = 1$$

But it is evident that

$$P(1/A) = 1/6$$

(if the dice is true our chance of obtaining 1 is 1 in 6)
and that

$$F(1/B) = 0.5$$

(if the dice is false our chance of obtaining 1 is 1 in 2).

Hence

$$P_1(A) = k_1 \times 0.8 \times \tfrac{1}{6},$$

$$P_1(B) = k_1 \times 0.2 \times \tfrac{1}{2},$$

$$1 = k_1 \left(\frac{0.8}{6} + \frac{0.2}{2}\right) \quad k_1 = 6/1 \cdot$$

and $P_1(A) = 0.57$ (when $P_1(B) = 0.43$).

Mr. Brown throws the dice a second time and again obtains 1 ($y_2 = 1$). For this second throw $P_1(A)$ is an *a priori* probability (see fig. 2.3).

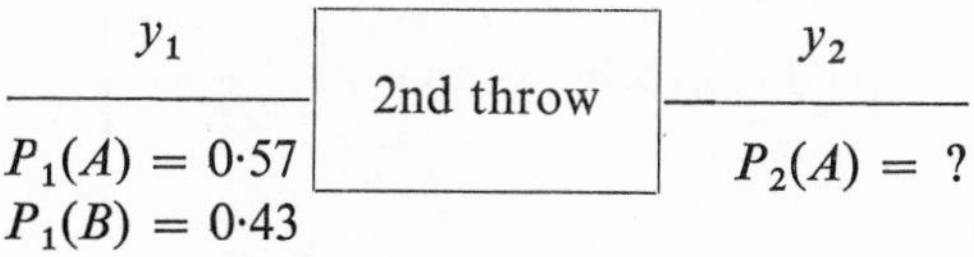

FIG. 2.3

We could now write

$$P_2(A) = k_2 P_1(A) \times P(1/A),$$

$$P_2(B) = k_2 P_1(B) \times P(1/B),$$

$$P_2(A) = k_2 0.57 \times \tfrac{1}{6} = 0.095 k_2 = 0.31,$$

$$P_2(B) = k_2 0.43 \times \tfrac{1}{2} = 0.215 k_2 = 0.69.$$

The final answer is therefore as follows. After two throws the probability of the dice being true is 0.31.

2.3 PROBABILITY OF THE EXISTENCE OR ABSENCE OF A SIGNAL IN A GAUSSIAN NOISE *A POSTERIORI* AFTER A SINGLE ATTEMPT

Let us suppose that a signal $S(t)$ could assume only two values, $S(t) = 0$ or $S(t) = V$, with an equal probability *a priori*:

$$P_0(S = 0) = P_0(S = V) = 0.5.$$

This signal is accompanied by a gaussian noise $n(t)$. At a given time we measure $S(t) + n(t) = y(t)$ and find a certain value y_0 which is the *a posteriori* probability that $S = V$, with $P_1(S = V)$.

Let us suppose $S = 0$. To say that the noise is gaussian is to imply that the probability that $y(t)$ lies between y and $y + dy$ is given by

$$P(y/S = 0) \, dy = k \exp \left(-\frac{y^2}{2N} \right) dy,$$

where N is the mean value of y^2 if $S = 0$, i.e. the mean value of n^2.

On the other hand, if we assume that $S = V$, it is evident that

$$P(y/S = V) \, dy = k \exp \left[-\frac{(y - V^2)}{2N} \right] dy$$

A calculation similar to that in the preceding paragraph gives

$$P_1(V) = k_1 P_0(V) \times P(y_0/S = V),$$

$$P_1(0) = k_1 P_0(0) \times P(y_0/S = 0),$$

so that,

$$P_1(V) = k_1 \times 0.5 \times \exp \left[-\frac{(y_0 - V)^2}{2N} \right]$$

and

$$P_1(0) = k_1 \times 0.5 \times \exp \left(-\frac{y_0^2}{2N} \right)$$

If $\qquad y_0 = 0.5V, \qquad P_1(V) = P_1(0) = 0.5.$

If $\qquad y_0 > 0.5V, \qquad P_1(V) > P_1(0).$

Example 1: $N = 0.1V^2$, $y_0 = V$: we find

$$P_1(V) = 0.5k_1 = 1 - 0.66 \cdot 10^{-2},$$

$$P_1(0) = 0.5k_1 \times 0.66 \cdot 10^{-2} = 0.66 \cdot 10^{-2}.$$

There is less than 1 per cent chance that $S = 0$.

Example 2: $N = 10V^2$, $y_0 = V$: we find

$$P_1(V) = 0{\cdot}5k_1 = 0{\cdot}515,$$
$$P_1(0) = 0{\cdot}5k_1 \times 0{\cdot}95 = 0{\cdot}485.$$

There is almost as much chance that $S = 0$ as there is that $S = V$.

REMARK

In the first example we could say that the power of the signal being V^2 and that of the noise $0{\cdot}1V^2$, the signal-to-noise ratio was equal to 10 (10 dB).

In the second example the ratio was equal to $0{\cdot}1$ (-10 dB).

2.4 *A POSTERIORI* PROBABILITY OF THE EXISTENCE OR ABSENCE OF A SIGNAL IN A GAUSSIAN NOISE AFTER SUCCESSIVE ATTEMPTS [1]

2.4.1 Let us assume that we must determine whether or not there is a signal after knowing that

(1) If there is a signal ($x = A$) without noise, we receive successively

$$S_1(A) = 10, \qquad S_2(A) = -10, \qquad S_3(A) = 10;$$

(2) If there is no signal ($x = B$) and no noise, we receive successively

$$S_1(B) = 0, \qquad S_2(B) = 0, \qquad S_3(B) = 0.$$

But in fact, we receive S_1, S_2 and S_3 each of these added to a random value n_1, n_2 and n_3, obtained by the sampling of a gaussian noise whose mean square is N, but white (in other words, the values n_1, n_2 and n_3 are independent, just as in the game of dice, where each value obtained has a probability of $1/6$ even if it had previously been obtained 6 times consecutively).

Let $P_0(A)$ and $P_0(B)$ be the *a priori* probabilities respectively of x being equal to A and x being equal to B.

After receiving $S_1 + n_1 = y_1$, we could write

$$P_1(A) = k_1 P_0(A) \exp\left[-\frac{(y_1 - S_1(A))^2}{2N}\right],$$

$$P_1(B) = k_1 P_0(B) \exp\left[-\frac{(y_1 - S_1(B))^2}{2N}\right],$$

$$P_1(A) = k_1 P_0(A) \exp\left[-\frac{(y_1 - 10)^2}{2N}\right],$$

$$P_1(B) = k_1 P_0(B) \exp\left(-\frac{y_1^2}{2N}\right).$$

E

After receiving $S_2 + n_2 = y_2$, we could write

$$P_2(A) = k_2 P_1(A) \exp\left[-\frac{(y_2+10)^2}{2N}\right],$$

$$P_2(B) = k_2 P_1(B) \exp\left(-\frac{y_2^2}{2N}\right).$$

Finally after receiving $y_3 = S_3 + n_3$:

$$P_3(A) = k_3 P_2(A) \exp\left[-\frac{(y_3-10)^2}{2N}\right],$$

$$P_3(B) = k_3 P_2(B) \exp\left(-\frac{y_3^2}{2N}\right).$$

In short,

$$P_3(A) = k P_0(A) \exp\left[-\frac{\Sigma[y_i - S_i(A)]^2}{2N}\right],$$

$$P_3(B) = k P_0(B) \exp\left[-\frac{\Sigma y_i^2}{2N}\right],$$

but we should also write

$$P_3(A) = k' P_0(A) \exp\left(-\frac{\Sigma S_i(A)^2}{2N}\right) \exp\left(\frac{\Sigma y_i S_i(A)}{N}\right),$$

$$P_3(B) = k' P_0(B).$$

If, for example, we take the case $(N = 100)$, where

$$n_1 = +10, \qquad n_2 = +7, \qquad n_3 = -5$$

and $x = A$ (which we are supposed to ignore), we receive

$$y_1 = 20, \qquad y_2 = -3, \qquad y_3 = +5.$$

The evaluation of $\Sigma S_i(A)^2/2N$ gives us $+1{\cdot}5$. We also find that

$$\frac{\Sigma y_i S_i(A)}{N} = \frac{200+30+50}{100} = 2{\cdot}8,$$

$$P_3(A) = k' P_0(A) \exp(1{\cdot}3) = k' P_0(A) \times 3{\cdot}7,$$

$$P_3(B) = k' P_0(B).$$

If *a priori* there is the same chance of having or not having a signal, i.e. if

$$P_0(A) = P_0(B) = 0{\cdot}5,$$

we find

$$P_3(A) = 0{\cdot}79;$$

$$P_3(B) = 0{\cdot}21.$$

A posteriori there is an 80 per cent chance that $x = A$.

2.4.2   There is an essential difference between the example just dealt with and the radar problem. We have assumed that there was only one possible position for the signal. In the case of the radar we do not know the location of the target, i.e. we do not know *a priori* where the signal is, if it exists.

To overcome this first lacuna, let us reconsider the preceding example, and let us assume that we receive 10 successive signals. If there were signals without noise, we could then receive

Position 1

$$S_{11} = 10 \qquad S_{12} = -10 \qquad S_{13} = 10 \qquad S_{14} = \;\; 0 \;\; 0 \;\; 0 \;\;\; 0 \;\;\; 0 \;\;\; 0 \;\;\; 0$$

Position 2

$$S_{21} = \;\; 0 \qquad S_{22} = 10 \qquad S_{23} = -10 \qquad\qquad 10 \;\; 0 \;\; 0 \;\;\; 0 \;\;\; 0 \;\;\; 0 \;\;\; 0$$

Position 7

$$0 \qquad\qquad 0 \qquad\qquad 0 \qquad\qquad 0 \;\; 0 \;\; 0 \;\; 10 - 10 \;\; 10 \;\;\; 0$$

Position 8

$$0 \qquad\qquad 0 \qquad\qquad 0 \qquad\qquad 0 \;\; 0 \;\; 0 \;\;\; 0 \;\; 10 - 10 \;\; 10$$

given that there are 8 possible positions for θ, from 1 to 8.

2.4.2.1   Let us suppose, for example, that the signal received is a superposition of a signal in the position 2 ($x = A$, $\theta = 2$) and of a gaussian noise ($N = 100$), giving for $n_1, n_2, \ldots, n_{10}$ the following values:

$$1, \; 0, \; 15, \; 5, \; -1, \; 1, \; 4, \; 2, \; -17, \; 3$$

the signal received being finally

$$y_1 = 1; \quad y_2 = 10; \quad y_3 = 5, \, 15, \, -1, \, 1, \, 4, \, 2, \, -17; \quad y_{10} = 3.$$

What could a receiver signify which does not *a priori* know that $x = A$ and $\theta = 2$ but which only knows *a priori* probabilities $P_0(A\theta)$ that there is a signal at θ and $P_0(B)$ that there is no signal?

Knowing y, the *a posteriori* probabilities can be written as

$$P_1(A\theta) = k_1 P_0(A\theta) \exp\left(-\frac{\sum\limits_i S_{\theta i}^2}{2N}\right) \exp\left(+\frac{\sum\limits_i y_i S_{\theta i}}{N}\right)$$

$$P_1(B) \;\; = k_1 P_0(B)$$

(In fact it is sufficient to carry out the summation over the duration of the signal, since outside it the signal $S = 0$.)

Knowing y, the *a posteriori* probability that there is a signal at any position can be written as

$$P_1(A) = k_1 \sum_\theta P_0(A\theta) \exp \left(-\frac{\sum_i S_{\theta i}^2}{2N} \right) \exp \left(+\frac{\sum_i y_i S_{\theta i}}{N} \right)$$

We obtain the following results:

$$-\frac{\sum_i S_{\theta i}^2}{2N} = -1 \cdot 5 \qquad\qquad \text{(independent of } \theta)$$

$$\frac{\sum_i y_i S_{1i}}{N} = -0 \cdot 4 \qquad \frac{\Sigma y S_2}{N} = 2 \qquad \frac{\Sigma y S_3}{N} = -1 \cdot 1$$

$$\frac{\Sigma y S_4}{N} = 1 \cdot 7 \qquad \frac{\Sigma y S_5}{N} = 0 \cdot 2 \qquad \frac{\Sigma y S_6}{N} = -0 \cdot 1$$

$$\frac{\Sigma y S_7}{N} = -1 \cdot 5 \qquad \frac{\Sigma y S_8}{N} = 2 \cdot 2$$

the corresponding exponentials being

$$0 \cdot 22$$
$$0 \cdot 67 \qquad 7 \cdot 4 \qquad 0 \cdot 33$$
$$5 \cdot 5 \qquad 1 \cdot 2 \qquad 0 \cdot 92$$
$$0 \cdot 3 \qquad 9 \cdot 1$$

In addition if we assume that

$$P(A\theta) = \frac{0 \cdot 5}{8} \quad \text{(independent of } \theta),$$

$$P(B) \ = 0 \cdot 5,$$

we find

$$P_1(A) = k_1 \times \frac{0 \cdot 5}{8} \times 0 \cdot 22 \, [0 \cdot 67 + 7 \cdot 4 + \ldots + 9 \cdot 1]$$

$$= k_1 \times \frac{0 \cdot 5}{8} \times 0 \cdot 22 \times 25 \cdot 4 = 0 \cdot 35 k_1 = 0 \cdot 41,$$

$$P_2(B) = 0 \cdot 5 k_1 = 0 \cdot 59.$$

When we know only
— the values of y,
— the nature of the signal if it exists,
— the value of N,
— the *a priori* probabilities that have been defined above,
we deduce:
— that there is a probability of 0·57 that there is no signal

.... of $\dfrac{0·41 \times 0·67}{25·4} = 0·01$ that there is a signal in position 1

.... of 0·12   that there is a signal in position 2
.... of 0·005 3
.... of 0·09   4
.... of 0·02   5
.... of 0·01   6
.... of 0·005 7
.... of 0·15   8

REMARK

If we had certainly known *a priori* that there was a signal then, these eight positions being *a priori* equally probable, the experiment would have led us to conclude that
— the probability of position 2: 0·29
— the probability of position 8: 0·37.

2.4.2.2 Let us assume that the experiment was conducted with a weaker noise ($N = 25$ instead of 100), the samples of the noise being divided by 2, the signal received (signal position $2 +$ noise) becoming

0·5   10 $-2·5$ 12·5 $-0·5$ 0·5   2   1 $-8·5$ 1·5

We then find

$$\frac{\sum\limits_i S_{\theta i}^2}{2N} = -6$$

$$\frac{\Sigma y S_1}{N} = -2·8 \qquad \frac{\Sigma y S_2}{N} = 8 \qquad \frac{\Sigma y S_3}{N} = -4·2$$

$$\frac{\Sigma y S_4}{N} = 5 \qquad \frac{\Sigma y S_5}{N} = 0·4 \qquad \frac{\Sigma y S_6}{N} = -0·2$$

$$\frac{\Sigma y S_7}{N} = -3 \qquad \frac{\Sigma y S_8}{N} = 4·4$$

the corresponding exponentials being

$$2\cdot5 \ \cdot 10^{-3}$$

0·07	$3 \ \cdot 10^3$	0·02
$0\cdot15\cdot10^3$	1·5	0·8
0·05	$0\cdot08\cdot10^3$	

Then

$$P_1(A) = k_1 \times \frac{0\cdot5}{8} \times 2\cdot5 \cdot 10^{-3}[3200] = 0\cdot5k_1 = 0\cdot5;$$

$$P_1(B) = k_1 \times 0\cdot5 = 0\cdot5.$$

This time we conclude

— that there is a probability of 0·5 for the absence of the signal

....	of 10^{-5}	for a signal in position.......... 1
....	of 0·48	 2
....	of 10^{-6}	 3
....	of 0·02	 4
....	of 10^{-4}	 5
....	of 10^{-4}	 6
....	of 10^{-5}	 7
....	of 0·005	 8

2.4.2.3 Let us finally assume that the experiment was conducted with an even weaker noise ($N = 6\cdot2$) corresponding to the samples of noises of sub-section 2.4.2.2 divided by 2, the signal received (signal position 2+noise) becoming:

0·2	10	−6·2	11·3	−0·2	0·3	1	0·5	−4·3	0·7

This time we get:

$$-\frac{\sum_i S_{\theta i}^2}{2N} = -24$$

$$\frac{\Sigma y S_1}{N} = -26 \qquad \frac{\Sigma y S_2}{N} = 44 \qquad \frac{\Sigma y S_3}{N} = -28$$

$$\frac{\Sigma y S_4}{N} = 19 \qquad \frac{\Sigma y S_5}{N} = 1 \qquad \frac{\Sigma y S_6}{N} = 0$$

$$\frac{\Sigma y S_7}{N} = -6 \qquad \frac{\Sigma y S_8}{N} = 9$$

with the following corresponding exponentials

$$3 \cdot 7 \cdot 10^{-11}$$

$$0 \qquad 1 \cdot 3 \cdot 10^{19} \qquad 0$$

$$2 \cdot 10^{8} \qquad 3 \qquad 0$$

$$0 \qquad 10^{4}$$

$$P_1(A) = k_1 \times \frac{0 \cdot 5}{8} \times 3 \cdot 7 \cdot 10^{-11} \times 1 \cdot 3 \cdot 10^{19} = 1 - 2 \cdot 10^{-8},$$

$$P_1(B) = k_1 \times 0 \cdot 5 = 2 \cdot 10^{-8}.$$

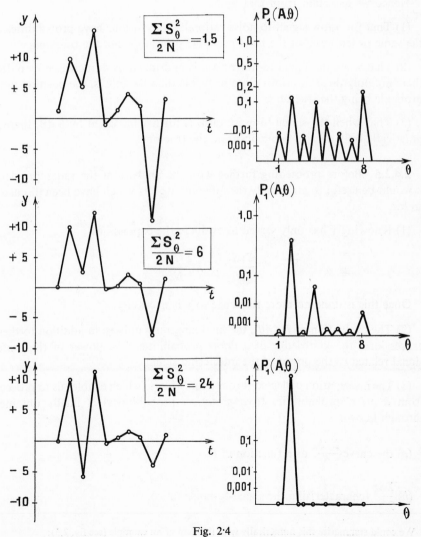

Fig. 2·4

The probability that there is no signal or that there is a signal in a position other than 2 is less than 10^{-7}.

2.4.2.4   Figure 2.4 shows on the left-hand side the signal received as function of time t, and on the right-hand side the probability of existence as a function of the position θ in the three cases envisaged. These correspond successively to the same experiment but with the signal-to-noise ratio (represented by $\Sigma S_\theta^2/2N$) increasing with each trial.

Hence we ascertain from that figure,

(1) That for a low signal-to-noise ratio all the positions have probabilities of the same order and that the most probable position is not the true one;

(2) That when the signal-to-noise ratio is multiplied by 4 (increased by 6 dB), there are only three positions more probable than the others, the position most probable being the true one;

(3) That when the signal-to-noise ratio is further increased by 6 dB, there is practically only one probable position, the true one.

2.4.2.5   Before proceeding further with the analysis of the radar problem, it would be useful to grasp fully the different aspects which have been discussed so far.

(1) Knowing y has only served to evaluate the expressions

$$\frac{\Sigma y S_1}{N}, \ldots, \frac{\Sigma y S_\theta}{N}.$$

Once this is done no more reference to y is necessary.

(2) The evaluation of $P_1(A\theta)$, the final aim, only utilises, in addition to these expressions, the knowledge of *a priori* probabilities, the power of the useful signal related to the power of the interfering signal.

(3) The information collected through knowing y (which enables us to proceed from *a priori* probabilities to *a posteriori* probabilities) is finally obtained through knowing

(a) the curve $\dfrac{\Sigma y S_\theta}{N}$ as a function of θ,

(b) $\dfrac{\Sigma S_\theta^2}{2N}$ (characterising the signal-to-noise ratio).

We could summarise this numerically with the help of an example (see fig. 2.5):

For a position to be more probable than others (e.g. 100 times), for there to be no risk of ambiguity, it is necessary that

$$\exp\left(\frac{\Sigma y S_i}{N}\right) > 100 \exp\left(\frac{\Sigma y S_j}{N}\right) j \neq i$$

$$\boxed{\frac{\Sigma y S_i}{N} > 4{\cdot}6 + \frac{\Sigma y S_j}{N}}$$

This inequality defines a "threshold of ambiguity".

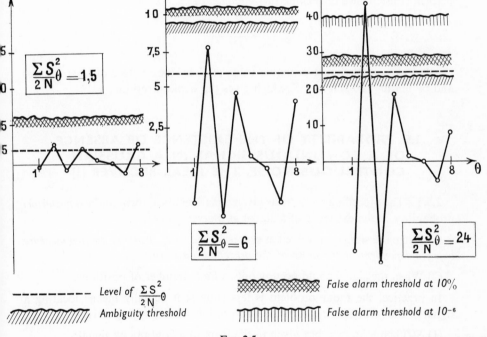

$$\boxed{\frac{\Sigma S^2_\theta}{2N} = 1{,}5}$$

$$\boxed{\frac{\Sigma S^2_\theta}{2N} = 6}$$

$$\boxed{\frac{\Sigma S^2_\theta}{2N} = 24}$$

— — — — — — Level of $\frac{\Sigma S^2_\theta}{2N}$

////////// Ambiguity threshold

XXXXXXX False alarm threshold at 10%

||||||||||| False alarm threshold at 10^{-6}

FIG. 2.5

In this case to write that the probability that the signal exists at i is at least 90 per cent would practically mean writing

$$\frac{\exp\left(\dfrac{\Sigma y S_i}{N} - \dfrac{\Sigma S^2_\theta}{2N}\right)}{8} > 10$$

$$\boxed{\frac{\Sigma y S_i}{N} > \frac{\Sigma S^2_9}{2N} + 4{\cdot}4}$$

If this inequality is verified, the probability of committing a mistake by saying that there is signal at i is less than 0·1: we could say that
The probability of a false alarm is less than 10 per cent;
The inequality (2) defines a threshold of false alarm at 10 per cent.
Similarly the inequality (3) given below defines the threshold of false alarm at 10^{-6}.

$$\boxed{\frac{\Sigma y S_i}{N} > \frac{\Sigma S_\theta^2}{2N} + 15 \cdot 9}$$

2.4.2.6 We notice that if we are to find the *maximum* of $\Sigma y S_i / N$, i.e. to find the "correlation" between y and each of the S_i, it is only because it is the mathematical consequence of seeking the *minimum* of

$$\frac{\Sigma (y - S_i)^2}{2N}$$

i.e. that we seek the most probable value of S_i by the method of least squares and by finding the value of S_i which gives the weakest residue.

2.5 PROBABILITY OF THE EXISTENCE OR ABSENCE OF A CONTINUOUS SIGNAL IN A GAUSSIAN CONTINUOUS NOISE. THE IDEAL RECEIVER [1]

2.5.1 The preceding section has given a mathematical form to the *a posteriori* probability of the existence of a signal at a given place:

(1) When the signal is received at successive instants, *the noise at each measure being independent of the noise of the preceding measure*;

(2) When the signal could occupy only a finite number of positions.

In practice, the radar problem is less simple: it actually means locating a signal of the form $S(t - t_{01})^1$ in the midst of the accompanying noise $n(t)$:

(1) $S(t)$ being known, but given in the form of a continuous signal;

(2) $n(t)$ being known only by its statistical properties and by also being continuous;

(3) t_{01} assuming all values t_0 (of a given interval).

Using a classical method, we shall try to replace the continuous functions $S(t)$ and $n(t)$ by successive samples such that we are led to the study of independent successive trials.

---

[1] In fact of the form $kS(t - t_{01})$ (see section 2.1). But in order not to overburden the calculations, we make $k = 1$ here. It is easily seen that this simplification does not change anything in the conclusions.

2.5.2 Let us assume that the signal $S(t)$ lasts a time T and occupies a frequency band of width Δf ($\Phi(f)$ being zero for $|f| > \Delta f/2$, in other words, $S(t)$ is now assumed to be a "video" signal).

Let us also assume the noise $n(t)$ accompanying the eventual signal $S(t-t_{01})$ is a *gaussian* noise uniformly occupying the same frequency band Δf, its mean power being N.

We define by $p(t_0)$ the *a priori* probability that there is a signal $S(t-t_0)$ (signal at t_0). (In fact here we mean the density probability.)

We measure $y(t)$, which is the sum of $n(t)$ and an eventual signal $S(t-t_0)$. Knowing $y(t)$ what is the *a posteriori* probability distribution $p(t_0/y)$?

We know that if we sample $y(t)$ at consecutive intervals of time distant from each other by $1/\Delta f$, then we make the maximum of independent measurements (compare with section 1.7).

Let $t_1, t_2, \ldots, t_n$ be the $T\Delta f$ instants of the sampling, and $y(t_1), y(t_2), \ldots, t(t_n)$ the corresponding values of $y(t)$.

As in sub-section 2.4.2, we can write

$$p(t_0/y) = k_1 p(t_0) \exp \left[-\frac{\Sigma[y(t_i) - S(t_i - t_0)]^2}{2N} \right]$$

$$p(t_0/y) = k_2 p(t_0) \exp \left[-\frac{\Sigma S(t_i - t_0)^2}{2N} \right] \times \exp \left[\frac{\Sigma[y(t_i) \cdot S(t_i - t_0)]}{N} \right],$$

$$p(t_0/y) = k_2 p(t_0) \exp \left[-\frac{\Sigma S(t_i - t_0)^2 \cdot 1/\Delta F}{2N/\Delta F} \right] \times \exp \left[\frac{\Sigma y(t_i) \cdot S(t_i - t_0) \cdot 1/\Delta F}{N/\Delta F} \right]$$

which we can replace by

$$p(t_0/y) = k_2 p(t_0) \exp \left(-\frac{1}{2b} \int_T S(t-t_0)^2 \, dt \right) \times \exp \left(\frac{1}{b} \int_T y(t) \cdot S(t-t_0) \, dt \right)$$

$$(1)$$

where $b = N/\Delta F$ represents the density of the power of the noise for unit width of the band, i.e. by Hz.

REMARKS

We notice that the above expression has a meaning even if the (gaussian) noise $n(t)$ does not occupy uniformly the band Δf, i.e. even if the spectral density of $n(t)$ is not constant in Δf. If such is the case, then b represents the average density only.

It must be recalled that this expression assumes that the noise $n(t)$ is gaussian, which is a correct assumption:

(1) Because it has been shown that a noise possesses more entropies (i.e. it is more jamming) if it is gaussian.

(2) Because, on the other hand, if the noise (jamming) is not gaussian then the totality of anti-jamming systems have precisely the effect of making it gaussian.

But should the noise $n(t)$ be decidedly not gaussian, then the theories presented here would have to be modified.

Another observation that is essential is the following. The passage from the series to the integrals could appear to be not rigorous enough, or to be rigorous only if $T\Delta f$ is large enough. It is not so, as is shown by various other proofs (which are simpler, but which do not allow one to understand—as the previous proof does, due to Woodward—what happens exactly, and the various conclusions that can be drawn from it).

First conclusion

The knowledge of $y(t)$ intervenes only by the expression

$$\int_T y(t) \cdot S(t-t_0)\, \mathrm{d}t$$

It follows that a receiver (calculator) which performs the calculation of the average product, over the period during which the signal is received, of the received signal by the signal which is assumed to exist, is a receiver sufficient to contain all the information about $y(t)$.

Definition of an ideal receiver

When we have information about the probability of the target's existence (see section 3.3 on the considerations of the probability of a false alarm), if we are satisfied in comparing the different possible positions of t_0 to seek the most probable position, then it is easy to see that since the integral

$$\int_T S(t-t_0)^2\, \mathrm{d}t$$

being independent of t_0, we could replace (1) by the following:

$$p(t_0/y) = k_3 p(t_0) \times \exp\left(\frac{1}{b}\int_T y(t) \cdot S(t-t_0)\, \mathrm{d}t\right) \qquad (2)$$

And if, in addition, we assume that $p(t_0)$ as a function of t_0 is not variable by very much in comparison with the variations of the other factor (a hypothesis quite normal in the extreme majority of practical applications), we could, in order to find the maxima of $p(t_0/y)$ (i.e. to find the most probable positions), replace expression (2) by the following

$$p(t_0/y) = K \times \exp\left(\frac{1}{b}\int_T y(t) \cdot S(t-t_0)\, \mathrm{d}t\right) \qquad (3)$$

i.e. the most probable positions are these that render maximum

$$C(t_0) = \frac{1}{b}\int_T y(t) \cdot S(t-t_0)\, dt \qquad (4)$$

Thus we conclude that *we have to find the cross-correlation of the signal received and the signal transmitted* in order to obtain an expression

(1) Whose size represents the possibility of the presence of a target,

(2) Whose maxima correspond to the most probable positions of the target.

We shall, therefore, say that *a receiver is ideal when it makes this correlation of the received signal with the transmitted signal.*

CHAPTER 3

PERFORMANCE OF RADARS EQUIPPED
WITH IDEAL RECEIVERS

3.1 TWO METHODS OF MAKING AN IDEAL RECEIVER

It was explained in Chapter 2 why an ideal receiver had to make the calculation of

$$C(t_0) = \frac{1}{b} \int_T y(t) \cdot S(t - t_0) \, dt.$$

The first procedure to obtain $C(t_0)$ consists of effectively applying this formula by forming the product of $y(t)$ (the signal received) by as many values of $S(t - t_0)$ as desired—values which we obtain from a sample (reference) of transmitted signal conveniently retarded—and then by integrating this product over the time T. We thus obtain a receiver called a correlation receiver. The noisy radar or the pulse Doppler radar, described in sections 4.1 and 4.2, use correlation receivers.

But we could obtain $C(t_0)$ differently, by using the theorem of convolution (see section 1.5).

Denoting the Fourier transform of the signal received $y(t)$ by $\mathscr{Y}(f)$ we could write the identity,

$$C(t_0) = \frac{1}{b} \int_T y(t) \times S(t - t_0) \, dt \equiv \frac{1}{b} \int_{\Delta f} \mathscr{Y}(f) \Phi(-f) \exp(2\pi j f t_0) \, df \qquad (5)$$

Thus by making $y(t)$ pass through a filter called "matched" to the transmitted signal $S(t)$, having $\Phi(-p/2\pi j)$ for a transfer function, we obtain at the output of the filter the expression $C(t)$ modulo a constant factor, i.e. something like a $C(t_0)$ in "real time".

Could such a filter exist?

It is easy to show that if such a filter does exist, its response to a Dirac pulse is $S(-t)$, i.e. that if $S(t)$ begins to exist at $t = 0$, the response of a matched filter to a Dirac pulse (also placed at $t = 0$) ends at the instant of excitation, which is evidently physically impossible.

Thus such a matched filter cannot exist.

63

On the contrary, nothing prevents us from conceiving a filter which gives as a response to a Dirac pulse $\delta(t)$ and in the same conditions a signal of the form $S(T_1 - t)$, from the moment that T_1 is greater than the duration T of the signal $S(t)$, i.e. a filter equivalent to a delay-line, resulting in a delay T_1, followed by a matched filter. The passage of $y(t)$ through such a filter (which we shall again call "matched") as an extension, gives at the output no longer $C(t)$ but $C(t-T_1)$, which does not worry us once we know T_1.

Another way of characterising a matched filter consists in noting that

(1) The amplitude of its transfer function is equal to $|\Phi(f)|$,

(2) The phase of its transfer function is the opposite of the argument of $\Phi(f)$.

Thus we see that the matched filter fed at the input with a replica of the transmitted signal $S(t)$ gives a signal at the output

(1) Whose Fourier transform has for absolute value $|\Phi(f)|^2$,

(2) Zero phase.

In other words, a matched filter removes the phase modulation of a signal $S(t)$ passing through it. Therefore a receiver having a matched filter is also an ideal receiver. A good classical radar uses (to some degree) a receiver with a matched filter (see section 4.4) and so does the pulse compression radar (see section 4.5).

3.2 NATURE OF THE OUTPUT SIGNAL OF AN IDEAL RECEIVER

Let us suppose that there is a target "at t_{01}". The signal $y(t)$ received can be expressed (see section 2.1) as

$$y(t) = kS(t-t_{01})+n(t) \tag{6}$$

and the output of an ideal receiver can be written as

$$C(t_0) = C_u(t_0)+C_p(t_0) \tag{7}$$

with

$$C_u(t_0) = \frac{1}{b}\int_T kS(t-t_{01}) \cdot S(t-t_0) \, \mathrm{d}t \tag{8}$$

$$C_p(t_0) = \frac{1}{b}\int_T n(t) \cdot S(t-t_0) \, \mathrm{d}t \tag{9}$$

The output signal of an ideal receiver is the sum

(1) Of a "useful" signal $C_u(t_0)$, the only one which we will have in the absence of the noise;

(2) Of an "interfering" (parasitic) signal $C_p(t_0)$, the only one which we will have in the absence of the target.

3.2.1   Properties of the useful signal

$C_u(t_0)$ is, modulo a factor kT/b, the autocorrelation function of the useful signal $S(t)$, on condition that $\tau = t_0 - t_{01}$:

$$C_u(t_0) = \frac{kT}{b} \times \frac{1}{T} \int_T S(u) \cdot S(u - \tau) \, du \qquad \text{with} \qquad u = t - t_{01}$$

$$C_u(t_0) = \frac{kT}{b} \, \rho(t_0 - t_{01}). \tag{10}$$

$C_u(t_0)$ is therefore maximal for $t_0 - t_{01}$, which is a consolation since we find that in the absence of noise ($n(t)$ and hence $C_p(t_0)$ being zero) $C(t_0)$ is maximal (and therefore $p(t_0/y)$) for $t_0 = t_{01}$. In the absence of noise the ideal receiver indicates that the most probable position of the target is its true position.

The form of $C_u(t_0)$ depends only on $|\Phi(f)|^2$, modulo a factor, since the Fourier transform of $\rho(\tau)$ is equal to $|\Phi(f)|^2$ modulo a factor. It follows that the form of the useful signal at the output of the radar equipped with an ideal receiver depends only on the absolute value of the Fourier transform of the transmitted signal and not at all on the phase of this Fourier transform.

Two radars, for example, transmitting signals $S_1(t)$ and $S_2(t)$ of very different durations could give the same useful signal at the receiver if their spectrums differ only in the phases of their components.

The value of $C_u(t_0)$ for $t_0 = t_{01}$ (the amplitude of the useful signal at the range of the target) is easily obtained as:

$$C_u(t_{01}) = \frac{1}{bk} \int_T [kS(t - t_{01})]^2 \, dt.$$

As $[kS(t - t_{01})]^2$ is the "power" of the signal received, its integral over the duration T of the signal is the energy of the signal received such that the amplitude of the useful signal is given by

$$C_u(t_{01}) = \frac{1}{k} \cdot \frac{E}{b} = \frac{R}{k} \tag{11}$$

where R denotes the signal-to-noise ratio in energy of the received signal.

$$R = \frac{\text{Energy of the received signal}}{\text{Spectral density of the accompanying noise}} \tag{12}$$

the ratio being a pure number, which is expressed in decibels.

REMARK

In sub-section 2.5.2 we assumed that $S(t)$ had a video spectrum, such that the maximum of $C(t_0)$ is "practically" unique (see section 3.4).

F

3.2.2 Properties of the interfering signal

The interfering signal can be written as

$$C_p(t_0) = \frac{1}{b}\sum n(t_i) \cdot S(t_i - t_0) \cdot \frac{1}{\Delta f},$$

t_i being the instants of sampling, each apart by $1/\Delta f$.

It is thus, modulo a factor $1/b\Delta f$, the sum of $T\Delta f$ independent terms which are the product of a known value by a random gaussian variable $n(t_i)$ of mean value zero, having a certain variance $N = \overline{n^2(t_i)}$, the noise power in the band Δf.

$C_p^2(t_0)$ is also, therefore, a random gaussian variable of mean value zero, and whose variance $\overline{C_p^2(t_0)}$ is the sum of the variances of each of the terms.

$$\overline{C_p^2(t_0)} = \frac{1}{b^2\Delta^2 f}\sum N \cdot S^2(t_i - t_0) = \frac{1}{b}\sum S^2(t_i - t_0)\times\frac{1}{\Delta f}$$

$$\overline{C_p^2(t_0)} = \frac{1}{b}\int_T S^2(t - t_0)\,\mathrm{d}t = \frac{1}{bk^2}\int [kS(t - t_0)]^2\,\mathrm{d}t$$

$$\overline{C_p^2(t_0)} = R/k^2 \tag{13}$$

3.2.3 Conclusions

We could therefore say that the signal at the output of an ideal receiver is, modulo a factor $1/k$, the sum

(1) Of a function having a maximum amplitude R at $t_0 = t_{01}$ (useful signal);

(2) Of a random gaussian function of mean value zero and standard deviation $\sqrt{R}$ (interfering signal);

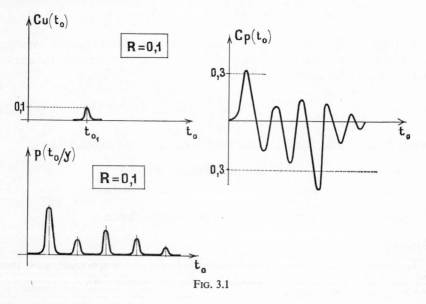

FIG. 3.1

Or again that it is, modulo a factor $\sqrt{R}/k$, the sum

(1) Of a function having a maximum of amplitude $\sqrt{R}$ at $t_0 = t_{01}$ (useful signal);

(2) And a random gaussian interfering signal of mean value zero and standard deviation 1.

If, therefore, $R \ll 1$, $C(t_0)$ has many maxima, the value t_{01} not corresponding normally to a specific maximum and $p(t_0/y)$ also has numerous maxima (see fig. 3.1).

If, on the other hand, $R \gg 1$, $C(t_0)$ has almost certainly a maximum very close to t_{01} (see fig. 3.2).

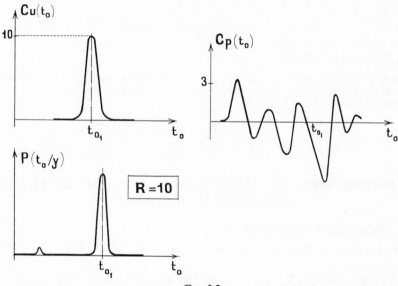

FIG. 3.2

3.2.4 Remarks

At the output of the receiver, the power of the useful signal is

$$C_u^2(t_{01}) = R^2/k^2,$$

the power of the interfering signal is

$$\overline{C_p^2(t_0)} = R/k^2.$$

The signal-to-noise ratio in power is therefore equal to R (see the remark at the end of section 3.4).

We could say that an ideal receiver gives at the output a signal-to-noise ratio equal in power to the signal-to-noise ratio in energy at the input.

Classical theories have made use of the signal-to-noise ratio in power SB at the input of the receiver. Modern theories replace it with the signal-to-noise ratio in energy, the only one which has a physical meaning and the only one which appears in what follows.

In the case in which the transmission signal $S(t)$ (and hence the useful signal received) has a constant power P during its duration T, we could write,

$$SB = \frac{P}{N} = \frac{E}{T} \times \frac{1}{b\Delta f}$$

$$SB = \frac{R}{T\Delta f}$$

If $T\Delta f \approx 1$ (case of a classical radar), $SB \approx R$.

If $T\Delta f$ is very large, $R \gg SB$ such that it is sometimes said that the receiver improves the signal-to-noise ratio in the ratio $T\Delta f$, a ratio which could be very high, attaining 10^5 or 10^6.

It is also possible to consider a spectral density b' equal to the quotient $N/(\Delta F/2)$ of the noise power by the width of the positive frequency band occupied by that noise.

Under these conditions, R can be written as,

$$R = \frac{E}{N/\Delta f} = \frac{2E}{b'}.$$

3.3 PROBABILITY OF FALSE ALARM AND OF DETECTION AMBIGUITY IN DISTANCE

3.3.1 False alarm probability

The calculations in sections 2.5 and 3.2 do not, in fact, differ from those in section 2.4.

Let us therefore assume that a signal $S(t - t_0)$ exists at a certain range t_{01} (and that its spectrum is video, centred at zero frequency).

If the noise is significant, we find in general an *a posteriori* probability distribution $p(t_0/y)$ having a number of peaks of similar importance. We do not *know* anything.

When the noise power diminishes, the number of peaks also diminishes. We could be mistaken over the position t_0 of the signal.

When the noise power becomes very weak, the probability distribution $p(t_0/y)$ practically consists of only a single peak around t_{01} (see figs. 3.1, 3.2 and 3.3, and compare with fig. 2.4).

In other words, if there is a target, there is a good chance of mislocating it and assuming a noise signal to be the target if $R \ll 1$; while on the contrary, there is a good chance of correct location of the target if $R \gg 1$ (i.e. not making a great error over the position of t_{01}).

It is customary (this corresponds to most practical methods) to define a threshold in the following way:

We fix the threshold so that in the absence of a useful signal (for example, when t_0 is very different from t_{01}) $C_p(t_0)$, which is equal to $C(t_0)$, has a very low probability of crossing it, and we take into account only those values of t_0 for which $C(t_0)$ crosses this threshold.

Hence, when $C(t_0)$ crosses the threshold we say that there is a target; but when $C(t_0)$ does not cross it, we say that there is no target.

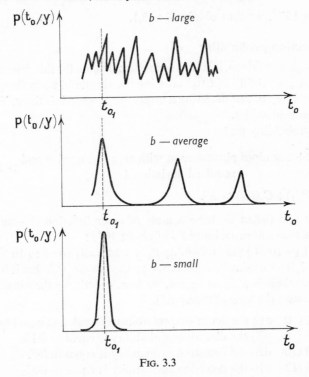

FIG. 3.3

It is possible that $C_p(t_0)$ will cross the threshold, and we decide that there is a target while there is in fact none, thus obtaining a false alarm. The probability that, for a certain value t_0, $C(t_0)$ crossing the threshold is called the false alarm probability.

The higher the false alarm probability the greater is the possibility of detecting dummy targets, and the greater is the chance—in the case of a proximity fuse radar—of destroying the target for no real reason, or of seeing a large number of dummy targets on the radar display.

The tolerable false alarm probability (the average number of false plots per second) is given by operational or technical considerations, such as saturation of computers, and this fixes the threshold.

Referring this threshold to the standard deviation of the parasitic signal $C_p(t_0)$, the false alarm probability P_f shall be given, for example, by the probability that a random gaussian function of zero mean value and standard deviation 1 crosses the threshold K:

$$P_f = \frac{1}{\sqrt{2\pi}} \int_K^{+\infty} \exp{(-v^2/2)}\,dv \qquad (14)$$

For $P_f = 10^{-3}$, we thus obtain $K \approx 3.1$.

3.3.2 Detection probability

Under these conditions, it is interesting to calculate for this false alarm probability P_f the probability of $C(t_0)$ crossing the threshold when there is a target, i.e. the probability of our detecting a target at t_{01} when it is there. This is called the detection probability.

It is the probability that

$$\sqrt{R}+\text{a random phenomenon with zero mean value and} \atop \text{standard deviation 1} > K$$

$[C_u(t_{01})+C_p(t_{01}) > K]$.

We easily find (when we have a table of error function Θ—see Appendix) that for a false alarm probability P_f of about 10^{-3}:

If $R = 0.1\,(-10\text{ dB})$ the probability P_d is practically equal to 10^{-3} (the signal $C_u(t_{01}) = 0.1$ is so weak when compared to the noise $C_p(t_0)$ that it is not significant: whether there is a signal or not, we have practically the same probability that $C(t_0)$ crosses the level of threshold).

If $R = 1\,(0\quad\text{dB})$ the detection probability is weak and equal to 0.02.
If $R = 4\,(6\quad\text{dB})$ the detection probability is equal to 0.15.
If $R = 10\,(10\quad\text{dB})$ the detection probability is equal to 0.5.
If $R = 16\,(12\quad\text{dB})$ the detection probability is equal to 0.85.
If $R = 25\,(14\quad\text{dB})$ the detection probability is equal to 0.98.
If $R = 36\,(15.5\text{ dB})$ the detection probability is equal to 0.999 (see fig. 3.4).

(See also the first figure at the end of the text.)

In addition, we generally have

$$P_d = \frac{1}{\sqrt{2\pi}} \int_{K-\sqrt{R}}^{+\infty} \exp{(-v^2/2)}\,dv \qquad (15)$$

We see that the possibility of the existence of ambiguous peaks due to noise forces us to take precautions, so that we can hope to detect the targets only if the value of R is sufficiently large (i.e. of the order of 13 dB here if we desire a detection probability of 0·9).

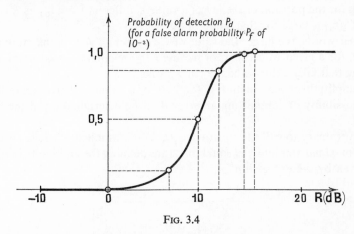

FIG. 3.4

The detection probability of 0·5 is obtained when the probability of $C_p(t_0)$ —random gaussian phenomenon with a zero mean—being greater than $K - \sqrt{R}$ is 0·5, which is clearly obtained for $K - \sqrt{R} = 0$, $R = K^2$.

We see naturally that for a given P_f (K given), P_d is an increasing function of R.

3.3.3 Ambiguity in distance

3.3.3.1 The first aspect of ambiguity

The function $C_u(t_0)$ always gives the *maximum maximorum* for $t_0 = t_{01}$, but it could

(1) Decrease more or less slowly when t_0 moves away from t_{01}.

(2) Give other maxima less important, for values of t_0 different from t_{01} (see fig. 3.5).

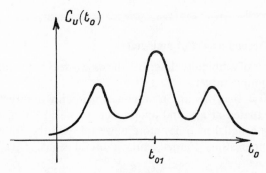

FIG. 3.5

This clearly shows that if R is very large, then $C(t)$ shall always be maximal for t_0 very close to t_{01}; but that once R is not so large, we have as much chance of giving for the position of the target a value t_0 different from t_{01} as R is small, and as $C_u(t_0)$ is large for that value of t_0.

In other words, the larger the value of $C_u(t_0)$ (for $t_0 \neq t_{01}$), the more chance we have, for a given value of R, of finding $C(t_0)$ maximal at that point, and of assuming that false value to be the correct one.

The amplitude of the function $C_u(t_{01} + \theta)$ for a value of θ gives an indication of the possibility of committing an error θ in the determination of the target's position.

It is customary to call the function $C_u(t_{01} + \theta)$ "ambiguity". It is normed so that the maximal ambiguity is equal to 1, thus defining the ambiguity in distance $\mathscr{A}(\theta)$ given by the expression

$$\mathscr{A}(\theta) = \frac{\displaystyle\int_T S(t) \cdot S(t - \theta)\, dt}{\displaystyle\int_T S^2(t)\, dt} \tag{16}$$

REMARK

In electronics, scientists have the habit (sometimes wrong and sometimes justified) of using imaginary notations: of writing exp ($j\omega t$) instead of cos ωt. If such is the case here, we must replace the above expression[1] with the following:

$$\mathscr{A}(\theta) = \frac{\displaystyle\int_T S(t) \cdot S^*(t - \theta)\, dt}{\displaystyle\int |S(t)|^2\, dt} \tag{17}$$

3.3.3.2 The second aspect of ambiguity

The first aspect of ambiguity describes the case (ideal but rare) where we have to deal with a unique target.

Let us suppose that we are now concerned with a target designated as "interesting", situated at t_{01}, and another target called "parasitic" situated at $t_{01} + \theta$, emitting a signal p^2 times more powerful than the "interesting" target, i.e. that the "interesting" target emits a useful signal $C_u(t_0)$ and that the

---

[1] And, as in every similar case, to be careful in the interpretation of these calculations.

"parasitic" one emits the signal $pC_u(t_0 - \theta)$ whose value at t_{01}, at the position of the interesting target, is equal to

$$pC_u(t_{01} - \theta) = pC_u(t_{01} + \theta)$$

or

$$p \mathscr{A}(\theta) \times C_u(t_{01})$$

In other words, at the site of the interesting target, the parasitic target gives a signal whose amplitude is $p|\mathscr{A}(\theta)|$ times that of the interesting target.

In other words, the parasitic signal has a power, at the position of the interesting target, whose ratio with the power of the interesting signal is

$$p^2 |\mathscr{A}^2(\theta)|,$$

i.e. the ratio of the powers of the echoes of the targets multiplied by the square of the ambiguity at the relative distance θ of the parasitic target (with respect to the interesting target).

The weaker the ambiguity at the position of the interfering target, the less does it disturb the interesting target.

The ambiguity $\mathscr{A}(\theta)$ gives the positions (peaks of $\mathscr{A}(\theta)$) where parasitic targets are not recommended to be sought: these are better found situated in the minima of $|\mathscr{A}(\theta)|$.

3.4 REVISION OF RESULTS WHEN THE USEFUL SIGNAL IS A MICROWAVE SIGNAL

For reasons of convenience (constructing antennae, propagation) in the case of radars we are led to utilise a signal $S(t)$ occupying a frequency spectrum of very small width with respect to one of the frequencies of the spectrum: for example, a spectrum lying between 10,000 and 10,001 MHz.

In this case (see, in particular, sub-section 1.6.1) the autocorrelation function of the useful signal possesses a large number of maxima (around 10,000 in the given example, each of them 10^{-10} sec apart).

In other words, $C_u(t_0)$ can be written as

$$\gamma_u(t_0) \cos(2\pi f t_0 + \varphi_1),$$

where f is fixed in the order of 10,000 MHz here) and $\gamma_u(t_0)$ and φ_1 vary slowly as functions of t_0 (with respect to the rapid variation of $\cos(2\pi f t_0 + \varphi_1)$.

This implies that, even for a large R, the a posteriori distribution $p(t_0/y)$ will possess a large number of peaks (10^{-10} sec apart in the given example) due to the fact that $C(t_0)$ is also of the form

$$C(t_0) = \gamma(t_0) \cos(2\pi f t_0 + \varphi)$$

where $\gamma(t_0)$ is the envelope (positive) of $C(t_0)$, which contains relatively inaccurate information on the position of the target, and φ contains information to the fourth or fifth decimal of this position. Since, in practice, we can never attain this degree of precision, it is not useful to conserve the information given by φ and to keep a distribution with a large number of peaks close to each other. (It is not feasible to consider measuring the position of an aircraft or missile at 0·1 mm!)

A radar, even an ideal one, could therefore destroy this information over φ, which we do by assuming that all the values of φ are equiprobable and by integrating over φ, which gives

$$p(t_0/y) = k'p(t_0) \int_0^{2\pi} \exp\left[\gamma(t_0)(2\pi f t_0 + \varphi)\right] \mathrm{d}\varphi$$

$$p(t_0/y) = k'p(t_0) I_0[\gamma(t_0)]$$

(I_0 is the modified Bessel function

$$I_0 \approx \exp x\,(2\pi x)^{-\frac{1}{2}}\left[1 + \frac{1}{8x} + \ldots\right]\bigg)$$

Therefore a receiver detecting a signal $C(t_0)$ with a "characteristic of detection" of the form $I_0(x)$ can also be considered as an ideal receiver. In addition, as the moment R is very large (which, as we have seen, was indispensable), $I_0(\gamma(t_0))$ behaves like $\exp(\gamma(t_0))$.

Under these conditions, it can be considered that the computations and the formulae given in this chapter remain valid, bearing in mind the remark at the end of sub-section 3.2.4, i.e. if R is defined to be the ratio between

— twice the energy E of the received signal;

— and the spectral density b of the noise relative to the band Δf of the positive frequencies occupied by the signal.

REMARKS

(1) It is, however, sometimes very expensive (for instance, in the case of certain correlation radars) to achieve the high quality promised by the theory, and failure to do this results in a loss on R (which can easily fall as low as 3 dB). For this reason, and taking into account the degree of approximation with which the figure giving the equivalent echoing areas of real targets is known (see Chapter 5), the curves giving the detection probability versus R can give only an order of the magnitude of the range of a radar, while they mainly allow comparison of the behaviour of two radars in front of the same target.

(2) A relatively simpler way of physically explaining this result consists of noting that there are, when the signal $S(t)$ is a microwave signal, two ways of

defining the signal-to-noise ratio in power at the output of the ideal receiver computing $C(t_0)$.

The first way consists of defining this ratio, say SB_A according to the general philosophy explained so far, as being the ratio between

(1) The square of the maximum amplitude of $C_u(t_0)$.
(2) The noise power.

The second method consists of defining this ratio, say SB_B, as being the ratio between

(1) The mean power of $C_u(t_0)$ around t_{01}.
(2) The noise power.

It appears that $SB_A = 2SB_B$.

Having $SB_A = \dfrac{2E}{b}$ and $SB_B = \dfrac{E}{b}$ allows the possibility of a bridge between the assumption of a "video" signal $S(t)$ considered up to now and the assumption of a signal $S(t)$ modulating a carrier frequency.

3.5 PRECISION OF RANGE MEASUREMENT

Let us recall the hypothesis already formulated. The useful signal $S(t-t_{01})$ lasts for a time T during which we make the measurement, and occupies a spectrum of width Δf, while the noise $n(t)$ accompanying it is gaussian and occupies the same frequency band of width Δf.

The problem is now to determine with what precision is it possible to evaluate the value of t_{01} when there is a target, and therefore $S(t-t_{01})$.

If $R \ggg 1$, at the point where we could completely neglect $C_p(t_0)$ compared to $C_u(t_0)$ in $C(t_0)$, and if, on the other hand, *a priori* distribution of $p(t_0)$ varies sufficiently little with t_0 in a zone around t_{01}—which is true in most cases—the maximum of $p(t_0/y)$ corresponds to the maximum of $C(t_0)$, and hence to that of $C_u(t_0)$. This is found to be at t_{01}, since $C_u(t_0)$[1] is the autocorrelation function of $S(t-t_{01})$.

When $R \gg 1$ but we are not permitted to neglect $C_p(t_0)$ compared to $C_u(t_0)$, we logically admit that the value of t_{01} is the value of t_0 that renders $C(t_0)$ maximal, and this time we commit an error due to the noise $C_p(t_0)$. We are thus led to examine the behaviour of $C(t_0)$ around its maximum, and firstly, the behaviour of $C_u(t_0)$ around $t_0 = t_{01}$.

We write $\tau = t_0 - t_{01}$; hence (see section 3.2.1)

$$C_u(\tau) = \frac{k}{b} \int_T S(u) \cdot S(u-\tau) \, \mathrm{d}u,$$

which could be written as

$$C_u(\tau) = C_u(0) + C_u''(0) \frac{\tau^2}{2}$$

---
[1] Modulo a constant factor.

for τ weak, and since $C'_u(0) = 0$, with (sub-section 1.5.4):

$$C''_u(\tau) = -\frac{k}{b} \int_T S'(u) \cdot S'(u-\tau) \, du,$$

and

$$C''_u(0) = -\frac{k}{b} \int_T S'^2(t) \, dt = -\frac{k}{b} \int_{+\Delta f/2}^{+\Delta f/2} |\Psi(f)|^2 \, df,$$

if $\Psi(f)$ is the Fourier transform of $S'(t)$, the first derivative of $S(t)$. The Fourier transform $\Phi(f)$ for this is zero for $|f| > \Delta f/2$ (compare with sub-section 1.5.1).

Since $\Psi(f) = 2\pi j f \Phi(f)$, we have

$$C''_u(0) = -\frac{4\pi^2 k}{b} \int_{\Delta f} f^2 |\Phi(f)|^2 \, df = -\frac{4\pi^2}{bk} \int_{\Delta f} f^2 k^2 |\Phi(f)|^2 \, df$$

Let us recall that [eq. (11)] $C_u(0) = R/k$, and that

$$\int_T k^2 S^2(t) \, dt = E = \int_{\Delta f} k^2 |\Phi(f)|^2 \, df,$$

we write

$$\int_{\Delta f} f^2 |\Phi(f)|^2 \, df = B^2 \int_{\Delta f} |\Phi(f)|^2 \, df, \tag{18}$$

defining thus the moment of the second order B [1] of the spectrum $|\Phi(f)^2|$.

B is, in a certain way, the radius of gyration of a plate limited by the axis of frequencies and the curve $|\Phi(f)|^2$.

Finally, we have the expression

$$C_u(\tau) = \frac{R}{k}[1 - 2\pi^2 B^2 \tau^2]$$

and

$$C(\tau) = \frac{R}{k}[1 - 2\pi^2 B^2 \tau^2] + C_p(\tau),$$

with

$$C_p(\tau) = \frac{1}{b} \int_T n(u+t_{01}) \cdot S(u-\tau) \, du.$$

The maximum of $C(\tau)$ is given by $C'(\tau) = 0$

$$-\frac{4\pi^2 B^2 \tau^2 R}{k} + C'_p(\tau) = 0$$

[1] According to the convention borrowed from probabilities.

This results in τ satisfying the expression

$$\tau = \frac{k}{4\pi^2 B^2 R} \, C_p'(\tau),$$

while if the noise $n(t)$ were negligible it results in $\tau = 0$.

The value of τ thus obtained represents, therefore, the error committed in the range measurement t_{01}.

To know more, we must know $C_p'(\tau)$ a little better, which could also be written (with the usual notations) as

$$C_p'(\tau) = -\frac{1}{b}\int_T n(u+t_{01}) \cdot S'(u-\tau) \, du,$$

$$C_p'(\tau) = -\frac{1}{b\Delta f}\sum n(t_i+t_{01}) \cdot S'(t_i-\tau).$$

Arguing as in sub-section 3.2.2, $C_p'(\tau)$ appears as a gaussian random variable of mean value zero and variance given by

$$\overline{C_p'^2(\tau)} = \frac{1}{b^2\Delta^2 f^2}\sum N \cdot S'^2(t_i-\tau) = \frac{1}{b}\sum S'^2(t_i-\tau)\frac{1}{\Delta f},$$

$$\overline{C_p'^2(\tau)} = \frac{1}{b}\int_T S'^2(t-\tau) \, dt = \frac{1}{b}\int_T S'^2(t) \, dt,$$

$$\overline{C_p'^2(\tau)} = \frac{1}{b}\int_{\Delta f} |\Psi(f)|^2 \, df = \frac{4\pi^2}{bk^2} B^2 E = \frac{4\pi^2 B^2 R}{k^2}.$$

Thus the error τ committed in the measurement of t_{01} appears to be gaussian of mean value zero and standard deviation given by

$$\sqrt{\overline{\tau^2}} = \frac{k}{4\pi^2 B^2 R} \times \frac{2\pi B}{k} \sqrt{R}$$

$$\boxed{= \frac{1}{2\pi B\sqrt{R}}} \tag{19}$$

an equation known as Woodward's formula.

N.B. To obtain the standard deviation of the range measurement of a target from the radar, it is evidently sufficient to multiply the result by $c/2$ (c being the speed of light).

Example: 1 μs gives 150 m.

If R is sufficiently large, we shall therefore commit a gaussian error over the determination of t_{01} (whose standard deviation is given by expression (19)) where $R = E/b$ is the ratio between the energy of the signal in the measurement of time and the spectral density of the noise, and B is the moment of the second order of the spectrum of the transmitted signal.

IMPORTANT REMARKS

(1) In fact, the transmitted signal is in the microwave whose spectrum is centred on a frequency f_0. The preceding formula applies on condition that B is defined by

$$\int_{\Delta f} (f - f_0)^2 |\Phi^2(f)| \, df = B^2 \int_{\Delta f} |\Phi^2(f)| \, df \tag{20}$$

and $R = \dfrac{2E}{b}$ (see section 3.4).

(2) The value of B depends only on the amplitude of $\Phi(f)$ and not on its argument (phase of the spectrum); (compare with section 3.2.1).

(3) If the spectrum has the form of a bell, $2B$ is practically its width at 3 dB. If, on the other hand, the spectrum of $S(t)$ is rectangular in the interval $\Delta f (|\Phi(f)|$ = constant), we have the relation

$$2B = \frac{\Delta f}{\sqrt{3}}$$

(4) If the transmitted signal $S(t)$ is periodic of period T_R (period of recurrence), i.e. if it is constituted by a regular sequence of elementary signals, it is evident that the signal received $S(t - t_{01})$ is identical to the signal $S(t - t_{01} - T_R)$. In other words, the measurement of t_{01} is made with precision, but we could, theoretically speaking, commit an error kT_R, k being an integer. And in this case, the spectrum of $S(t)$ is a spectrum of lines each apart by $1/T_R$ (compare with sub-section 1.7.1).

The transmission of a periodic signal $S(t)$ creates, therefore, an ambiguity in the measurement of t_{01}. It is often a question of theoretical ambiguity; the order of size of t_{01} being generally known, we eliminate, *ipso facto*, the values $t_{01} + kT_R$ (k being an integer).

This ambiguity is found in the graph of the function of ambiguity $\mathscr{A}(\theta)$ associated with $S(t)$. Since $\Phi(f)$ is constituted with lines regularly spaced apart by $1/T_R$, the same applies to $|\Phi(f)|^2$, and hence $\mathscr{A}(\theta)$—whose Fourier transform, modulo a factor, is $|\Phi(f)|^2$—is a periodic function of θ whose period is

$$\frac{1}{1/T_R} = T_R$$

In practice, for $S(t)$ to be really periodic it is necessary that its duration T be infinite, which cannot be so. Therefore, $S(t)$ shall never be periodic, no more than $\mathscr{A}(\theta)$, which will consist of a peak at $\theta = 0$ surrounded by peaks for $\theta = kT_R$, peaks of altitude around unity. There remains a very real ambiguity.

3.6 RANGE DISCRIMINATION

3.6.1 General

Inasmuch as we could think that what has been presented so far is almost certain (there have been very few obstructions in arriving logically at eq. (19)), this sub-section should be considered as an introduction which deserves to be rendered more cartesian.

The problem to be studied is the following. This time we have to deal with two targets having the same bearing but at close ranges. To what extent could we ascertain the two targets and determine their respective positions with precision?

We must take into account that when we are in the presence of a unique target we could locate it with great precision if R is very large, and with an infinite precision on assuming R to be infinitely large.

But, on the other hand, if two targets are very near, even if R is extremely large, we cannot distinguish them. This is easily understood by the following.

Let us suppose R to be very large, and two identical nearby targets, one at t_{01}, and the other at t_{02} (very near). The target at t_{01} shall give

$$C_{1u}(t_0) = R[1 - 2\pi^2 B^2 (t_0 - t_{01})^2];$$

the target at t_{02} shall give

$$C_{2u}(t_0) = R[1 - 2\pi^2 B^2 (t_0 - t_{02})^2].$$

The set of two targets, therefore, giving a C_u:

$$C_{1u}(t_0) + C_{2u}(t_0) = 2R\left[1 - 2\pi^2 B^2 \left(\frac{t_{01} - t_{02}}{2}\right)^2 - 2\pi^2 B^2 \left(t_0 - \frac{t_{01} + t_{02}}{2}\right)^2\right],$$

i.e. an expression which has only one maximum for

$$t_0 = \frac{t_{01} + t_{02}}{2}.$$

In other words, if the two targets are sufficiently near so that the limited developments utilised is good, even if R is extremely large, we see only one target and cannot distinguish the two of them.

In order that two targets be distinguished (when they are in the same direction), it is necessary that for $t_0 = t_{02}$: $C_{1u}(t_0)$ (of the first target) be practically zero.

In other words, two targets θ apart will be distinguished only if $C_u(\tau)$ for $\tau = t_{02} - t_{01} = \theta$, i.e. $C_u(\theta)$ is very small such that $C_u(\tau) + C_u(\tau - \theta)$ gives two distinct maxima.

We could thus define an interval $\theta_{\min}$, beyond which we could consider that the two identical targets are distinguished, and on this side of which we could consider that they are no longer so.

REMARK

In the case of transmission of a periodic signal of recurrence period T_R, it is evident that a target at a range t_{01} and another at $t_{01}+kT_R$ would both be confused on the radar display (this problem is often purely theoretical).

3.6.2 First general rule

Whatever be the definition of range discrimination it is only a function of the form of the useful signal at the output of the ideal receiver.

Thus, the range discrimination depends only on $|\Phi(f)|^2$, i.e. the amplitude of the transmitted spectrum and not on its phase.

3.6.3 An attempt to analyse the problem

3.6.3.1 First example. Classical radar

Let us consider the example of an ideal radar transmitting a rectangular signal non-modulated in frequency and of duration T when we are in the presence of two identical targets of the same radial speeds, whose radial dis-

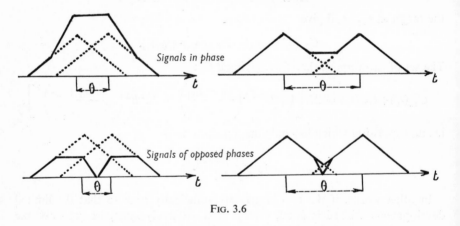

FIG. 3.6

tances differ by θ. Figure 3.6 represents the output signal of the radar for $\theta < T$ and $\theta > T$ according to the signals received from the two targets being in phase or in opposite phases. (The autocorrelation function of the transmitted signal is a triangle of base $2T$.)

We see, in this example, that when θ is greater than T, we shall obtain in the envelope of the output signal two maxima corresponding to real positions of the targets, whatever be the phases of the respective signals received. But we also see that if θ is less than T we obtain a single maximum if the signals are in phase and two maxima if they are in opposite phases, and that in this case the maxima are flat and do not by themselves give the positions of each of the targets. We could say that

— if $\theta < T$ the signals cannot be separated,

— if $\theta > T$ the signals are separable.

We must realise that, if this way of looking at things is quite realistic in practice it is theoretically pessimistic. If, since the noise is negligible, we effectively receive the signals on the left of fig. 3.6 and knowing that individual signals are triangular of duration $2T$, we could in theory deduce from the study of the received signals that we are in the presence of two targets at such and such a position. (It is sufficient to ascertain that the signal has a length greater than $2T$ in order to deduce that there is a target found at the first instant increased by T and another at the last instant decreased by T.)

This remark on angular measurements has, on the other hand, enabled us to see that the classical notions on resolution in optics were obsolete and pessimistic (see section 6.8) although they were based on the fundamental ideas which we shall try to use here for range measurement.

With this reservation we shall therefore generally be led to admit that, when the output signal of the radar has only one maximum in the presence of a unique target, two targets are separable if the sum of the envelopes of the signals (radar output) corresponding to each of the targets gives two maxima. On the contrary, if the sum of the envelopes of the two signals gives only one maximum, we shall admit that the two targets are non-separable.

We could utilise this idea by defining an "ambiguity of resolution" $A^2(\theta)$:

The ambiguity of resolution shall be defined as follows. When we are in the presence of two targets, with the larger one assumed to be the reference at a radial distance presumed to be the origin for θ and to which corresponds a signal of energy equal to 1, and the smaller target at a radial distance θ (with respect to the first), the ambiguity of resolution is equal to A^2 at the distance θ when, for a signal energy of the second target equal to A^2, the second target is just separable from the larger one ($A^2 < 1$). In other words, if a target at a distance θ has an equivalent echoing area greater than A^2 times the equivalent echoing area of the target of reference (see Chapter 5) it is separable; in the other case, it is not separable.

3.6.3.2   Gaussian signal non-frequency modulated

Let us consider a transmitted signal of the form

$$S(t) = \exp\left(-\pi t^2/T^2\right)$$

($S(t)$ is in fact equal to $\exp\left(-\pi t^2/T^2\right) \exp\left(j\omega_0 t\right)$ but we do not take into account $\exp\left(j\omega_0 t\right)$ since we are interested in the envelope of the signal.)

A target of reference shall give a signal

$$C_u(t) = \exp\left(-\pi t^2/2T^2\right)$$

Another target, at a distance θ and of equivalent echoing area A^2 times that of the reference target shall give

$$A \exp\left[-\pi(t-\theta)^2/2T^2\right]$$

It is therefore required, for a given A, to determine when

$$|\exp\left(-\pi t^2/2T^2\right)| + A|\exp\left[-\pi(t-\theta)^2/2T^2\right]|$$

G

gives two maxima. We find (after relatively complicated calculations with many changes of variables) that the following result is attained:

$$
\begin{aligned}
\text{for } A &= 1 & \text{when } |\theta| &> 1\cdot1T \\
A &= 0\cdot5 & \text{when } |\theta| &> 1\cdot4T \\
A &= 0\cdot1 & \text{when } |\theta| &> 1\cdot9T \\
A &= 10^{-2} & \text{when } |\theta| &> 2\cdot3T \\
A &= 10^{-3} & \text{when } |\theta| &> 2\cdot6T.
\end{aligned}
$$

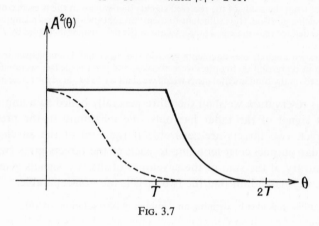

FIG. 3.7

With the accepted definition we deduce the following table, representing $A^2(\theta)$ as a function of $|\theta|$.

$|\theta|$	$\leqq 1\cdot1T$	$1\cdot4T$	$1\cdot9T$	$2\cdot3T$	$2\cdot6T$
$A^2(\theta)$	1	0·25	10^{-2}	10^{-4}	10^{-6}

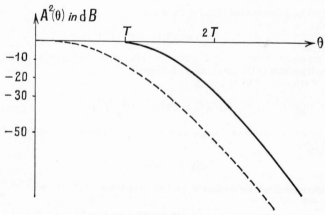

FIG. 3.8

This table corresponds to the mathematical expression

$$A^2(\theta) = \left(1 - \frac{1}{u^2} + \sqrt{1 - \frac{2}{u^2}}\right)^2 u^4 \exp\left(-2u^2\sqrt{1 - 2/u^2}\right)$$

with

$$u^2 = \frac{\pi\theta^2}{2T^2} \quad \text{for} \quad u^2 > 2$$

and

$$A^2(\theta) = 1 \quad \text{for} \quad u^2 < 2,$$

and to the curve given in fig. 3.7 [the interrupted line represents the curve $\mathscr{A}(\theta)$].
Figure 3.8 shows the same curves, but with $A^2(\theta)$ being expressed in decibels.

3.6.3.3   Rectangular pulse non-frequency modulated and of duration T

We easily find that, whatever be A, two targets (at the same radial speed) are not separable (with the accepted definition) if $|\theta| < T$ and are always separable if $|\theta| > T$ (see fig. 3.9).

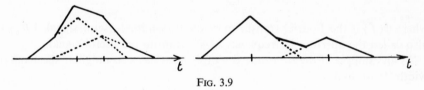

FIG. 3.9

Thus

$$A^2(\theta) = 1 \quad \text{if} \quad |\theta| < T$$
$$A^2(\theta) = 0 \quad \text{if} \quad |\theta| > T$$

(see fig. 3.10 with the curve $\mathscr{A}^2(\theta)$).

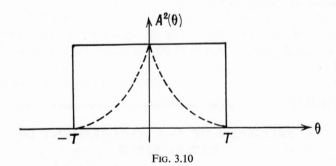

FIG. 3.10

3.6.4   An approximated formula

The value of θ beyond which $A^2(\theta)$ decreases could be considered as the range resolution of the radar.

Let θ_{min} be this value: in effect two targets closer than θ_{min} cannot be distinguished whatever their respective amplitudes.

It is convenient, when we do not have time to make the complete calculation, to use an approximated formula giving θ_{min} without much error in numerous cases:

$$\theta_{min} = \int |\mathscr{A}^2(\theta)| \, d\theta \tag{21}$$

This definition of range resolution of a radar could appear a little arbitrary, but it is very useful. It has the advantage of being written in another form[1] with the help of classical mathematical transformations: we could in effect write θ_{min} in the form

$$\theta_{min} = \frac{\int |\varPhi(f)|^4 \, df}{\left[\int |\varPhi(f)|^2 \, df \right]^2} \tag{22}$$

where $\varPhi(f)$ is the Fourier transform of the transmitted useful signal. $1/\theta_{min}$ is also called the aperture in frequency of the transmitted useful signal.

As an example, if the transmitted useful signal has a rectangular spectrum of width Δf we find

$$\theta_{min} = \frac{1}{\Delta f}$$

3.6.5 Important remark

It was shown in sub-section 1.7.2 that during a time T a frequency could not be defined within a range of $1/T$.

In the same way, we could say that two identical signals less than $1/\Delta f$ apart can be separated when the spectrum of the signals has a width limited by Δf (which theoretically assumes signals of infinite length, but in practice this is not necessarily so).

Thus the range resolution of a radar, according to this reasoning, could not be better than $1/\Delta f$.

3.7 PRECISION OF THE MEASUREMENT OF RADIAL SPEED

At this point it is well to remember that we have assumed the signal received $S(t - t_{01})$ to be identical (modulo a factor) to a signal transmitted after a delay of t_0.

---

[1] The results recalled in Chapter 1 are sufficient to prove it, since the Fourier transform of $\mathscr{A}(t)$ is equal to

$$\frac{|\varPhi(f)|^2}{\int |\varPhi(f)|^2 \, df}$$

This is so only if the target is immobile, or has a radial speed of zero. If, on the other hand, the target has a radial speed V_R which is not zero, and if, as in most cases,[1] the width Δf of the spectrum transmitted is very weak compared to the central frequency f_0 (corresponding to the wavelength λ), we could admit that the signal received from the target is obtained by shifting the spectrum of $S(t - t_{01})$ by a frequency f_D, called the Doppler frequency, and given by

$$\boxed{f_D = \frac{2V_R}{\lambda}} \tag{23}$$

In practice, the case which we have just described is the ideal one where either $f_D = 0$ or we know f_D, which enables us to shift the spectrum of the signal received artificially by $-f_D$, and thus return to the preceding problem.

This is the case of the measurement of the position of the target whose speed is known, or whose speed is sufficiently low. (In practice, this signifies that we know the frequency f_D with an exactitude better than $1/T$ approximately.)

The question that we now ask ourselves is to know how exactly could we measure f_D if, on the contrary, the position of the target is known (with an exactitude better than $1/\Delta f$). This case is treated in the same way as the earlier one.

In fact, we transmit a spectrum $\Phi(f)$ which returns displaced by f_D and submerged in noise, and we propose to evaluate the theoretical error with which we could measure f_D. All our arguments remain valid on condition that we permutate time and frequency.

We are thus led to define from the envelope $\sigma(t)$ of the useful signal, a time T_f in the following way.

We define the origin of time such that

$$\int_T t\sigma^2(t)\,\mathrm{d}t = 0$$

(at the centre of gravity of the energy of the signal).

We define T_f through

$$\int_T t^2\sigma^2(t)\,\mathrm{d}t = ET_f^2 = T_f^2 \int_T \sigma^2(t)\,\mathrm{d}t \tag{24}$$

If the signal is rectangular, of duration T, we have

$$2T_f = \frac{T}{\sqrt{3}}, \qquad T_f = \frac{T}{2\sqrt{3}}.$$

---

[1] It is not absurd, on the contrary, to make radars which transmit a signal occupying a spectrum of width Δf of the order of the central frequency f_0. However, the study of such radars is not dealt with in this section.

The standard deviation of the best measurement that we could make of f_D is given by

$$\boxed{\frac{1}{2\pi T_f \sqrt{R}}} \tag{25}$$

which corresponds to a standard deviation of the measurement of V_R equal to

$$\boxed{\frac{\lambda}{4\pi T_f \sqrt{R}}} \tag{26}$$

In particular, if the signal is rectangular, of duration T, the standard deviation of the measurement of the radial speed is given by

$$\boxed{\frac{\lambda\sqrt{3}}{2\pi T \sqrt{R}}} \tag{27}$$

Numerical example:

$$\lambda = 0.1 \text{ m}; \quad T = 5 \cdot 10^{-3} \text{ s}; \quad R = 20.$$

We could theoretically measure the radial speed at 0·3 m/s.

REMARK

There is another method of measuring the Doppler speed of targets, which consists of deriving the successive positions of the targets, whose accuracy is given by analogous but different formulae.

3.8 AMBIGUITY IN RADIAL SPEED

Just as we were led in section 3.3 to define a function of the distance θ called a function of ambiguity $\mathscr{A}(\theta)$, we define in an analogous way a function of ambiguity of the Doppler frequency F by means of an expression which follows from that of eq. (17):

$$\mathscr{X}(F) = \frac{\int_{\Delta f} \Phi(f) \cdot \Phi^*(f - F) \, df}{\int |\Phi(f)|^2 \, df} \tag{28}$$

recalling the fact that

$$\int |\Phi(f)|^2 \, df \equiv \int |S(t)|^2 \, dt.$$

This function is maximal and equal to 1 for $F = 0$. It also has two aspects:

(1) The amplitude of $\mathscr{X}(F)$ gives an indication of the possibility of committing an error F in the determination of the Doppler frequency (radial speed) of a target whose distance is known. The bigger $\mathscr{X}(F)$ is for a certain value of F, the greater chance we have of making an error equal to F in the measurement of the Doppler frequency.

(2) When there are two targets at the same distance, one called "interesting" having a certain Doppler frequency f_D, and the other called "parasitic" having a Doppler frequency $f_D + F$ and being p^2 times more energetic than the "interesting" target, this parasitic target gives at the frequency f_D a response having a power $p^2 |\mathscr{X}^2(F)|$ times that of the interesting target. In other words, the weaker is $|\mathscr{X}(F)|$, the less disturbing is the parasitic target.

EXAMPLE

Let us consider a transmitted signal constituted, as in the case of a classical radar, by a certain number n of elementary rectangular signals, spaced regularly, each of them lasting a time τ, and the distance between two consecutive signals being T_R (τ being very small in comparison to T_R) (see fig. 3.11).

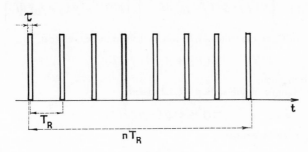

FIG. 3.11

Such a signal represents in the domain of time the equivalent of a spectrum of lines in the domain of frequencies. But we have seen in section 3.5 that when the spectrum of the signal was constituted by lines distanced from $1/T_R$:

We could make an error equal to kT_R over the measurement of t_{01};

We confused two targets distanced by kT_R.

As a corollary, with a transmitted signal as shown in fig. 3.11, we could conclude:

That we could commit an error equal to k/T_R over f_D;

That we could confuse two targets whose Doppler frequencies differ by k/T_R. This corresponds in the function $\mathscr{X}(F)$ to the existence of peaks for $F = k/T_R$.

3.9 SPEED DISCRIMINATION

We could repeat here, *mutatis mutandis*, all that has been discussed in section 3.6.

3.9.1 General rule

The (radial) speed resolution, i.e. the possibility of distinguishing two targets at the same range because their Doppler frequencies are sufficiently different, depends only on $\sigma(t)^2$, i.e. on the envelope of the transmitted signal (of the form of the transmitted signal assumed to be centred on the zero frequency).

3.9.2 Trial analysis of the problem

3.9.2.1 First example. Gaussian signal non-frequency modulated

We shall define here an ambiguity of resolution $A_1^2(F)$, a function of F, in the following way.

When we are in the presence of two targets at the same distance, with one of them, e.g. the larger, assumed to be a reference at a Doppler frequency which is regarded as the origin of F, and the weaker at a Doppler frequency F (with respect to the first), the ambiguity of resolution is equal to A_1^2 at the frequency F when an energy of the signal of the second target is equal to A_1^2 times that of the first, and the two targets are just separable ($A_1^2 < 1$).

Let us consider the expression

$$\Gamma(f_0) = \int \Phi(f) \cdot \Phi^*(f-f_0)\, df = \left[\int \Phi^*(f) \cdot \Phi(f-f_0)\, df \right]^*,$$

Corollary of $C_u(\tau)$, the value $A_1^2(F)$ will be defined to be such that

$$|\Gamma(f)| + A_1\ |\Gamma(f-F)|$$

just presents two maxima.

Recalling the example of sub-section 3.6.3.2, where

$$\sigma(t) = \exp\left(-\pi t^2/T^2\right),$$

we find that $\Phi(f)$ can be written as

$$\Phi(f) = k_1 \exp\left[-\pi(Tf)^2\right]$$

and hence $\Gamma(f)$ in the form

$$\Gamma(f) = k_2 \exp\left[-(\pi/2)(Tf)^2\right].$$

From which we get for $A_1^2(F)$ the expression

$$A_1^2(F) = \left[1 - \frac{1}{v^2} + \sqrt{1 - \frac{2}{v^2}}\right]^2 v^4 \exp\left(-2v^2\sqrt{1-2/v^2}\right)$$

with

$$v^2 = \frac{\pi}{2}(TF)^2 \qquad \text{for} \qquad v^2 > 2$$

and

$$A_1^2(F) = 1 \qquad \text{for} \qquad v^2 < 2,$$

i.e.

$$A_1^2(F) = A^2(FT^2).$$

3.9.2.2   Rectangular pulses non-frequency modulated of duration T

If we evaluate here the expression $\Gamma(f)$ we find that it is equal to a Fourier transform of a rectangular signal of duration T:

$$\Gamma(f) = \frac{\sin \pi f T}{\pi f T}$$

and this gives a *maximum maximorum* equal to 1 for $f = 0$ and an infinity of secondary maxima for (nearly)

$$|f| = \frac{1}{2T} + \frac{2k}{T} \qquad \text{(with } k \geqq 1)$$

whose amplitude is (nearly) equal to

$$\frac{1}{\pi T f},$$

such that $|\Gamma(f)| + A_1|\Gamma(f-F)|$ always presents a large number of maxima. The definition accepted earlier becomes null and void. In fact, it is not absurd to accept that two targets whose Doppler frequencies differ by F are separable if

$$\Gamma(f) + A_1\Gamma(f-F)$$

presents a maximum $f = F$ higher than the neighbouring maxima (see fig. 3.12).

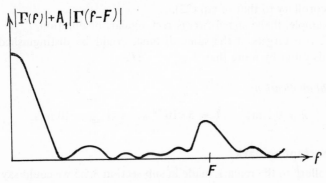

FIG. 3.12

We find that for $A_1 = 1$, there is a possible separation if F is greater than $1\cdot1/T$ (nearly). We also find that for $F \gg 1/T$ there is separation for

$$A_1^2 > \frac{1}{(\pi F T)^2}$$

which gives the following approximate values for $A_1^2(F)$,

$$A_1^2(F) = 1 \qquad \text{for} \qquad F < \frac{1\cdot1}{T},$$

$$A_1^2(F) = \frac{1}{(\pi F T)^2} \qquad \text{for} \qquad F > \frac{1\cdot1}{T}.$$

3.9.3 Approximated formula

The value of F beyond which $A_1(F)$ decreases may be considered as the Doppler frequency resolution of a radar.

Let F_{min} be that value: two targets nearer to each other than F_{min} in Doppler frequency (and at the same radial distance) cannot be separated whatever their respective amplitudes.

It is convenient to use here an approximated formula giving F_{min} without much error in numerous cases:

$$F_{min} = \int |\mathscr{X}^2(F)| \, dF, \tag{29}$$

which can be written as

$$F_{min} = \frac{\displaystyle\int_T |\sigma(t)|^4 \, dt}{\left[\displaystyle\int_T |\sigma(t)|^2 \, dt\right]^2} \tag{30}$$

a formula corollary to that of eq. (22).

As an example, if the signal $S(t)$ is rectangular, of duration T, we find that $F_{min} = 1/T$: two targets at the same distance could be distinguished if their radial speeds differ by more than $V_{min} = \lambda/2T$.

Numerical application:

$$\lambda = 0{\cdot}1 \text{ m}; \qquad T = 5 \cdot 10^{-3} \text{ s}; \qquad V_{min} = 10 \text{ m/s}.$$

3.9.4 Important remark

As a corollary to the remark made in sub-section 3.6.5 we could say that it is not possible to separate two targets (at the same distance) with different Doppler frequencies with a transmission signal of duration T if the Doppler frequencies of these two targets differ by less than $1/T$.

3.10 AMBIGUITY IN RANGE–SPEED

3.10.1 Generalities

In the preceding sections we have described the more or less important possibilities of making an error in the range measurement of a target whose Doppler frequency was assumed to be known, or of making an error in the measurement of the Doppler frequency of a target whose radial distance was known; i.e.

We have also spoken of the troubles related to an interesting target by a parasitic target being found either at the same Doppler frequency but at a different range, or at the same range with a different Doppler frequency;

All these being mathematically contained in the functions of ambiguity $\mathscr{A}(\theta)$ or $\mathscr{X}(F)$.

In reality the problem is more general. We must:

Measure the radial distance and the Doppler frequency at the same time;

Estimate the difficulties created in an interesting target by a parasitic target which is neither at the same range nor as the same Doppler frequency. It is clear that the arguments are analogous.

What is $\mathscr{A}(\theta)$? It is, conveniently normed, the response at $t_0 = \theta$ and $f_D = 0$ of a target found at $t_0 = 0$ with a Doppler frequency $f_D = 0$. We are led to consider this time the response $\mathscr{A}(\theta, F)$ for $t_0 = \theta$ and $f_D = F$ of a target found at $\theta = 0$ and at $f = 0$, i.e. the correlation of the signal $S(t)$ received from a target at $t_0 = 0$ and $f_D = 0$, with the reference $S(t)$ shifted by θ in time and F in frequency, after having conveniently normed it, say,

$$\mathscr{A}(\theta, F) = \frac{\int_T S(t) \cdot S^*(t-\theta) \exp(+2\pi jFt) \, dt}{\int |S(t)|^2 \, dt} \tag{31}$$

What is $\mathscr{X}(F)$? It is, conveniently normed, the output of a matched filter to a signal situated at $t_0 = 0$ and at $f_D = F$, fed by a signal corresponding to a target situated at $t_0 = 0$ and at $f_D = 0$. This time we will be led to consider the output of a filter matched to a signal situated at $t_0 = \theta$ and at $f_D = F$, fed by a signal corresponding to a target situated at $t_0 = 0$ and at $f_D = 0$, after having conveniently normed it,

$$\mathscr{X}(\theta, F) = \frac{\int \Phi(f) \cdot \Phi^*(f-F) \exp(+2j\pi f\theta) \, df}{\int |\Phi(f)|^2 \, df} \tag{32}$$

These two processes of reasoning lead to the same result because

$$|\mathscr{A}(\theta, F)| = |\mathscr{X}(\theta, F)|.$$

In practice, we often use $|\mathscr{A}(\theta, F)|$, or $|\mathscr{A}(\theta, F)|^2$ for reasons that will become clear later.

$\mathscr{A}(\theta, F)$ (or its derivatives $|\mathscr{A}(\theta, F)|$ and $|\mathscr{A}^2(\theta, F)|$) is the function of ambiguity in two dimensions.

This ambiguity has two aspects:

(1) The amplitude of $\mathscr{A}(\theta, F)$ gives an indication of the possibility of making an error of θ in range together with an error of F in Doppler frequency in the determination of the two coordinates of the target. The closer $|\mathscr{A}(\theta, F)|$ is to 1, the more probable that there will be a simultaneous error of θ and of F.

(2) When two targets are in the same direction the one called "interesting" being at a certain distance t_0 with a certain Doppler frequency f_D, and the other called "parasitic" being at a distance $t_0 + \theta$ with a Doppler frequency $f_D + F$ and being p^2 times more energetic than the interesting target, the parasitic target gives at the range t_0 and at the frequency f_D a response having a power $p^2 |\mathscr{A}^2(\theta, F)|$ times larger than that of the interesting signal. In other words, the smaller is $|\mathscr{A}(\theta, F)|$, the less does the parasitic target impede the interesting one.

$|\mathscr{A}^2(\theta, F)|$ represents the troubles related to the interesting target by the other targets, as a function of their relative positions (θ, F).

MATHEMATICAL PROPERTIES OF THE FUNCTION OF AMBIGUITY

(1) It is maximal for $\theta = 0$ and $F = 0$.

(2) It is symmetrical with respect to that point: $|\mathscr{A}(\theta, F)| = |\mathscr{A}(-\theta, -F)|$.

(3) The volume contained inside this ambiguity is constant:

$$\iint |\mathscr{A}^2(\theta, F)| \, dF \, d\theta = 1 \tag{33}$$

In other words, we could reduce the ambiguity at a point only on the condition of having it increasing elsewhere.

We recall that we have defined (in an approximate manner) the discrimination in range (i.e. the possibility of distinguishing two targets with the same speed by their different ranges) θ_{min} and in Doppler frequency F_{min} (i.e. the possibility of distinguishing two targets at the same range by their different Doppler frequencies) by respectively

$$\theta_{min} = \int |\mathscr{A}^2(\theta, 0)| \, d\theta \tag{21'}$$

and by

$$F_{min} = \int |\mathscr{A}^2(\theta, F)| \, dF \tag{29'}$$

It is important to note, in this respect, that relation (33) does not imply that the product of θ_{min} and F_{min} defined by eqs. (21') and (29') is constant. In particular, there could exist signals such that the levels of $|\mathscr{A}^2|$ are ellipses having for their main axes the axes of θ and of F (see fig. 3.13), such that the volume of ambiguity is obviously equal to 1 and also such that the product $\theta_{\min} \times F_{\min}$ is very small, when, for example, the ambiguity contains a central peak at 0 ($\theta = 0$, $F = 0$), with a flat plain around this peak where the ambiguity

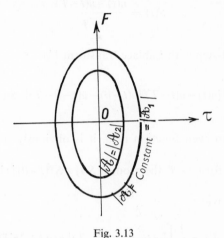

Fig. 3.13

decreases slowly when we get far away from 0. In order to fix our ideas, if the ambiguity revolved around 0 and had the form $\mathscr{A}^2(\rho)$ (with $\rho^2 = \tau^2 + F^2$), the integral

$$F_{\min} = \theta_{\min} = 2 \int_0^\infty \mathscr{A}^2(\rho)\, d\rho$$

could be very small, while the integral

$$\int_0^\infty 2\pi\rho\mathscr{A}^2(\rho)\, d\rho$$

is equal to 1. In this case, the volume where the ambiguity $|\mathscr{A}^2|$ is greater than 0·8, for example, could be very small, while the volume where the ambiguity $|\mathscr{A}^2|$ is greater than 10^{-6} would be very large. (That is why speaking of surface of ambiguity instead of volume of ambiguity could be interpreted wrongly.)

3.10.2 First example. Rectangular pulse non-frequency modulated of duration T

Let us consider the case where the transmitted signal has a constant amplitude during its duration T and is not modulated in frequency. This would be the case of a radar transmitting a signal similar to those of classical radars but effecting over this signal a reception completely matched (by correlation, for example).

In this case we could write (by neglecting the carrier frequency, see section 3.4):

$$S(t) = \frac{u(t) - u(t-T)}{\sqrt{T}}$$

with $u(t)$ being unit-step with Laplace transform $1/p$:

$$\mathscr{A}(\theta, F) = \int [u(t) - u(t-T)][u(t-\theta) - u(t-\theta-T)] \exp(+2\pi jFt) \frac{dt}{T}.$$

As $|\mathscr{A}^2(\theta, F)|$ is an even function of θ, it is obviously sufficient to calculate it for $\theta > 0$.

It is evident that for $\theta > T$, the product $S(t) \times S^*(t-\theta)$ is identically zero, and hence also is $\mathscr{A}^2$.

For $\theta < T$, we have

$$\mathscr{A}(\theta, F) = \frac{1}{T} \int [u(t-\theta) - u(t-T)] \exp(+2\pi jFt) \, dt$$

$$= \frac{1}{T} \cdot \frac{\exp[+\pi jF(\theta+T)] \cdot \sin \pi F(T-\theta)}{\pi F}$$

$$\boxed{|\mathscr{A}^2(\theta, F)| = \frac{[\sin \pi F(T-\theta)]^2}{\pi^2 F^2 T^2}}$$

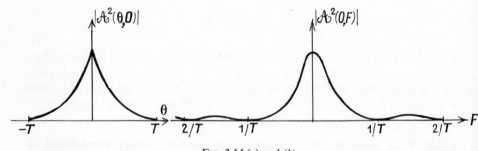

FIG. 3.14 (a) and (b)

Figure 3.14(a) shows $|\mathscr{A}^2(\theta, 0)|$ as a function of θ. Figure 3.14(b) shows $|\mathscr{A}^2(0, F)|$ as a function of F. Figure 3.14(c) shows in the plane (θ, F) the positions of the points where $|\mathscr{A}^2| = 0$. Figure 3.14(d) shows in the plane (θ, F) the positions of points where $|\mathscr{A}^2| = 0\cdot5$, $0\cdot25$ and $0\cdot04$.

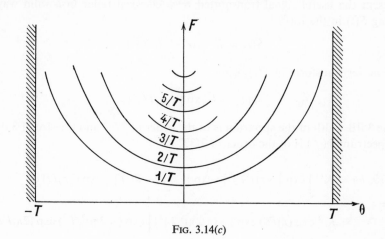

Fig. 3.14(c)

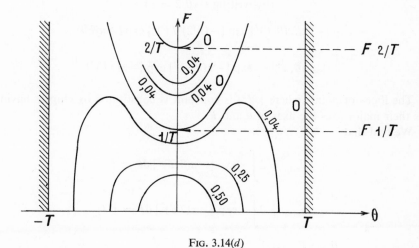

Fig. 3.14(d)

We find that

$$\theta_{min} = 2\int_0^\infty \frac{(T-\theta)^2}{T^2}\, d\theta = 2T/3,$$

$$F_{min} = 2\int_0^\infty \left[\frac{\sin \pi FT}{\pi FT}\right]^2 dF = 1/T,$$

$$\theta_{min} \cdot F_{min} = 2/3.$$

3.10.3   Second example. Gaussian signal non-frequency modulated

In practice, in a classical radar the spectrum used is limited and finally we represent the useful signal transmitted by a classical radar in a valid way by writing $S(t)$ in the form

$$S(t) = K' \exp [-\pi(t/T)^2],$$

the Fourier transform of $S(t)$ being

$$\Phi(f) = k \exp [-\pi(Tf)^2]$$

The 3 dB width of the spectrum is of the order of $2T/3$ and the size of 3 dB of the spectrum $\Phi(f)$ is of the order of $2/3T$.

$$\mathscr{A}(\theta, F) = K'^2 \int \exp [-\pi(t/T)^2] \cdot \exp \{-\pi[(t-\theta)/T]^2\} \exp (2\pi jFt) \, dt$$

$$= K'^2 \exp (\pi jF\theta) \exp [-(\pi/2)(\theta/T)^2] \int \exp (-2\pi u^2/T^2) \exp (2\pi jFu) \, du$$

(by writing $t - \theta/2 = u$)

$$= \exp [-(\pi/2)(\theta/T)^2] \exp [-(\pi/2)(TF)^2] \exp (+\pi jF\theta)$$

$$\boxed{|\mathscr{A}^2(\theta, F)| = \exp [-\pi(\theta/T)^2] \exp [-\pi(TF)^2]}$$

The locus of points where $|\mathscr{A}^2|$ is constant is constituted by ellipses having as their major axes the axes of θ and F.

We find that

$$\theta_{min} = 2 \int_0^\infty \exp [-\pi(\theta/T)^2] \, d\theta = T,$$

$$F_{min} = 2 \int_0^\infty \exp [-\pi(TF)^2] \, dF = 1/T,$$

$$\theta_{min} \cdot F_{min} = 1.$$

3.10.4   Gaussian signal linearly frequency modulated

This is a (mathematically) simple example of a signal transmitted by a pulse compression radar. (In fact pulse compression radars use in preference rectangular signals modulated in frequency.)

We could write the transmitted signal in the form

$$S(t) = \exp [-\pi(t/T)^2] \exp [-j(\pi/K)t^2],$$

i.e. we consider a signal whose frequency varies linearly as a function of time with a slope $df/dt = 1/K$.

In this case $\mathscr{A}(\theta, F)$ is written

$$k \int \exp\left[-\pi(t/T)^2\right] \exp\left[-j(\pi/K)t^2\right] \exp\left\{-\pi[(t-\theta)/T]^2\right\} \exp\left[+j(\pi/K)(t-\theta)^2\right]$$
$$\exp\left(+2\pi jFt\right) dt$$

$$= k \exp\left(-\pi\theta^2/2T^2\right) \exp\left(+\pi jF\theta\right) \int \exp\left[-2\pi(u/T)^2\right] \exp\left[-2\pi ju(\theta/K-F)\right] du$$

(by writing $u = t - \theta/2$)

$$= \exp\left(-\pi\theta^2/2T^2\right) \exp\left(+\pi jF\theta\right) \exp\left[+(\pi/2)(F-\theta/K)^2 T^2\right]$$

$$\boxed{|\mathscr{A}^2(\theta, F)| = \exp\left(-\pi\theta^2 T^2\right) \exp\left[+\pi T^2(F-\theta/K)^2\right]}$$

The locus where $|\mathscr{A}^2|$ is constant is constituted by ellipses whose equation is

$$-\frac{\theta^2}{T^2} + \left(F-\frac{\theta}{K}\right)^2 T^2 = \text{constant},$$

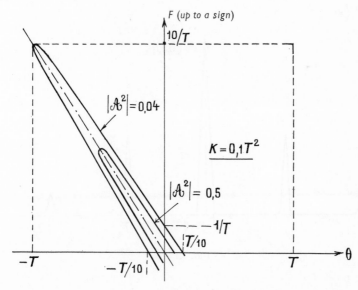

FIG. 3.15

i.e. such that the diameter of the direction of the axis of F is the line whose equation is $F = \theta/K$ (see fig. 3.15).

H

In other words, the ambiguity is concentrated on the line $F = \theta/K$. This corresponds entirely to the results found in Chapter 4.

On the other hand, we find

$$\theta_{min} = \frac{T}{\sqrt{1 + T^4/K^2}}$$

T^2/K being, nearly, what we shall call in Chapter 4, the pulse compression ρ (much greater than 1):

$$\theta_{min} \approx T/\rho, \qquad F_{min} = 1/T.$$

The product $\theta_{min} \cdot F_{min}$ does not always have a physical meaning because the ambiguity is concentrated on a direction which is not that of one of the axes θ or F.

3.10.5 Train of rectangular pulses

As an example, figs. 3.16 (a)–(e) represent the function $|\mathscr{A}^2(\theta, F)|$ in the case of a train of three rectangular signals of duration τ with a period of repetition equal to T_R.

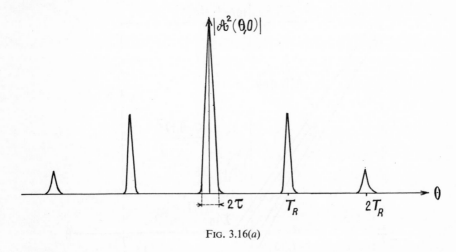

FIG. 3.16(a)

Figure 3.16(a) shows $|\mathscr{A}^2(\theta, 0)|$ as a function of θ. Figure 3.16(b) shows $|\mathscr{A}^2(0, F)|$ as a function of F. Figure 3.16(c) shows $|\mathscr{A}^2(T_R, F)|$ as a function of F. Figure 3.16(d) shows $|\mathscr{A}^2(2T_R, F)|$ as a function of F. Figure 3.16(e) represents the curves of levels of $\mathscr{A}^2$.

(The shaded areas correspond to zones where ambiguity is greater than 0·25 and the circumferences of the circles correspond to the locus $|\mathscr{A}^2| = 0·1$.)

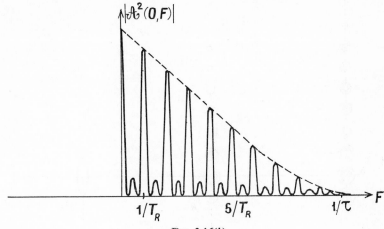

FIG. 3.16(b)

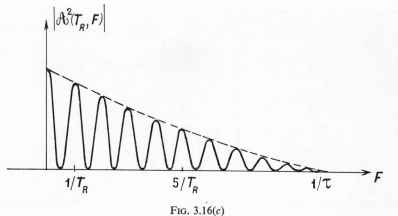

FIG. 3.16(c)

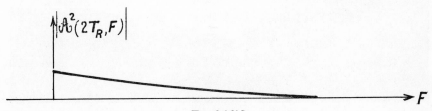

FIG. 3.16(d)

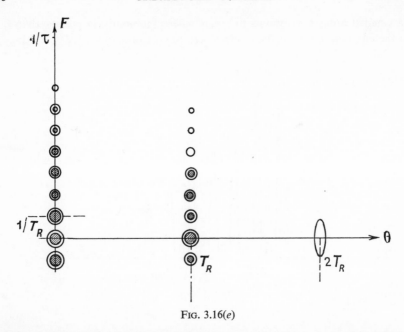

Fig. 3.16(e)

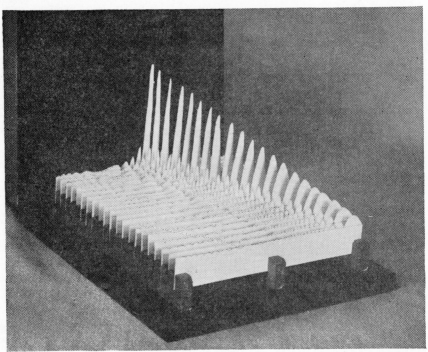

Fig. 3.17

3.10.6 Chirp signal

Figure 3.17 shows the function of ambiguity $|\mathscr{A}(\theta, F)|$ of a rectangular pulse modulated in frequency corresponding to a product $T\varDelta f$ of 20 (pulse compression ratio).

The origin $\theta = 0$, $F = 0$ is in the centre background of the figure. The axis of θ is parallel to the boundary in front of the lid of the box.

3.11 DISTANCE–SPEED RESOLUTION

We could define an ambiguity of resolution $A^2(\theta, F)$ by generalising that which has been said in sub-sections 3.6.3 and 3.9.2.

The value of $A^2(\theta, F)$ will be defined as being such that

$$|\mathscr{A}(t, f)| + A|\mathscr{A}(t-\theta, f-F)|$$

gives just two maxima.

3.11.1 Gaussian signal non-frequency modulated (compare with sub-section 3.10.3)

We seek the value of A such that

$$\exp\left[-(\pi/2)(Tf)^2\right]\exp\left[-(\pi/2)(t/T)^2\right] + A\exp\left\{-(\pi/2)[T(f-F)]^2\right\}\exp\left\{-(\pi/2)[(t-\theta)/T]^2\right\}$$

gives just two maxima.

We could find this result (here in a rigorous way and in general with an excellent approximation) by finding out when the section of the surface

$$|\mathscr{A}(t, f)| + A|\mathscr{A}(t-\theta, f-F)|$$

by the plane $f = (F/\theta)t$ gives just two maxima, i.e. here, when

$$\exp\left[-\frac{\pi}{2}\left(\frac{T^2F^2}{\theta^2}+\frac{1}{T^2}\right)t^2\right] + A\exp\left[-\frac{\pi}{2}\left(\frac{T^2F^2}{\theta^2}+\frac{1}{T^2}\right)(t-\theta)^2\right]$$

gives two maxima. We find that

$$A^2(\theta, F) = A^2\left[\sqrt{\theta^2 T^2\left(\frac{T^2F^2}{\theta^2}+\frac{1}{T^2}\right)}, 0\right],$$

$$A^2(\theta, F) = A^2(\sqrt{\theta^2 + T^4F^2}, 0),$$

thus obtaining the results shown in fig. 3.18. The shaded area corresponds to $A^2 = 1$.

A point of the plane θ, F where $A^2(\theta, F) = A_0^2$ is such that two targets whose radial distances differ by θ and the Doppler frequencies by F are separable if the ratio

$$\frac{\text{Equivalent echoing area of the smallest}}{\text{Equivalent echoing area of the largest}}$$

is greater than A_0^2.

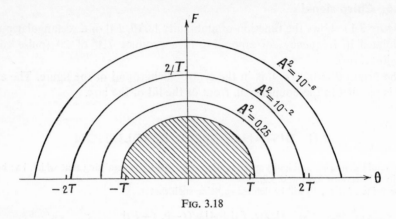

FIG. 3.18

The line round the shaded area is special: it corresponds to an impossibility of separation whatever be the respective levels of the two targets. We could call the shaded area a zone of total ambiguity, or simply a zone of ambiguity.

3.11.2   Gaussian signal linearly frequency modulated

We find here in an identical manner,

$$A_2^2(\theta, F) = A_1^2[\sqrt{\theta^2 + T^4(F - \theta/K)^2}]$$

given the ambiguity found in sub-section 3.10.4, which gives the curves of fig. 3.19.

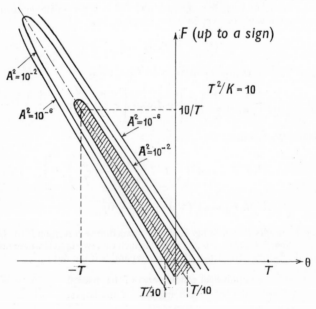

FIG 3.19

3.11.3 Rectangular pulse non-frequency modulated

By referring to what has been said in sub-section 3.9.2.2, when $F(T-|\theta|)$ is sufficiently large (with respect to 1), we could admit that there is a separation if

$$A^2 > \frac{1}{(\pi FT)^2}.$$

The curve $A^2(\theta, F) = 1$ has been determined, as in sub-section 3.11.1, by limiting the surface $|\mathscr{A}(t, f)| + |\mathscr{A}(t-\theta, f-F)|$ with planes $f = (F/\theta)t$.

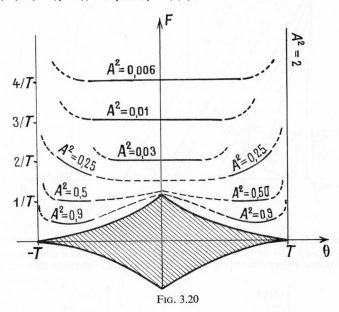

Fig. 3.20

And finally $A^2(\theta, F)$ is approximately represented as in fig. 3.20.

3.11.4 Rectangular pulse linearly frequency modulated

Figure 3.21 shows approximately the ambiguity A^2 of a rectangular signal of duration T linearly modulated in frequency between $(f_0 - 5/T)$ and $(f_0 + 5/T)$.

3.11.5 Random signal

Let us consider a signal of transmission composed of a noise of constant power (randomly modulated in phase) occupying a rectangular spectrum of width Δf, when we cut into this noise with a rectangular pulse of duration T (see fig. 3.22). The value of the product $T\,\Delta f$ is assumed to be large (for example, 10^6) but not infinite, i.e. that T is large with respect to $1/\Delta f$, but finite.

Under these conditions, the expression for $C_u(\theta)$ is very close to the autocorrelation function of the spectral density of the original noise (rectangular spectral density), but it is not rigorously identical to it. The difference comes from two separate sources.

The autocorrelation function is to be multiplied by $|(T-\theta)/T|$ in order to take into account the fact that the signals $S(t)$ and $S^*(t-\theta)$ exist together only during the time $T-\theta$, which allows us to find $C_u(\theta) = 0$ for $\theta \geqq T$.

In other respects, $|T/(T-\theta)|\,C_u(\theta)$ shall be equal to the autocorrelation function only if the $(T-\theta)$ could be considered to be infinitely large with respect to $1/\Delta f$. Since it is nothing like that, it has to be considered that $|T/(T-\theta)|\ C_u(\theta)$ is equal to the autocorrelation function of $S(t)$, plus a correcting term due to the finite character of $(T-\theta)$, and which is predominant when θ is large.

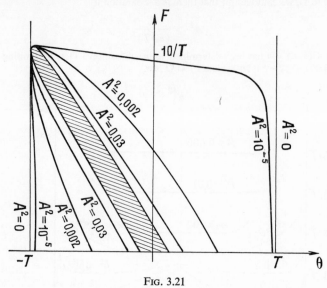

FIG. 3.21

More generally, because of the finite character of $(T-\theta)$, the expression $\mathscr{A}(\theta, F)$ is equal to that which it would be if T were infinite, multiplied by $|(T-\theta)/T|$, plus a correcting term. This correcting term could be evaluated by assuming the point (θ, F) sufficiently far from the centre

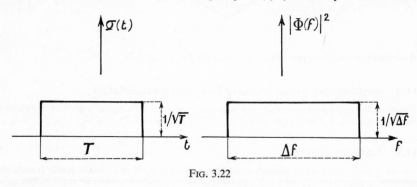

FIG. 3.22

of coordinates in order to admit that $S(t)$ and $S^*(t-\theta)\exp(-2\pi jFt)$ are independent. It can be written as:

$$\sigma = \int S(t) \cdot S^*(t-\theta)\exp(-2\pi jFt)\,dt$$

$$\sigma = \sum S(t_i) \cdot S^*(t_i-\theta)\exp(-2\pi jFt_i) \cdot \frac{1}{\Delta f}$$

where t_i is the $(T-\theta)\,\Delta f$ instants of sampling $(1/\Delta f$ apart).

The real part of σ is a random gaussian variable, since $(T-\theta)\, \Delta f$ is large (except for θ really very near to T), of mean value zero since $S(t_i)$ and $S^*(t_i-\theta)\exp(-2\pi j F t_i)$ are assumed independent, characterised by its variance,

$$(T-\theta)\, \Delta f \left[\frac{1}{\Delta f^2}\cdot\frac{1}{T^2}\cdot\frac{1}{2}\right] = \frac{T-\theta}{2T^2\Delta f}.$$

It is similar for the imaginary part of σ, so that the absolute value of σ possesses a Rayleigh distribution and the mean value of $|\sigma^2|$ is given by

$$\overline{|\sigma^2|} = \left|\frac{T-\theta}{T}\right|\cdot\frac{1}{\Delta T f}.$$

We therefore find that a target situated at the values of θ and F, which easily allow us to distinguish it from the target of reference if T were infinite, may not be so easily differentiated because of the term σ. It is not illogical to admit that, on average and in an order of sizes, it will be possible to separate only if

$$A^2 > \left|\frac{T-\theta}{T}\right|\cdot\frac{1}{T\Delta f}.$$

Finally, $A^2(\theta, F)$ is well represented by fig. 3.23 (where $T\Delta f = 10^6$).

It is to be noted that, with the approximations made, fig. 3.23 also shows the ambiguity $|\mathscr{A}^2(\theta, F)|$.

The surface of ambiguity is composed of a central peak of low volume surrounded by a plain whose amplitude is of the order of $1/T\Delta f$.

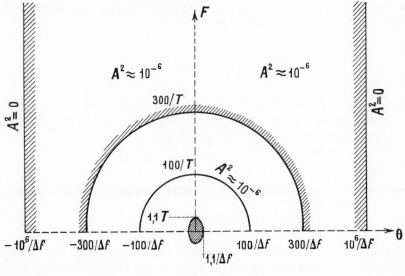

FIG. 3.23

IMPORTANT REMARK

From the preceding we could conclude that in the case of a transmission of a "slice of a random signal" we could reduce the ambiguity to a desired level by increasing $T\Delta f$ to infinity. In fact, even here there is a limitation: the value of ΔTf has an upper limit.

In effect, in the presence of a target of radial speed V_R, the Doppler deviation is not constant over the whole spectrum: it differs by

$$\frac{2V_R\,\Delta f}{c}$$

(c being the speed of light) between the extremal frequencies of the spectrum used. We could not, therefore, make a coherent measurement over a very long time T, because it is necessary that

$$\frac{1}{T} > \frac{2V_R\,\Delta f}{c}$$

$$\boxed{T\Delta f < \frac{c}{2V_R}}$$

We obtain the same result by writing that the time T must be less than the time required by the target to move a distance corresponding nearly to $1/\Delta f$, i.e. the distance $c/2\Delta f$, which gives us

$$V_R T < \frac{c}{2\Delta f}, \qquad T\Delta f < \frac{c}{2V_R}.$$

In a way, we could say that the more the target is capable of great speeds, the more difficult is its location. This is what is sometimes called the Heisenberg principle applied to radar.[1]

Numerical application:

$$V_R = 50 \text{ m/s}, \qquad T\Delta f < 6 \cdot 10^6;$$

$$V_R = 6{,}000 \text{ m/s}, \qquad T\Delta f < 5 \cdot 10^4.$$

N.B. Part of the difficulty comes from the fact that while we have assumed throughout the preceding discussion that the Doppler effect gives a translation of the frequency spectrum, it really has the effect of a similarity on the scale of frequencies. When radars utilise this property (this part of the theory is yet to be evolved, at least to our knowledge) these limitations will take a different form.

---

[1] See, in particular, in this field, *Mr. Tompkins in Wonderland*, Cambridge University Press.

3.12 REMARKS ON CLUTTER ELIMINATION

3.12.1 Application of notions of ambiguity to effects of clutter

When we are in the presence of a useful target of equivalent echoing area σ_u and of an interfering target of equivalent echoing area σ_p situated at (θ, F) with respect to the useful target, we have seen that the power of the interfering signal at the site of the useful signal was given by

$$\sigma_p |\mathscr{A}(\theta, F)|^2,$$

in comparison with the power σ_u of the useful signal.

When we are in the presence of a great number of interfering targets of equivalent echoing area σ_{pi}, situated at (θ_i, F_i) with respect to the useful target and sending back signals without phase-reference between them (which is often the case), the power of the total interfering signal at the site of the useful signal is given by

$$\sum \sigma_{pi} |\mathscr{A}(\theta_i, F_i)|^2, \text{ in comparison with } \sigma_u.$$

Similarly, if we are in the presence of clutter (or diffused interfering echoes) characterised by the density of equivalent echoing area [expressed in $m^2/Hz \cdot s$, as $V(\theta, F)$], their power at the site of the useful target can be written as

$$\iint |\mathscr{A}^2(\theta, F)| \times V(\theta, F) \, d\theta \, dF, \text{ in comparison with } \sigma_u.$$

According to whether this integral is smaller or greater than σ_u, we have more or less hope of obtaining valid information about the useful target.

We could note that if $V(\theta, F)$ is a constant, the integral does not depend on the signal transmitted. Fortunately, this is never the case, and this is why engineers could choose the signal transmitted according to the case.

As an example, let us suppose that we have to detect an echoing area 1 m^2 in the presence of clutter such that

$$V(\theta, F) = 10^4 \text{ m}^2/\text{Hz} \cdot \text{s for 5,000 Hz} < F < 5,100 \text{ Hz and}$$

$$-200 \, \mu\text{s} < \theta < 200 \, \mu\text{s and}$$

$$V(\theta, F) = 0 \text{ outside these intervals}$$

(see fig. 3.24).

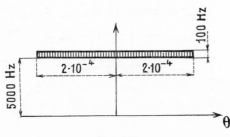

FIG. 3.24

These numbers correspond, for example, to a clutter occupying a large zone around the useful target with a density of 10^{-8} m^2 of equivalent echoing area per m^3 of volume, when we utilise a radar beam of 10^{-2} rd in bearing and of $6 \cdot 10^{-3}$ rd in elevation, the useful target being at 100 km from the radar.

If the transmitted signal is gaussian, non-frequency modulated of duration 10 μs, the double integral

$$\int\int |\mathscr{A}^2(\theta, F)| \cdot V(\theta, F) \, d\theta \, dF$$

is near to $2 \cdot 10^{-5} \times 100 \times 10^4 = 20$, and the useful target cannot be located correctly (see fig. 3.25).

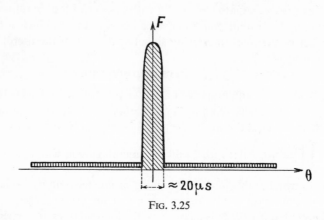

FIG. 3.25

But if the transmitted signal is gaussian, non-frequency modulated of duration 400 μs (see fig. 3.26), the integral

$$\int\int |\mathscr{A}^2(\theta, F)| \cdot V(\theta, F) \, d\theta \, dF$$

is near to $4 \cdot 10^{-4} \times 10^2 \times 10^{-6} \approx 4 \cdot 10^{-4}$, which is negligible.

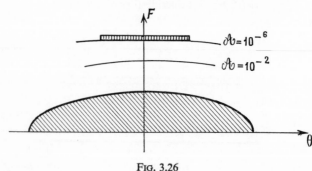

FIG. 3.26

However, radar can distinguish two targets having the same radial speeds by means of radial distances only if these differ by more than 75 km (500 μs). Otherwise the accuracy of the radar's measurement of the radial speed will be mediocre.

Another possibility consists of utilising a gaussian signal of duration $T = 10 \, \mu$s but linearly frequency modulated, with $k = 0 \cdot 01 T^2$ (pulse compression ratio of the order of 100), thus obtaining the result shown in fig. 3.27, where we see that the integral

$$\iint |\mathscr{A}^2(\theta, F)| \cdot V(\theta, F) \, d\theta \, dF$$

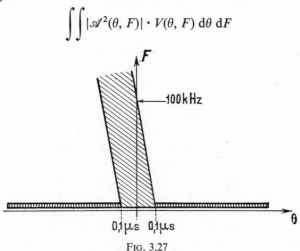

FIG. 3.27

is near to $2 \cdot 10^{-7} \times 100 \times 10^4 = 0 \cdot 2$, which is good. We notice that we would have obtained the same result with a gaussian signal non-frequency modulated of duration $T = 0 \cdot 1 \, \mu$s (i.e. having, everything else being equal, a peak power 100 times higher). We say that we have reduced the clutter in the ratio of compression.

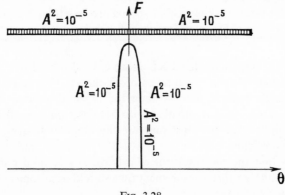

FIG. 3.28

Finally, we could utilise a signal of transmission modulated in phase in a random way as that analysed in sub-section 3.11.5, with $\Delta f = 10$ MHz and $T = 0.01$ s $(T\Delta f = 10^5)$ thus obtaining for the double integral a value

$$4 \cdot 10^{-4} \times 10^2 \times 10^{-5} \approx 4 \cdot 10^{-4}$$

which is completely negligible (see fig. 3.28).

However, the discrimination in radial distance is of the order of 20 m, the discrimination in Doppler frequency is of the order of 100 Hz (these values have a meaning for two analogous targets) and the peak power to be transmitted is 1,000 times weaker than in the case of the pulse compression radar envisaged above, everything being equal elsewhere. We must note, in order to be complete, even in an example, that if the interfering targets are punctual, few and very powerful, their effect is constant on a radar using such a signal, however constant the position of the useful target. This is not the case in a radar using the signal shown in sub-section 3.25—classical radar—on which the interfering targets have an effect only if they are at a radial distance of less than 2,000 m from the useful target. Assuming that we are in the presence of a unique, interfering, punctual target of equivalent echoing area 10^6 m^2, the radar transmitting a signal randomly phase modulated would be found incapable of correctly locating the useful target of less than 10 m^2 of equivalent echoing area, while the classical radar would not have this incapacity. This brings to our notice a comment which underlines the deficiency of the notion of ambiguity, i.e. that if such is the case, we could know very quickly where (in θ and F) the unique interfering target is and what its level is, and hence to subtract from the signal received $y(t)$ the corresponding signal, thus eliminating, at least partially, the harmful effect of the interfering target.

3.12.2 Elimination of fixed echoes

In a radar we often try to eliminate the targets whose speeds are very low since these targets are cumbersome and useless. In reality, we could not attain the speed of targets in a direct way but only their radial speeds. We try, therefore, to eliminate the targets whose radial speeds are less than a certain threshold, i.e. the targets whose Doppler frequencies are less than a certain threshold $f_{D\,min}$.

3.12.2.1 To eliminate the fixed echoes we must therefore be able to measure with sufficient precision the radial speed of the targets. (We could utilise certain habitual properties of fixed echoes—their forms and distances—but the corresponding apparatus, for their usefulness, do not enter into our discussion here.) This clearly implies that we must measure the Doppler frequency of a target with sufficient precision.

It is known that the measurement of a frequency is valid only if it lasts a sufficient time and that this measurement time should be as long as the processed signal is submerged in the noise.

The mathematical form which this known result takes leads us to formula (25) of section 3.7, which expresses that the standard deviation of the error committed over the measurement of the frequency is

(1) Inversely proportional to the duration of the measurement (in fact, to T_f);

(2) Inversely proportional to the square root of the signal-to-noise ratio in energy R.

The relative error over the measurement of the Doppler frequency, and hence of the radial speed, is therefore as weak as the Doppler frequency is high, i.e. as the wavelength of the radar is small.

Suppose that we wish to eliminate the fixed targets and not the mobile ones whose Doppler frequency is 2,000 Hz (100 m/s of radial speed in band S). If the standard deviation of the error committed over the measurement of the Doppler frequency f_D is 1,000 Hz, we could adopt the principle of elimination of targets whose measured Doppler frequency is less than 1,000 Hz ($f_{D\,min} = 1,000$ Hz), and we would obtain a probability

— of 0·15 for not eliminating a fixed target;

— of 0·15 for eliminating an interesting target.

But this value of 1,000 Hz, which is really a maximum, could be obtained (as is shown by the application of formula (25)) only if the measurement lasts at least almost 100 μs.

In this respect, it is least important that the signal on which the measurement is made should be composed of two short pulses 100 μs apart or of a single pulse of 100 μs duration. (T_f has practically the same value in the two cases.)

3.12.2.2 If, during the measurement of the radial speed, the central frequency of the transmitted microwave signal changes in a significant way (for example, by 20 MHz in band S), we measure, in fact, the radial speed of the displacement of the "centre of reflection", which is usually extremely high. The elimination of fixed echoes becomes impossible (see Chapter 5).

3.12.2.3 In order that the elimination of fixed echoes be satisfactory, it is not sufficient to measure the radial speeds with precision.

It is necessary, when two targets (one fixed and the other mobile) are in close proximity (at the same distance, for example)

— that we can distinguish each of the targets (i.e. separate them) by their difference in Doppler frequency to measure the speed of each;

— that, if we cannot distinguish them, the speed of the virtual target (a complex combination of the two non-separable targets) should not be very low, otherwise we eliminate the fixed target and the mobile one.

3.12.2.4 The first hypothesis is satisfied when the radar has good discrimination in Doppler frequency. This could be obtained only

— if the time of measurement of the Doppler frequency is sufficient, which is evident (if the precision of measurement is poor, the discrimination is also poor),

— if, during this time of measurement, the duration of transmission of the signal is long.

This means that a radar transmitting two short pulses of 5 μs 1,000 μs apart has a poor discrimination in Doppler frequency of the order of 100 kHz, while a radar transmitting a rectangular pulse of 1,000 μs duration has a good discrimination (of 1 kHz).

We see that the elimination of fixed echoes does not pose any theoretical problem in the case of radars of very long pulses (i.e. CW radars).

3.12.2.5   In the case of classical radars, the elimination of fixed targets poses a problem when we wish to avoid eliminating the mobile targets situated in the same position: we say that there is a limit to the sub-clutter visibility.

Indeed, if the fixed target has an equivalent echoing area larger than the mobile target situated in the same position (in the ratio k^2), generally the set of two targets behaves like a target of a slower speed. This virtual speed of the set of two targets (corresponding to a Doppler frequency F_D much less than the Doppler frequency f_D of the mobile target alone) could be sufficiently low to fall in the domain of eliminated speeds.

Generally, when k^2 increases, the number of mobile targets eliminated also increases, and from a certain value of k^2—called "sub-clutter visibility" of the system (S.C.V.)—all the targets are eliminated. We can understand this better by means of an example.

Suppose that a transmitted signal consists of two short pulses (at the same frequency) with a time T apart.

The receiver receives from a mobile target

— a first signal of the form sin (ωt);
— a second signal, after T, of the form sin $(\omega t + 2\pi f_D T)$.

The measurement of $f_D T$ allows that of f_D. We notice, at this stage, that the measurement of $f_D T$ being defined modulo an integer, by eliminating the fixed targets we eliminate, *ipso facto*, the targets having Doppler frequencies $1/T$, $2/T$, called "blind frequencies".

Hence if we do not want a blind frequency to fall in the domain of useful frequencies and if the maximal useful frequency is $f_{D \max}$, it is necessary to take

$$f_{D \max} T < 1, \qquad f_{D \max} < 1/T.$$

Numerical application:

$$f_{D \max} = 25 \text{ kHz} \qquad T < 40 \text{ } \mu\text{s}.$$

Let us consider what happens when a mobile target is in the same position as a fixed target of equivalent echoing area k^2 times larger.

We receive

— a first signal of the form

$$\sin \omega t + k \sin \omega t = (1+k) \sin \omega t$$

— a second signal, after a time T, of the form

$$\sin{(\omega t + 2\pi f_D T)} + k \sin{\omega t} = \sqrt{k^2 + 1 + 2k \cos{(2\pi f_D T)}} \, [\sin{(\omega t + 2\pi f_D T)}],$$

with

$$\tan{(2\pi F_D T)} = \frac{\sin{(2\pi f_D T)}}{k + \cos{(2\pi f_D T)}}.$$

In practice, when k is large (with respect to 1) we have the relation,

$$\tan{(2\pi F_D T)} = \frac{\sin{(2\pi f_D T)}}{k}.$$

If $f_D T$ is small, we thus obtain $F_D \approx f_D/k$: the virtual radial speed of the set (the fixed target and the mobile target) is equal to the radial speed of the mobile target divided by k.[1]

In any case, the maximal value of F_D is given by

$$\frac{1}{2\pi T} \arctan{\left(\frac{1}{k}\right)} = \frac{1}{2\pi T k} \qquad \text{(if } k \gg 1).$$

Suppose that we wish to eliminate all the targets whose Doppler frequencies are less than $f_{D\,\text{min}}$. We eliminate all the mobile targets situated at the same place as the fixed target of equivalent echoing area k^2 times larger when

$$\frac{1}{2\pi T k} < f_{D\,\text{min}},$$

$$k^2 > \frac{1}{(2\pi T f_{D\,\text{min}})^2}.$$

This admissible maximal value of k^2 constitutes the S.C.V. of the system.

Numerical application:

$$T = 100 \ \mu s, \qquad f_{D\,\text{min}} = 100 \ \text{Hz},$$

$$\text{S.C.V.} = \frac{1}{(2\pi \times 10^{-2})^2} = 250 = 24 \ \text{dB}.$$

The sub-clutter visibility is 24 dB.[2]

---

[1] The preceding calculation assumes that the signals retransmitted by the fixed target and the mobile target have the same phase. The rigorous calculation should take into account a possible difference in phase. When this is carried out, slightly different numerical results are found.

[2] In the example chosen, the frequency F_D is found to be equal to or less than f_D/k (equal if f_D is low). It could be shown that f_D/k is the value that is obtained for F_D with an ideal radar, and that no radar could provide a value greater than F_D.

J

REMARKS

(a) When the target is unique and fixed, the two pulses have the same amplitude. When the target is unique and mobile, the two pulses have the same amplitude.

When the target is complex (fixed target and mobile target at the same position), the two pulses do not have the same amplitude: the ratio of the amplitudes is equal to

$$\frac{\sqrt{k^2+1+2k \cos (2\pi f_D T)}}{k+1}.$$

It varies, hence, between 1 for a target which is mobile and of very low speed, and $(k-1)/(k+1)$ for a target having a radial speed half of the first blind speed.

Hence theoretically we could use the difference between the amplitudes of the two pulses to know that we are in the presence of a fixed and a mobile target simultaneously.

In reality, we should not fail to see that:

If k is large, we are led to detect a very small relative difference between the amplitudes of the two pulses.

For example, if

$$f_D = 2,000 \text{ Hz} \qquad T = 100 \ \mu\text{s}$$

$$k = 16 \qquad\qquad k^2 = 24 \text{ dB}$$

$$\frac{\sqrt{k^2+1+2k \cos (2\pi f_D T)}}{k+1} = 0.97$$

That the argument does not take into account the presence of the noise which initially accompanies useful signals.

(b) In the case studied, we see that we have an interest in increasing the interval T between the two pulses in order to increase the precision of the measurement of the radial speed. With the adopted figures, in the example 100 μs appears to be a minimum leading to a figure of 1,000 Hz for $f_{D \text{ min}}$, which gives an S.C.V. in the neighbourhood of 0 dB.

(c) We also see that the S.C.V. decreases when T increases. But since the increase of T often permits the diminution of $f_{D \text{ min}}$, the two effects very often compensate each other.

(d) The system studied here poses two specific problems:

(1) If the radar is classical, it is necessary to close the receiver during the transmission of the second pulse. If, therefore, T is very large, there will be a zone of blind distance for the radar. (If $T = 500 \ \mu$s, the radar will not detect the echoes situated at 75 km, and beyond, at a certain distance.)

If, on the contrary, we adopt a very low value for T, a fixed target which extends over a great radial distance will be poorly eliminated. Supposing that $T = 100$ μs and that a fixed target has a depth greater than 15 km, we will receive,

— the first pulse corresponding to the front of the fixed target;

— the second pulse transmitted from the front of the fixed target at the same time as the first pulse is sent from the point of the target situated 15 km away. The measurement of f_D no longer has any meaning.

3.12.2.6   Classical M.T.I.

Let us first recall that the classical M.T.I. utilises the pulses that are transmitted during two successive recurrences, which prohibits the use of a radar randomly changing the frequency at each period of recurrence.

Otherwise, we obtain a result as if the value of T was equal to the period of recurrence, which is generally of the order of 5 ms. The blind frequencies are therefore very close (of the order of 200 hertz).

If, therefore, we wish to eliminate the targets whose Doppler frequency is less than 100 Hz $= f_{D\ min}$ (in absolute value), we also eliminate the targets whose Doppler frequency is between 100 Hz and 300 Hz; 300 Hz and 500 Hz. In other words, we could suppress the radar.

This disappointing result is found on the S.C.V. which is found to be less than 0 dB.

We could, therefore, only choose a very small $f_{D\ min}$, for example, of 5 Hz. But in the S band [1] this signifies that we eliminate only the targets whose radial speed is less than 0·25 m/s (just as when there is wind, we can see the leaves of trees because they move).

On the other hand, if the radar were panoramic it would have generally turned through a non-negligible angle during the time which separates two pulses, and the pulses could correspond to centres of reflection of the fixed target of different distances (mainly if the radar beam is very fine). The fixed target has, from then onwards, a non-zero virtual radial speed and connot be eliminated.

3.13   CONCLUSIONS

All that has been said so far must be summarised so that the reader, if he has not understood it (which is normally the fault of the author) can remember only the following conclusions. These conclusions must be known by any engineer who is concerned with radars.

---

[1] λ in the neighbourhood of 0·1 m.

It is obvious that what follows applies to an ideal radar, and that a practical radar cannot be better than an ideal one; but practical radars can often attain the theoretical limits of an ideal radar.

(A) To detect a target with a sufficient probability it is necessary and sufficient that the ratio R

$$R = \frac{\text{energy received during measurement}}{\text{density of noise power (or jamming) in Hz}}$$

be sufficient. Hence the range of a radar (with a given target, a given wavelength and a given antenna) depends only on the ratio R.

The range of the radar does not depend, in particular, either on the form of the signal transmitted or on the form of its spectrum or its width. In particular: two identically good radars transmitting with the same cadence

— one of them a signal of (peak) power 100 MW during 4 μs;

— the other a signal of (peak) power 100 kW during 4 ms,

have the same range.

(B) With a given quality of detection, the precision of range measurement that could be attained by a radar depends only on the form of the spectrum of the signal transmitted.

Approximately, at a given range, the error made over the distance is inversely proportional to the width of the spectrum transmitted. When the target approaches the radar (R increasing) the precision improves.

(C) With a given quality of detection, and a given central frequency of transmission, the precision of the measurement of the radial speed that could be attained by a radar depends only on the form of the transmitted signal.

Approximately, the error made over the measurement of the radial speed is inversely proportional to the duration of the transmitted signal (or the duration of the measurement made).

(D) The probability of discriminating two targets does not depend on the energy transmitted.

We can distinguish two targets of the same speed situated a certain distance apart only if the form of the spectrum transmitted is correct, and in practice only if the spectrum transmitted has a sufficient [1] width.

Similarly, we could distinguish two targets at the same distance, of different radial speeds, only if the form of the transmitted signal is correct, and in practice only if the signal transmitted has sufficient duration (or if the duration of the measurement is sufficient).

---

[1] Only the amplitude of the spectrum intervenes, and not its phase. We could hence modify at will its phase without modifying the precision and the range discrimination of the radar.

This being so, it immediately appears that the radar having the best qualities is that

— which transmits the longest pulses,

— and which transmits the widest spectrum.

For the "Radarists" of the old school, these two qualities might seem contradictory: in fact, they are contradictory if the transmitted signal is modulated only in amplitude. If, on the other hand, the transmitted signal is modulated in frequency (or in phase) we could very well obtain a long signal occupying a wide spectrum.

But the main interest in transmitting a long signal (occupying a wide spectrum) rather than a short one (as is the case, unfortunately, of most of the existing radars) is in the fact that, with the range being fixed by the transmitted energy, we are led with short signals to transmit high instantaneous power, while with long signals peak power could be very much reduced.

Choice of the signal to be transmitted

This choice depends on three considerations:

(1) The first is relative to the range required, to fix not the power but the energy to be transmitted during the duration of the measurement, an energy which is often more easy to obtain with a long period of time and a low power than with high power and short period of time.

However, the duration of the measurement is limited to a maximum which depends either on the maximal time admissible to obtain the result of the measurement or the time during which the parameter to be measured is sufficiently constant (the precision required over their measurement being taken into consideration), or on the time during which we could consider that the received signal does not fluctuate greatly, taking into account the behaviour of the target and the movement of the radar antenna (see Chapter 5).

(2) The second consideration is relative to the precision required over the range measurement and the measurement of the radial speed, a precision which eliminates certain signals of a very narrow spectrum (imprecise radial distance) or very short duration (imprecise radial speed) or which eliminates certain signals giving ambiguous measurements.

(3) Finally, the third consideration takes into account the strength, the radial distance and the radial speed of the targets different from the interesting target, with respect to the same parameters of the interesting target.

Let us suppose that we have chosen a certain signal of transmission $S(t)$. To this signal corresponds, by a certain mathematical operation, what we call a function of ambiguity,

$$|\mathscr{A}^2(\theta, F)|$$

a function of the difference θ between the radial distance of a strange target and that of the interesting target, and also of the difference F between the radial speeds of these two targets.

This function $|\mathscr{A}^2(\theta, F)|$ could be defined, roughly, as representing the degree of difficulty created by the parasitic target in the detection of the interesting target.

Hence, knowing the geography of the clutter represented by

$$V(\theta, F)$$

which gives the strength of the clutter as a function of θ and F, the difficulty created by these strange targets is represented by the integral:

$$\iint |\mathscr{A}^2(\theta, F)| \cdot V(\theta, F) \, d\theta \, dF$$

It is clear that it is necessary to choose $\mathscr{A}^2(\theta, F)$, hence the transmitted signal $S(t)$, so this integral is the weakest possible. We have, hence, the means to choose the optimal modulation of the transmitted signal, after which we could choose the type of receiver to be used.

It is necessary to notice that this is not always carried out entirely because the signal transmitted in the direction of the target is the result of the modulation, by the antenna, of the output signal of the transmitter. For instance, in a panoramic radar, the movement of the antenna introduces a modulation of amplitude of the transmitted signal by the whole equipment, and the receiver has to be matched, not to the form of the signal at the output of the transmitter, but to the form of the signal received by the target, which is very different.

REMARK

On the other hand, it is not sufficient to choose the transmitted signal $S(t)$ to minimise the difficulties created by the clutter, i.e. the integral:

$$\iint |\mathscr{A}^2(\theta, F)| \cdot V(\theta, F) \, d\theta \, dF,$$

but it is necessary to choose $S(t)$ to maximise the response of the useful signal, i.e. the same expression in which $V(\theta, F)$ represents the geography of the interesting target. This consideration is not of use:

— when the dimensions of the useful target are small with respect to the range discrimination of the radar;
— when the Doppler spectrum of the useful target is narrow in comparison with the Doppler frequency discrimination of the radar, which was often the case until now.

But it becomes very important to take this into consideration:

— when the target is spread over a great range of distance and speeds (for example, the earth or moon);
— or when the range discrimination of the radar becomes very good, and this leads to a new evolution of radar.

Indeed, all that has been said so far depends on the hypothesis that the signal reflected by the target has the same form as that of the transmitted signal.

But, in fact, if the signal from the target comes from the transmission signal, it is modulated by the target, and it is necessary to use a receiver matched not to the transmitted signal but to the signal received when we transmit $S(t)$ over a given target.

The next evolution of radar will probably be towards utilising a receiver matched to a given target when it is illuminated by a certain signal transmitted by means of a certain antenna, and we will have thus the possibility:

— of obtaining a much improved response, i.e. one better separated from the noise;
— of obtaining a good response only over a given target.

We will arrive, for example, at a radar equipped with numerous outputs, each corresponding to a given type of target.

Choice of the receiver

Thus, due to the theorem of convolution and as long as we have not found any other analogous theorem (and it does not seem possible), we have two procedures to make a radar receiver:

— either by using correlators
— or by using matched filters.

When we use correlators we have a correlation radar, of which the pulse Doppler radar constitutes the oldest example. When we use a matched filter, we have a matched filter radar, of which the classical radar constitutes the oldest example and the pulse compression radar called CHIRP radar, is one of the most recent examples.

The choice between these two types of radars depends on technical considerations.

If the transmitted signal consists of a signal randomly modulated in phase, it is generally impossible to manufacture the matched filter, and we use correlators.

If the transmitted signal consists of pulses during which the frequency varies linearly as a function of time, it is often more economical to use a matched filter.

If the transmitted signal consists of a train of pulses non-phase modulated, the two types of receivers are, *a priori*, possible, and the choice between them depends on the exact value of the parameters of transmission and on practical considerations.

CHAPTER 4

ANALYSIS OF THE PRINCIPLES
OF RADARS

In this chapter we do not wish to describe in detail all types of existing radars but only to give an insight into their philosophy.

4.1 NOISY RADAR

The preceding chapters have shown that the ideal radar integrated over the time of measurement the product

(signal received) × (transmitted signal delayed by t_0)

and they tried to find the value of t_0 giving the maximum. In other words, we have an infinite number of samples of the transmitted signals delayed by all conceivable and possible values of t_0. Each of these samples is multiplied by the signal received, the whole being integrated over time T, and we seek the value of t_0 for which the integral gives the most important results.

In practice, we are led to use only a finite number of the samples of delayed transmitted signal.

(a) We could use only one of them, in which case the integrator will give the maximum signal when the target passes at the distance corresponding to the delay of the sample.

(b) We could also use a large number of them if, for example, we assume a precision of 450 m, we may use samples of the transmitted signals delayed by τ, $\tau+3$ μs, $\tau+6$ μs such that if there is a target, there will always be an integrator which will give a signal.

Case (b) differs from case (a) only by the number of correlators (the complexity of the equipment). It is therefore possible to restrict ourselves to study case (a) in detail, i.e. to examine the behaviour of a radar which tries to determine at a given instant whether there is a target at a certain distance, or, in other words, which measures the instants when a target passes at a certain given distance (with a certain precision).

121

4.1.1 Target with a fairly well-known velocity

Let us assume that we have a target with a radial velocity lying between $V_R - v_R$ and $V_R + v_R$ with, for example, $V_R = 300$ m/s and $v_R = 5$ m/s.

Let us also assume that the transmitted signal has a rectangular spectrum of width Δf centred on 150 MHz ($\lambda = 2$ m) and that we wish to know the instant when a target passes at a distance of $D = 500$ km from the radar, within ± 15 m.

Let us also admit that we will be satisfied with a false alarm probability of 10^{-3} and a detection probability of 0·9. This means that at maximum range (see fig. 3.4) we shall have $R = 20$ (13 dB).

The value of B is therefore determined by

$$15 \text{ m} \to 10^{-7} \text{ s} = \frac{1}{2\pi B\sqrt{20}},$$

$$2B = 700 \text{ kHz},$$

and, after remark (3) of section 3.5:

$$\boxed{\Delta f = 1\cdot 2 \text{ MHz}}$$

If we adopt this value of Δf, we know that, since the target has a radial velocity of V_R of 300 m/s, the need to make a measurement during a time greater than that which the target takes to cover 15 m, i.e. during a time greater than

$$\frac{15}{300} = 0\cdot 05 \text{ sec} = T$$

is out of the question.

A radial velocity v_R corresponds to a Doppler deviation

$$f_D = 2v_R/\lambda = 5 \text{ Hz}.$$

This value is less than $1/T$: the velocity is hence known with sufficient precision. The mean radial velocity corresponds to a Doppler frequency of 300 Hz. The signal to be transmitted will therefore be determined when we know the energy to be transmitted during the time T.

For this we will assume that the transmission antenna has an aperture of 20 m of diameter and hence a surface S_e of 300 m^2, i.e. a maximal theoretical gain of

$$G_e = \frac{4\pi \times S_e}{\lambda^2} = \frac{4\pi \times 300}{4} = 900.$$

The real gain will be much less, of the order of 600 (28 dB). The density of power at a distance D is therefore given by

$$\frac{600P}{4\pi D^2} = p,$$

where P is the transmitted power.

The target is assumed to radiate in an omnidirectional way a certain quantity $p\sigma_e$ of the transmitted power, by definition of σ_e: the equivalent echoing area (see Chapter 5).

It must be noted that the equivalent echoing area of a target has only a distant relationship to its actual area, i.e. with its dimensions: it depends on the wavelength, on the presentation of the target, and it fluctuates over time (see Chapter 5). This leads us to assume R to be greater than 13 dB in many cases.

Nevertheless, for a given wavelength of a given target in a certain situation, there corresponds an order of size of σ_e which we will assume equal to 1 m^2 (this is the normal value for a small aircraft).

The target therefore radiates a density of power equal to $G_e P \sigma_e / 4\pi D^2$ and the reception antenna (assumed to be identical to the transmission antenna but placed on the side), with an effective area of reception $S_R = \lambda^2 G_e / 4\pi$, finally receives the power

$$\frac{G_e P \sigma_e}{(4\pi D^2)^2} \times S_R = \frac{12 \cdot 10^4 P}{(4\pi D^2)^2}$$

The energy received, E, from the target, as a function of the energy transmitted E_e, is written as

$$E = \frac{G_e S_R \sigma_e}{(4\pi D^2)^2} E_e = \frac{12 \cdot 10^4 E_e}{(4\pi D^2)^2}$$

We must now know the density b of the noise power accompanying the useful signal. *If we do not encounter any jamming*, the value of b is given by

$$b = kT_B,$$

where k is the Boltzmann constant equal to $1{\cdot}4 \cdot 10^{-23}$ W/Hz $\cdot$ deg and T_B the effective noise temperature of the receiving system (in degrees Kelvin).

The noise temperature of the receiving system is the sum of the noise temperatures of each of its components (taking into account, if necessary, attenuations caused by these components). In order to simplify matters, we could write

$$T_B = T_H + T_R.$$

T_H being the noise temperature of the whole aerial + plumbing in microwave and T_R the noise temperature of the receiver itself (which could have one part in microwave).

We thus define the noise figure of the receiving system by the relation

$$N_B = \frac{T_B}{T_0} = \frac{T_H + T_R}{T_0}$$

where T_0 is a reference temperature equal to 290°K.

The noise figure of the receiver is, by definition, that which we find for the complete receiving system if we had $T_H = T_0 = 290°$, i.e.

$$N_R = \frac{T_0 + T_R}{T_0} = 1 + \frac{T_R}{T_0},$$

$$N_B = \frac{T_H}{T_0} + N_R - 1.$$

Numerical applications:

(1) $T_R = 2600°K$ $N_R = \dfrac{2890}{290} = 10 \text{ dB}$

    $T_H = 100°K$ $N_B = \dfrac{2700}{290} = 9\cdot7 \text{ dB} \approx N_R$

(2) $T_R = 290°K$ $N_R = \dfrac{580}{290} = 3 \text{ dB}$

    $T_H = 100°K$ $N_B = \dfrac{390}{290} = 1\cdot3 \text{ dB} \neq N_R$

We therefore finally find that at a distance D,[1]

$$R = \frac{2G_e S_R E_e \sigma_e}{(4\pi D^2)^2 kT_B} = \frac{2 \times 1\cdot2 \times 10^5 E_e}{(4\pi \cdot 25 \cdot 10^{10})^2 \times 1\cdot4 \times 10^{-20}}$$

by taking $T_B = 1000°K$, which is a reasonable value (and which corresponds to a noise figure of almost 5 dB).

Since R must be equal to 20 (by doing this we do not take into account the losses due to the imperfections of the receiver), the energy E_e to be transmitted is given by

$$\boxed{E_e = \frac{RkT_B(4\pi)^2 D^4}{2G_e S_R \sigma_e}} = \frac{20 \times 1\cdot4 \times 10^{-20} \times 160 \times 625 \cdot 10^{20}}{2 \times 1\cdot2 \times 10^5}, \tag{1}$$

E_e being expressed in joules.

We find in the present case

$$E_e \approx \boxed{12\cdot5 \text{ joules}}.$$

If the transmitted signal has a constant power during its duration (peak power) which we shall assume, it will mean that this power must be equal to

$$\frac{E_e}{T} = \frac{12\cdot5}{0\cdot05} = \boxed{250 \text{ W}}.$$

In fact, to be sure that the target receives the transmitted signal when it passes at the required distance, and if we do not know *a priori* when it will pass, we are

[1] See section 3.4.

led to transmit permanently and hence to transmit a mean power equal to 250 W.

The transmitted signal will, for example, be a noise uniformly occupying the frequency band lying between 149·4 MHz and 150·6 MHz, whose mean power will be 250 W.

Let us now suppose that the *target* is transmitting jamming in the form of a gaussian noise with a density p of 10^{-6} W/Hz (a transmitter of 50 W occupying a band of 50 MHz and utilising an omnidirectional antenna). Then the noise of the receiver is negligible *vis-à-vis* the jamming and the ratio R becomes equal to

$$\frac{2G_e E_e \sigma_e}{4\pi D^2} \times \frac{1}{p} = R,$$

which leads to

$$\boxed{E_e = \frac{4\pi D^2 R}{2G_e \sigma_e} \times p} = 0\cdot5 \cdot 10^5 \text{ joules}, \qquad (2)$$

and to a power (peak or mean) of 1 MW.

In short: *in the absence of jamming*

— the energy to be transmitted is proportional to the fourth power of the range;

— is inversely proportional to the gain of the antenna of transmission and to the gain of the antenna of reception;

— for a given surface of aerials, it is proportional to the square of the wavelength.

In the presence of a jamming target:

— the energy to be transmitted is proportional to the square of the range;

— and inversely proportional to the gain of the antenna of transmission, the gain at the reception no longer having any importance.

4.1.2 Diagram of the principle

Figure 4.1 illustrates the principle of such a noisy radar[1] in which

— component 1 creates continuously a noise uniformly occupying a band 1·2 MHz centred on 5 MHz;

— component 2 (mixer and filter) shifts this spectrum of noise around 150 MHz;

— component 4 is a local oscillator at 145 MHz;

---

[1] For reasons of discretion, this diagram does not correspond to any existing equipment (at least to the best of our knowledge).

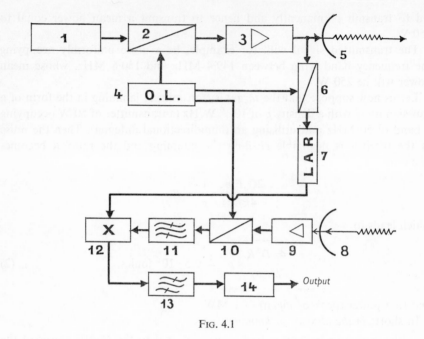

FIG. 4.1

— component 3 is a power amplifier, amplifying the level of 2 and thus
   transmitting in aerial 5 a microwave signal constituted by a noise occupying
   a band 1·2 MHz centred on 150 MHz;

— the power received in aerial 8 is amplified in the low noise preamplifier;

— the received signal is shifted in frequency in the mixer 10 such that the
   output is a signal centred on 5 MHz;

— mixer 10 is followed by a pass-band filter 11 centred on 5 MHz with a
   bandwidth of 1·2 MHz;

— on the other hand, a small part of the transmitted signal, after shifting of
   frequency in 6 which brings it to approximately 5 MHz, is delayed by a
   delay τ_0 corresponding to D, in the delay line 7;

— the output of 7 is multiplied with the output of 11 in a multiplier, and the
   product is then amplified in 12;

— the output of 12 is filtered through filter 13 centred at 300 Hz, of bandwidth
   40 Hz, and then processed in 14 (passed through the threshold and
   "presented" to the user or the computer which handles it).

The working of the whole apparatus is not very difficult to understand: when
the target is at a distance τ near τ_0, component 9 receives the signal collected
by the receiving antenna.

The preamplifier has the essential aim, due to its property of not giving a power output greater than a certain maximum, of protecting mixer 10, which is very fragile. As it has an important gain, it is the noise of the preamplifier that counts, the noise of the mixer, however important it may be, becoming negligible. This preamplifier transmits the useful signal centred on 150 MHz and a noise covering a very large band, in particular the zone of frequencies in the neighbourhood of 140 MHz.

If we do not take any precautions the noise around 140 MHz (which is not accompanied by a useful signal) by mixing with the 145 MHz of L.O. will give a parasitic noise around 5 MHz, which will double the noise of the receiver unnecessarily.

In order to avoid this, preamplifier 9 is followed by a filter, of 5 MHz bandwidth, for example, centred on 150 MHz.

Finally at the output of 10 we therefore obtain

— the useful signal of mean power E_R/T

— a parasitic noise of mean power $kT_B \times 5 \cdot 10^6$, i.e. a signal/noise ratio in power equal to

$$\frac{E_R}{T} \times \frac{1}{kT_B \times 5 \cdot 10^6} = \frac{E_R}{kT_B} \times \frac{1}{T \cdot 5 \cdot 10^6},$$

$$\frac{S_1}{B_1} = \frac{R}{2 \times 0.05 \times 5 \cdot 10^6} = \frac{20}{2 \times 0.25 \cdot 10^6} = 4 \cdot 10^{-5} = -44 \text{ dB},$$

by defining the signal-to-noise ratio in power by

$$\frac{S}{B} = \frac{\text{mean useful power}}{\text{mean parasitic power}}$$

At the output of 11, the noise power is equal to

$$kT_B \Delta f = kT_B \times 1.2 \cdot 10^6,$$

and the signal/noise ratio in energy is equal to

$$1.7 \cdot 10^{-4} = -38 \text{ dB}.$$

Multiplier 11 does the multiplication between the useful signal of reference $S(t-\tau_0)$ centred on 5 MHz and the received signal (accompanied by a noise), i.e. the signal $S(t-\tau)$ centred on 5 MHz + 300 Hz (within a range of 5 Hz). The product of these two signals gives

— a component at 300 Hz (± 5 Hz),

— a component at 10 MHz + 300 Hz (which is useless).

The pass-band filter of 2×20 Hz centred on 300 Hz makes the final integration (averaging) of the useful component, over a time equal to $1/20 = 0.05$ s $= T$.

When τ varies, the output of 13 shows the autocorrelation function of the signal of transmission assumed to be centred on 5 MHz, $\rho(\tau - \tau_0)$.

The demodulation (or simply the detection) of the output of 13 gives, when τ varies, the autocorrelation function of the transmitted signal assumed to be centred on the zero frequency.

We have therefore at the output a signal-to-noise ratio equal to $R/2$, i.e. to $(13 \text{ dB} - 3 \text{ dB}) = 10 \text{ dB}$ (see end of section 3.4).

The correlation has therefore improved the signal-to-noise ratio by $10 + 38 = 48$ dB, which represents *the product* $T\Delta f$.

Thus if we see the output signal of 11 (or of 10) on an oscilloscope, we will be seeing only the parasitic noise, the signal being extremely weak, while the examination of the output of 13 gives a signal "coming well out of the noise". This also means that multiplier 12 should have a dynamic of at least 48 dB, i.e. it should treat in the same way signals having levels different from 48 dB.

REMARK

In practice, we make the measurement on a sample of duration 0·05 sec of the (useful) noise transmitted permanently. Even if there were no parasitic noise, the result obtained would not exactly be the autocorrelation function corresponding to the spectrum of width Δf, but one affected by a certain fluctuation. This point was studied in sub-section 1.9.2, where we saw that the parasitic fluctuations have a power of 45 dB less than the power of the useful signal. They are therefore strictly negligible in most of the applications.

4.1.3   Target of unknown speed

If we do not know the radial speed of the target (assumed, however, of known sign: in the contrary case it is easy to modify the diagram a little in order to take into account no knowledge of the sign of the speed) it is sufficient to replace:

The unique chain 13–14 by a certain number of parallel chains having filters of 40 Hz centred on

260 Hz	340 Hz
220 Hz	380 Hz

the numbers of the channels (adjacent) by which the maximum signals are received, and the comparison between the amplitude, of those signals, giving at $\pm 2\cdot 5$ m/s the velocity of the target.

We also obtain, conforming to the theory (section 3.9), the possibility of distinguishing two targets whose velocities differ by 20 m/s.

In particular, if we wish to eliminate the slow targets and especially the fixed echoes, it is sufficient not to put in filters corresponding to low speeds. (In practice, this could be effected by direct transmission leaks in the reception antenna.)

REMARKS

(1) Figure 4.1 is the typical diagram of a correlation proximative fuse, in which we restrict ourselves to finding if and when the target is at a certain defined distance. If we wish to ensure a continued observation of all zones of distances, it is convenient, as has already been said, to multiply the receivers, each of them corresponding to a different value of τ_0.

But, in this case, it will remain impossible to distinguish two targets of very close speeds distant from each other by 120 m:

$$\left(\theta_{min} = \frac{1}{1 \cdot 2 \cdot 10^6} = 0 \cdot 8 \ \mu s \right)$$

(2) The zone of ambiguity is an ellipse whose axes are the coordinate axes and of lengths $d = 120$ m and $v = 20$ m/s.

4.2 "PULSE DOPPLER" RADAR

The pulse Doppler radar transmits pulses modulating a signal of the form $A \sin (2\pi f_0 t)$, i.e. the signal transmitted may be represented by the expression

$$S(t) = A \sin (2\pi f_0 t) \cdot F(t),$$

where $F(t)$ is a function which may be equal to only zero or 1, for example

equal to 1	for	$0 \leqq t \leqq T_0$
	for	$t_1 \leqq t \leqq t_1 + T_1$
	. . . .	
	for	$t_k \leqq t \leqq t_k + T_k$
	. . . .	
equal to zero	for	$T_0 < t < t_1$
	for	$t_1 + T_1 < t < t_1$
	. . . .	
	for	$t_k + T_k < t < t_{k+1}$
	. . . .	

In practice, very often $t_1, t_2, \ldots, t_k$ are distributed in an arithmetic progression in time (but this is not general), and all the values of $T_0, T_1, \ldots, T_k, \ldots$ are equal (but this is not indispensable).

On the other hand, it may be that the utilisation of transmission tubes (called non-coherent) makes the phase of the carrier $A \sin 2\pi f_0 t$ vary from pulse to pulse by a malfunction in the transmission tube. In this event, by means of a superheterodyne reception in which the phase of the local oscillator (called coherent) follows that of the transmitter, we return to the case where the transmitter is coherent (constant phase of the carrier). We therefore consider only this case.

K

However it may be possible to ensure the reception of a pulse Doppler radar in a matched filter (see section 3.1), we generally use a correlation receiver, very similar to that which has been described for the noisy radar.

We therefore calculate the expression

$$\int_T S(t-t_0) \cdot y(t) \, dt,$$

for a finite number of values of t_0.

The only difference from the radar described in section 4.1 is due to the particular nature of the transmitted signal $S(t)$. We could therefore write

$$\frac{1}{A} \int_T S(t-t_0) \cdot y(t) \, dt = \int \sin 2\pi f_0(t-t_0) \cdot F(t-t_0) \cdot y(t) \, dt$$

$$= \int_T [y(t) \cdot F(t-t_0)] \cdot \sin 2\pi f_0(t-t_0) \cdot dt.$$

Since, on the other hand, replacing $2\pi f_0(t-t_0)$ by $\sin 2\pi f_0 t$ results in making an error over t_0 of less than $1/f_0$ [which is always negligible in practice (compare section 3.4)] we calculate

$$\int_T [y(t) \cdot F(t-t_0)] \cdot \sin (2\pi f_0 t) \cdot dt.$$

We obtain the product $y(t) \cdot F(t-t_0)$ by allowing the received signal $y(t)$ to pass through the receiver only during the time intervals

$$t_0 \qquad , \qquad t_0 + T_0,$$
$$t_1 + t_0 \qquad , \qquad t_1 + t_0 + T_1,$$
$$\cdots \cdots \cdots \cdots$$
$$t_k + t_0 \qquad , \qquad t_k + t_0 + T_k.$$

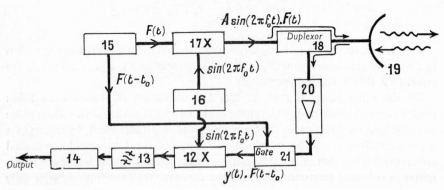

FIG. 4.2

We multiply $y(t) \cdot F(t - t_0)$ by $\sin 2\pi f_0 t$ by demodulating the first by the carrier of the transmission, thus obtaining, for example, the diagram shown in fig. 4.2, in a simplified way. (The reception here is assumed to be homodyne and not superheterodyne.)

In this diagram

— component 15 produces the function $F(t)$ and even shifts it by t_0,

— oscillator 16 produces the signal $\sin (2\pi f_0 t)$,

— multiplier 17 (modulator) provides the transmission signal carried towards aerial 19 (unique on the figure) through duplexor 18,

— gate 21 allows the signal to pass only when $F(t - t_0)$ is not zero,

— components 12, 13 and 14 are similar to those in fig. 4.1.

4.3 CW DOPPLER RADAR

Let us suppose that we are no longer interested in knowing the positions of the targets but only their speeds. In this case we could restrict ourselves to transmit a pure wave of power P_e.

The value of R at the point of reception depends only on the duration T of the measurement. This duration is limited by two factors:

(a) the passage time of the target in the beam of the radar;

(b) the time during which the radial velocity of the target remains constant within a certain quantity.

If we assume that the radial velocity of the target is constant during the time T_p of its passage in the beam of the radar, it is this time T_p which limits the range of the radar.

Let us suppose, in order to clarify our ideas, that the power transmitted is 250 W and that the radar has the characteristics admitted in section 4.1 for a noisy radar (antenna gain, wavelength, equivalent echoing area, noise temperature).

Let us suppose that the target remains in the beam of the radar for 1 sec $(T_p = T = 1)$.

The range of the radar in the absence of jamming will be therefore equal to

$$500 \text{ km} \times \left(\frac{1}{0 \cdot 05} \right)^{\frac{1}{4}} \approx 1100 \text{ km.}$$

At that distance we will still have $R = 20$.

The possible precision on the measurement of the radial speed is therefore given by formula (27) of Chapter 3. We find

$$\frac{2\sqrt{3}}{2\pi\sqrt{20}} = 0 \cdot 15 \text{ m/s}$$

at the maximum range.

But if two targets are simultaneously found in the radar beam they could be distinguished (and their radial speeds be measured) only if their radial speeds differ by more than $1/T = 1$ Hz, i.e. by more than 1 m/s.

The principle of Doppler radar is simple: we mix the received wave with the transmitted wave (if necessary after a certain number of transpositions) and we measure the frequency of mixing

— either with a counter if we have only one target;

— or by passing the mixing signal through a certain number of filters centred on different Doppler frequencies, and by examining the filters which emit a sufficiently strong signal, if we have many targets.

4.4 CLASSICAL PULSED RADAR

4.4.I Classical concept

The classical pulsed radar transmits with a certain recurrence frequency F_R pulses of duration T_i non-modulated in frequency (at least spontaneously).

During their existence these pulses have a power (peak power) P_c, the mean power transmitted, P_m, being evidently equal to

$$P_c \times T_i \times F_R = P_m$$

where $T_i F_R$ is the duty cycle of the radar.

Example:

$$P_c = 20 \text{ MW}; \quad T_i = 4 \text{ } \mu s; \quad F_R = 250 \text{ Hz}.$$

$$\text{Duty cycle} = 10^{-3}; \quad P_m = 20 \text{ kW}.$$

The energy transmitted during the duration of the pulse is radiated by a transmission antenna. The energy radiated by the target is received by reception antenna. The reception antenna is normally confused with the transmission antenna, which forces us to introduce a duplexor, so that during the duration of the transmission a sufficient fraction of the energy will not cause the receiver to deteriorate. The functioning of the radar corresponds to the diagram given in fig. 4.3.

The received signal is amplified in a low noise preamplifier followed by a filter for eliminating the image frequency (see section 4.1), and then frequency shifted such that its spectrum is centred on the intermediary frequency (for example, 30 MHz). To that effect, a local oscillator is used to transmit a frequency different by 30 MHz from the central frequency of transmission (by the intermediary of an automatic or manual control of frequency A.F.C. or M.F.C.).

The signal at the output of mixer 6 is therefore composed of 1 (or more) pulses coming from the target, accompanied by a gaussian noise occupying a wide spectrum (of the same size as that of the filter bandwidth of the low noise preamplifier).

The signal is amplified and filtered in a receiver at an intermediary frequency (in reality, the filter is indistinguishable from the amplifier), which means that

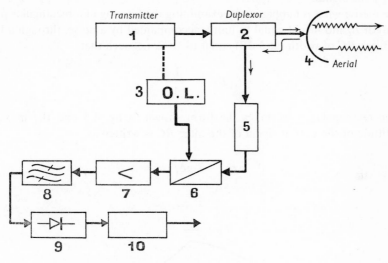

FIG. 4.3

only frequencies lying between 30 MHz $- \Delta f/2$ and 30 MHz $+ \Delta f/2$ are transferred.

We obtain a result as if we had transmitted a signal whose spectrum had a width Δf.

Generally, the Doppler frequency due to the speed of the target is very low compared to Δf and $1/T_i$, and we shall not, at least at this stage, take this into account. The problem is then to define the value of Δf.

The transmitted signal has a Fourier transform whose amplitude is shown in fig. 4.4, where f_0 is the central frequency of transmission. The received signal therefore occupies a spectrum whose Fourier transform is the same, except that the f_0 is to be replaced by the intermediary frequency (30 MHz).

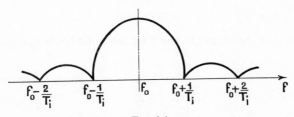

FIG. 4.4

If Δf is very wide in relation to $1/T_i$, we shall retain, in addition to the central lobe, many lobes which contain only very little useful energy, however important the noise power. At the output of 8 we shall have rectangular pulses but submerged in a large noise. If Δf is very narrow in relation to $1/T_i$ we will completely destroy the signal.

We realise what is happening by examining the filtering of a rectangular pulse of length T_i and height equal to unity, accompanied by a noise, through a low-pass filter RC of width (at 3 dB) equal to $\Delta f/2$, i.e. such that

$$RC = \frac{1}{\pi \Delta f}$$

The rectangular pulse takes the form shown in fig. 4.5 and the maximal amplitude of the output signal of the filter RC is written as

$$\boxed{\left| 1 - \exp\left(-T_i \pi \Delta f\right) \right| = \sqrt{S}}$$

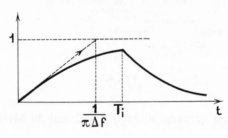

FIG. 4.5

If we assume that the gaussian noise has a constant density A, the noise power at the output of the filter is written as

$$= A \int_0^\infty \frac{1}{1 + \dfrac{\omega^2}{\pi^2 \Delta f^2}}\, d\omega \quad \left[\text{since the transfer function of the filter is equal to } \frac{1}{1 + p/\pi \Delta f} \right]$$

$$= A\pi \Delta f \times \frac{\pi}{2}$$

which means that at the output of the filter the noise has a standard deviation given by

$$\boxed{\pi \sqrt{A \frac{\Delta f}{2}}}$$

— if, therefore, $T_i \Delta f$ is large in relation to 1, the signal has an amplitude 1 and the noise has a very large standard deviation.

— if, on the other hand, $T_i \Delta f$ is small in relation to 1, the signal has an amplitude equal to

$$1 - \exp(-T_i \pi \Delta f) \approx T_i \pi \Delta f$$

while the standard deviation of the noise is given by $\pi \sqrt{A \cdot \Delta f / 2}$, which is therefore very large (since Δf is small).

When Δf tends to infinity (the pass band being very large), the signal-to-noise ratio

$$\frac{S}{B} = \frac{2}{\pi^2 A \Delta f}$$

tends to zero.

When Δf tends to zero (the pass band being very small) the ratio

$$\frac{S}{B} = 2\frac{\pi^2 T_i^2 \Delta f^2}{\pi^2 A \Delta f} = 2\frac{T_i^2}{A} \Delta f$$

also tends to zero.

There exists a mean value of Δf for which the ratio

$$\frac{\text{amplitude of the signal}}{\text{standard deviation of noise}} \text{ is maximal.}$$

In reality, the filters are of a better quality than the RC filter: their sides fall away steeply. For an ideal pass-band filter, we find that for Δf we must assume the value

$$\boxed{\Delta f = \frac{1 \cdot 2}{T_i}}$$

and this is thus shown in an approximate way below.

The Fourier transform of a pulse $S(t)$ of duration τ and of height $1/\tau$ is equal to

$$\Phi(f) = \frac{\sin \pi f \tau}{\pi f \tau}.$$

By filtering this pulse through a rectangular filter of size $2B$ we obtain the signal:

$$\sigma_B(t) = \int_{-B}^{+B} \frac{\sin \pi f \tau}{\pi f \tau} \exp(2\pi j f t) \, df,$$

whose central value (for $t = 0$) is equal to

$$\sigma_B(0) = \int_{-B}^{+B} \frac{\sin \pi f \tau}{\pi f \tau} \, df = 2 \int_0^B \frac{\sin \pi f \tau}{\pi f \tau} \, df,$$

writing $\pi f \tau = u$,

$$\sigma_B(0) = \frac{2}{\pi\tau} \int_0^{\pi B\tau} \frac{\sin u}{u} \, du$$

$$df = \frac{du}{\pi\tau},$$

$$\sigma_B(0) = \frac{2}{\pi\tau} \ \mathrm{Si}\,(\pi B\tau).$$

Hence as a first approximation, seeking the optimal value of B is the same as seeking the value of B that renders maximal the expression

$$\frac{2}{\pi\sqrt{B\tau}} \ \mathrm{Si}\,(\pi B\tau):$$

$$\frac{2}{\sqrt{\pi\tau}} \cdot \frac{\mathrm{Si}\,(\pi B\tau)}{\sqrt{\pi B\tau}}$$

For $\pi B\tau \to 0$: $\mathrm{Si}\,(\pi B\tau) \sim \pi B\tau$,

$$\frac{\mathrm{Si}\,(\pi B\tau)}{\sqrt{\pi B\tau}} \sim \sqrt{\pi B\tau} \to 0.$$

For $\pi B\tau \to \infty$: $\mathrm{Si}\,(\pi B\tau) \to \pi/2$,

$$\frac{\mathrm{Si}\,(\pi B\tau)}{\sqrt{\pi B\tau}} \to 0$$

$\pi B\tau$	0·5	1	1·5	1·7	1·9	2·1	2·3	2·5	3
$\mathrm{Si}\,(\pi B\tau)$	0·49	0·95	1·32	1·45	1·56	1·65	1·72	1·79	1·85
$\sqrt{\pi B\tau}$	0·71	1	1·22	1·30	1·38	1·45	1·52	1·58	1·73
$\dfrac{\mathrm{Si}\,(\pi B\tau)}{\sqrt{\pi B\tau}}$	0·70	0·95	1·08	1·11	1·13	1·14	1·13	1·12	1·07

The maximum is obtained for

$$\pi B\tau \approx 2\cdot1,$$

$$B\tau = 0\cdot65$$

$$\boxed{2B = 1\cdot3/\tau}$$

This evaluation is not rigorous because for the mean values of B (around the optimum) the signal $\sigma(t)$ is not necessarily maximal for $t = 0$.

In these conditions, the rectangular pulse which is fed into the filter emerges from it with a form which is no longer rectangular, and which is shown in fig. 4.6.

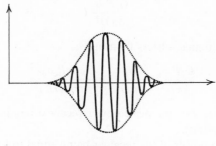

FIG. 4.6

With the curve of fig. 4.7 representing the variations of $\Phi^2(f)$ (the square of the Fourier transform of the signal) as a function of Δf, we see that we have lost practically nothing of the transmitted energy by keeping only the part lying between $f_0 - 0 \cdot 6/T_i$ and $f_0 + 0 \cdot 6/T_i$ (the corresponding loss is nearly 1 dB).

The signal at output of filter 8 is finally detected in component 9 and processed in 10 (threshold, etc.).

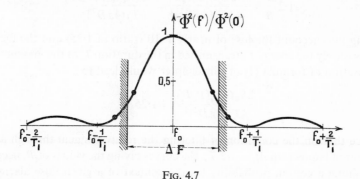

FIG. 4.7

The calculations show that, for a false alarm probability of 10^{-3}, the curve giving the probability of detection as a function of R is not very different from the ideal curve given in fig. 3.4.

Formulae (1) and (2) of this chapter, calculated for the correlation radar, therefore remain approximately valid: it is well, in this respect, to compare formula (1) with the well-known radar equation (as we do below).

The density of the transmitted power at a distance D is given by

$$p = \frac{G_e P_c}{4\pi D^2}$$

The power radiated (assumed omnidirectionally) by the target is therefore:

$$\frac{G_e P_c \sigma_e}{4\pi D^2}$$

and the reception antenna collects from it

$$\frac{G_e P_c \sigma_e}{4\pi D^2} \times \frac{S_R}{4\pi D^2} = \frac{G_R G_e P_c \sigma_e \lambda^2}{4\pi (4\pi D^2)^2},$$

which therefore constitutes the peak power received (G_R being the gain of the antenna at the reception).

The parasitic noise power of the receiver being equal to $kT_B\,\Delta f$, the signal-to-noise ratio is written as

$$\boxed{\frac{S}{B} = \frac{G_R G_e P_c \sigma_e \lambda^2}{4\pi k T_B\,\Delta f\,(4\pi D^2)^2}} \qquad \text{(equation of radar)}$$

Replacing Δf by $1{\cdot}2/T_i$, we find that

$$1{\cdot}2\,\frac{S}{B} = \frac{G_R G_e P_c T_i \sigma_e \lambda^2}{4\pi k T_B (4\pi D^2)^2} = \frac{S_R G_e \sigma_e (P_c T_i)}{k T_B (4\pi D^2)^2}$$

Taking into account the loss of nearly 1 dB (ratio of $1{\cdot}25$) and the fact that $P_c T_i$ is precisely the energy E_e transmitted in the duration T_i of the measurement, the utilisation of formula (1) of this chapter would lead to

$$\frac{2 S_R G_e \sigma_e (P_c T_i)}{k T_B (4\pi D^2)^2} = 1{\cdot}25R.$$

We see that on the condition of filtering the received signal through a pass-band filter of bandwidth $\Delta f = 1{\cdot}2/T_i$, the curves giving the values of R, necessary for obtaining a certain probability (in the context of a given false alarm), are also those that give twice the necessary values of the signal-to-noise ratio in power, for a perfect classical radar.

In the particular case of a classical pulsed radar, R therefore represents practically at some (3) decibels that which is usually called the signal-to-noise ratio.

If we therefore receive only one pulse per target, the energy to be transmitted in one pulse for detecting a target of 1 m² of equivalent echoing area under the conditions given in section 4.1 remains equal to about 15 joules in the absence of jamming.

If we require the same precision of ± 15 m over the range measurement, it is at least necessary (the practical radar not being better than the ideal radar) to assume $\Delta f \approx 1\cdot2$ MHz, i.e. T_i is, at most, equal to 1 μs (in practice, it is often necessary to assume T_i to be much shorter).

The peak power to be transmitted will therefore be at least of the order of $15/10^{-6} = 15$ MW (while in the correlation radar it would suffice to have 250 W).

In the presence of the jamming target given in section 4.1 it would now be necessary to transmit a peak power of 50,000 MW as a minimum (the peak power being not at all feasible).

The maximal recurrence frequency corresponds to the measure of preventing the receiver from receiving a signal corresponding to a first pulse after having sent a second pulse, this rendering the range measurement ambiguous, since the only *procedure that we have here to measure the range of targets is to measure the time between the beginning of the transmitted pulse and a characteristic point (the centre, for example) of the pulse received.*

For a range D of 500 km (3·3 ms) the maximal value of F_R is therefore 300 Hz.

If we assume that $T_i = 1$ μs and $F_R = 300$ Hz we find a duty cycle of the order of $3 \cdot 10^{-4}$.

We have not taken into account in what precedes

— atmospheric attenuations,

— the fact that the targets fluctuate,

— the fact that generally the radar makes the measurement over N pulses.

The last two points will be dealt with in the following chapters.

4.4.2 New concept

According to what has been described in section 3.1 for obtaining an ideal receiver, it is necessary to have a receiver having a transmittance such that

— the amplitude of gain of this filter is equal to $|\Phi(f)|$ (compare with fig. 4.4),

— the phase-shift caused by this filter is equal to the opposite of the argument of $\Phi(f)$ (i.e. zero for $f_0 - 1/T_i < f < f_0 + 1/T_i$, 180 degrees for $f_0 - 2/T_i < f < f_0 + 2/T_i$, etc),

$\Phi(f)$ being the Fourier transform of the transmitted pulse. Such a filter is difficult to make.

In practice, if we agree to sacrifice the energy contained in the frequencies less than $f_0 - 0\cdot6/T_i$ and in the frequencies greater than $f_0 + 0\cdot6/T_i$ (thus deliberately losing nearly 20 per cent of the transmitted energy) by conserving at the point of reception only the frequencies lying between $f_0 - 0\cdot6/T_i$ and $f_0 + 0\cdot6/T_i$, we obtain a result as if we had transmitted a signal $S(t)$ whose Fourier transform was characterised by

— a zero phase (a null argument),
— and an amplitude represented in fig. 4.8.

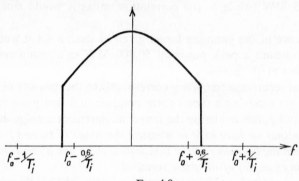

FIG. 4.8

The matched filter for such a signal has then to be given a null plane-shift and a transmittance (shown also in fig. 4.8).

The pass-band filter used is not very different from this, and gives very close results.

Thus, with respect to an ideal radar, the essential loss is due to the deliberate loss (of nearly 1 dB) of the energy transmitted outside the band $f_0 - 0.6/T_i$ and $f_0 + 0.6/T_i$, an energy transmitted uselessly.

But for this loss, the receiver (at $1.2/T_i$ of pass band) of classical radar appears to be very close to the matched filter.

REMARK

We should note that since the spectrum which is not situated in the band $f_0 - 0.6/T_i$ and $f_0 + 0.6/T_i$ is eliminated at the point of reception, it is just as futile to make expensive attempts to make one. In this respect, it is also useless to make expensive equipment—as has been made too often—in order to obtain steeply descending and ascending sides in the transmission pulse, which we expect mainly to be symmetrical.

4.5 PULSE COMPRESSION RADARS

4.5.1 Introduction

The transmitter of the classical radar whose diagram is shown in fig. 4.3 has not been described. In practice, there exist two types:

(1) The magnetron transmitters consisting of an auto-oscillator tube that

we light on only during the duration of the pulses T_i (with the help of a modulator).

(2) The amplifier transmitters containing a certain number of tubes in cascade.

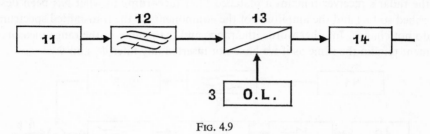

FIG. 4.9

Figure 4.9 illustrates the diagram for such a transmitter (replacing component 1 of fig. 4.3), in which

— component 11 transmits pulses of duration T_i with a recurrence frequency of F_R, and a carrier frequency of 30 MHz,

— component 13 shifts the spectrum of the signal coming from 12 to the transmission frequency f_0 by means of the local oscillator wave 3,

— component 14 consists of a cascade of amplifier tubes each of them transmitting a power greater than the preceding. The chain will successively consist, for example, of

— a T.W.T. providing a peak power of 10 W,

— a klystron amplifier providing a peak power of 30 kW,

— a klystron amplifier providing a peak power of 30 MW.

Since, finally, at the reception point we do not absolutely take into account the energy transmitted at the frequencies outside the interval $f_0 - 0\cdot6/T_i$, $f_0 + 0\cdot6/T_i$, there is no point in transmitting them, and the working of the set is not disturbed if we insert between 11 and 13 a filter, analogous to that which is used at the reception point, which

— modifies neither the amplitudes nor the phases of the spectral components between 30 MHz $- 0\cdot6/T_i$ and 30 MHz $+ 0\cdot6/T_i$, and which

— suppresses all other components.

But if we insert, in addition, between 12 and 13, an all band-pass filter having a characteristic $\Phi_1(f)$ such that

$$|\Phi_1(f)| = 1$$

and $\underline{/\Phi_1(f)} \neq 0$ (*the filter modifying only the phases of the spectrum crossing it*) and if we insert also between 8 and 9 (fig. 4.3) an all band-pass filter, of characteristic $\Phi_2(f)$), such that

$$\text{phase of } \Phi_2(f) = -\text{phase of } \Phi_1(f),$$

the radar's receiver remains a matched filter (according to what has been described so far) and the amplitude of the components of the transmitted spectrum do not change. In other words, the range and the quality of the range measurement remain the same as if we have not inserted any filter Φ_1 and Φ_2.

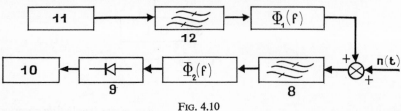

FIG. 4.10

In practice, the final result is as if we had the simplified chain of fig. 4.10.

The output of 11 is a rectangular pulse at 30 MHz of duration T_i. The output of 12 is a pulse at 30 MHz of duration nearly T_i and having the form indicated in fig. 4.6. The output Φ_1 is a pulse whose spectrum has always the width $1 \cdot 2/T_i$ but which is modulated in phase (or in frequency). The output of 8 consists of the output of Φ_1 plus a gaussian noise occupying a spectrum of width $1 \cdot 2/T_i$. The output of Φ_2 is a pulse of the same form as that of 12 (which is no longer modulated in frequency) and which is strictly what we would have obtained if Φ_1 and Φ_2 did not exist.

With respect to classical radar, the only difference is in the fact that the output signal of Φ_1 could have a duration T_e very much greater than T_i, since it is phase modulated, and the signal finally transmitted is much longer than T_i. We call the ratio T_e/T_i the pulse compression ratio of the radar.

In order to comprehend (more or less) physically the working of a pulsed compression radar here are some simple, useful hints.

Let us examine, for example, and compare:

(1) The spectrum of a continuous wave frequency modulated by a saw-tooth modulation, f_0 being the central frequency, the frequency of modulation being 1 kHz and the range of the modulation being 20 kHz (see fig. 4.11).

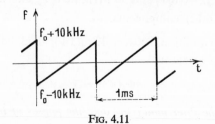

FIG. 4.11

(2) The spectrum of a sequence of pulses at the carrier frequency f_0, of quasi-gaussian form, of length 100 μs, repeated every thousandth of a second (see fig. 4.12).

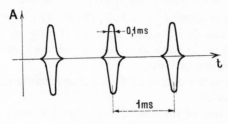

FIG. 4.12

The spectrum of 4.11 is shown in fig. 4.13. It is composed of lines 1 kHz apart whose envelope is practically a rectangle of width 20 kHz centred on f_0.

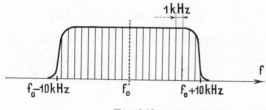

FIG. 4.13

But given the precision of the diagram, we could also say that the spectrum of 4.12 is represented by the same diagram of fig. 4.13: i.e. lines 1 kHz apart whose spectrum, centred on f_0, has a width of 20 kHz.

The only difference between the spectrum of 4.12 and that of 4.11 is that the phases of the lines are not identical.

Thus, by feeding wave 4.12 into a filter which does not modify the amplitudes of the components, but which cleverly changes the phases, we could pass from a sequence of signals of 0·1 ms to a continuous wave. Inversely, a complementary filter will transform the continuous wave 4.11 into a sequence of signals of 0·1 ms.

Let us hence suppose that we have made the complementary filters Φ_1 and Φ_2 (or, on the other hand, that we have been able to make a component which gives the same result as the output of $\Phi_1(f)$). We are led with respect to the classical radar studied in section 4.4, to transmit pulses of length T_e, much greater than T_i, but containing the same energy E_e and occupying the same spectrum as the pulses transmitted by classical radar.

The peak power transmitted is hence, with respect to classical radar, multiplied by the ratio T_i/T_e, much less than 1, and, at the input of the receiver, the signal-to-noise ratio is hence smaller (multiplied by the ratio T_i/T_e).

When we compress the long pulse received in the filter Φ_2 the amplitude of the useful signal is multiplied by $\sqrt{T_e/T_i}$ (hence its power by T_e/T_i) and the noise entering through Φ_2 has random phases. If these are changed in Φ_2 in a known way, they remain random, since an unknown quantity + a known quantity = an unknown quantity.

The noise power at the output of Φ_2 is hence equal to the input power (the noise is not compressed).

Finally at the output of the filter Φ_2, the signal-to-noise ratio is multiplied, with respect to the input, in the ratio T_e/T_i: we have "recuperated" the signal-to-noise ratio of the classical radar, having gained, in compression, the number of decibels lost in transmission.

Let us return to the radar problem posed above. We have seen that classical radar should, in the presence of jamming, transmit pulses

of length 1 μs,

of peak power about 15 MW.

If we utilise a pulse compression ratio of 100, we will obtain the same performances with a radar (of the same mean power) transmitting pulses of 100 μs occupying a spectrum of 1·2 MHz, and of a power of about 150 kW.

4.5.2 Pulse compression procedures

The signal at the output of the matched receiver has a duration nearly equal to the inverse of the width Δf of the spectrum transmitted. If the transmitted signal has a duration of T, we say that the receiver has compressed the signals in a pulse compression ratio

$$\boxed{T\Delta f = \rho}$$

There are two large families of pulse compression systems:
— the family of active generation,
— the family of passive generation.

4.5.2.1 Active generation

We create artificially and directly a signal whose spectrum $\Phi(f)$ is such that the filter at the reception is matched. For example, if we utilise at the point of reception a delay line whose time of propagation (of group) T_R decreases linearly with the frequency f (with a slope $dT_R/df = K$), the signal of transmission which corresponds to it is a signal linearly modulated in frequency, the frequency increasing with a slope $df/dt = 1/K$, of duration T sufficiently large so that $T^2/K \gg 1$ (K has the dimensions of the square of time).

This can be shown both mathematically and physically.

4.5.2.1.1 *Mathematically*, $\Phi(f)$ has a quasi-constant absolute value for

$$f_0 - \frac{T}{2K} < f < f_0 + \frac{T}{2K}$$

and a quasi-zero absolute value for

$$f < f_0 - \frac{T}{2K} \quad \text{and} \quad f < f_0 + \frac{T}{2K}.$$

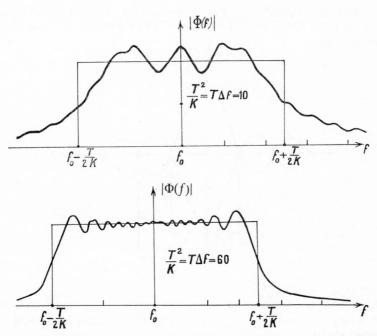

FIG. 4.14

However, the argument of $\Phi(f)$ is very close to

$$-\pi K(f - f_0)^2.$$

The complete calculation of $\Phi(f)$ has been made by numerous authors,[1] and there is no need to reproduce them here. Figure 4.14 shows the real form of $|\Phi(f)|$ when $T\Delta f$ is not infinitely large.

[1] Compare, for example, I. E. Chin and C. E. Cook "The mathematics of pulse compression", *Sperry Engineering Rev.*, **12**, No. 3 (1959), pp. 11–16.

L

The argument of $\Phi(f)$ is written as

$$-\frac{K(\omega-\omega_0)^2}{4\pi} = -\frac{K\omega^2}{4\pi}+\frac{K\omega\omega_0}{2\pi}-\frac{K\omega_0^2}{4\pi}.$$

The delay line at the reception point, having a propagation time of the form

$$T_R = T_0-Kf = T_0-K\frac{\omega}{2\pi}$$

behaves like a filter not modifying the components of the signals, passing across them and adding to their phase

$$\Phi = -T_0\omega+\frac{K\omega^2}{4\pi}+\varphi_0,$$

i.e. the opposite of the phase of $\Phi(f)$ if we take into account the fact that the terms of the form $T_0\omega$ give a delay of the set and the term φ_0 a phase displacement of the carrier.

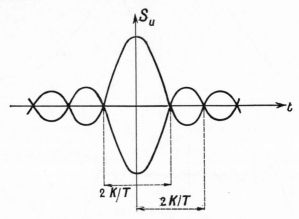

Fig. 4.15

Hence, on the condition of adding in the receiver a pass-band filter which conserves only the band $(f_0-T/2K)$, $(f_0+T/2K)$ the receiver is matched to the transmitted signal.

It is to be noted that after reception we obtain a signal non-modulated in frequency (zero phase) and whose spectrum has a constant amplitude between $f_0-T/2K$ and $f_0+T/2K$, i.e. a signal of the form

$$S_w(t) = K_1 \cos (2\pi f_0 t)\frac{\sin (\pi Tt/K)}{Tt/K}$$

(see fig. 4.15) containing a principal lobe of a width equal to $2K/T = 2/\Delta f$ (if Δf is the width of the spectrum) and of 3 dB width equal to $K/T = 1/\Delta f$ nearly, and secondary lobes, the first of them having a level of 13 dB below the main lobe.

4.5.2.1.2 *Physically*, the frequency f, being transmitted a certain time before the last frequency $f_0 + T/2K$, is delayed at the reception point by a period equal to the same delay with respect to the last frequency: all the frequencies hence leave from the receiver set (delay line) at the same time, i.e. in phase, giving a signal non-modulated in frequency and of high power.

REMARK

The variation of the phase inside the signal is equal to

$$\pi K(T^2/4K^2) = \pi T^2/4K = \pi T \Delta f/4 = \pi \rho/4,$$

where Δf is the width of the spectrum and ρ the compression ratio.

The higher is ρ, the greater is the total phase variation, and the better should be the relative precision of the curve phase versus frequency of the reception filter corresponding to a given absolute error over the phase (and to a given quality of compression). The higher is ρ, the more critical is the carrying out of the law of transmission or the reception filter.

4.5.2.2 Passive generation

In the passive generation, we utilise a short signal (incident) non-frequency modulated whose spectrum, centred on the frequency f_0, has a width Δf, i.e. whose all-component frequencies are in phase (i.e. simultaneous) and we pass them through a filter 1 which causes a certain delay depending on the frequency f, say

$$T_E = F_1(f) \text{ (without altering the amplitude of the components).}$$

If at the reception point we utilise a filter 2 whose transmission time is of the form

$$T_R = F_2(f) = T_0 - F_1(f) = T_0 - T_E$$

all the frequencies will finally be in phase at the output of the filter, returning a short signal identical to the first signal (within a delay of T_0), although the transmitted signal may be very long.

4.5.2.2.1 There are many procedures to obtain this result. The first which comes to mind is as follows. The signal at the output of filter 1 is recorded in the form of a signal corresponding to the relation $T'_E = F_1(f)$. Then the recording is returned before being read, providing a signal responding to the relation $T_E = T_1 - F_1(f)$, which is transmitted. We then utilise at the reception point, as filter 2, filter 1, which introduces a delay

$$T_R = T'_E = F_1(f) = T_1 - T_E$$

The procedure (patented since 1945 in Great Britain and U.S.A.) has probably never been used: applied to radars, a high quality of recording is required and a very expensive recorder is necessary (it would be more useful if applied to signals of low-pass band).

4.5.2.2.2 The second useful procedure (which was patented in France by Adamsbaum and Carpentier) consists of using a filter 1 such that the curve

$$T'_E = F_1(f)$$

presents a point of inflexion for the central frequency f_0 of the spectrum of the short incident signal (see fig. 4.16).

In practice, the incident signal could be a short signal modulating a carrier frequency f_0 in such a way that its spectrum is centred on f_0 and symmetrical with respect to f_0.

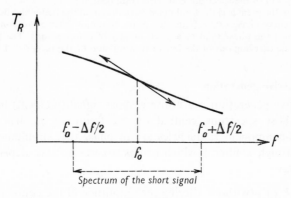

FIG. 4.16

In this case it is not generally incorrect to consider that the curve $T_R = F_1(f)$ is, in its useful part—between $f_0 - \Delta f/2$ and $f_0 + \Delta f/2$—, symmetrical about the point f_0 such that a symmetry about a vertical passing through f_0 is equivalent to a symmetry about a horizontal.

Hence, if we return with respect to f_0 the spectrum of the signal returning from filter 1, we obtain a signal corresponding to

$$T_E = T_2 - T'_E = T_2 - F_1(f),$$

which is transmitted.

Turning the spectrum is obtained by mixing (in a modulator) the signal coming from the filter 1 with a frequency $2f_0$. An incident frequency f gives two frequencies

$$(2f_0 + f) \quad \text{and} \quad (2f_0 - f).$$

The frequencies $(2f_0 + f)$ are eliminated, the frequencies $2f_0 - f$, i.e. $f_0 + (f_0 - f) = f_0 - (f - f_0)$ give the spectrum turned with respect to f_0.

It is hence sufficient at the reception point to pass the signal through a filter identical to the filter 1, which introduces a delay

$$T_R = F_1(f) = T_2 - T_E$$

This method has been much used.

4.5.2.2.3 A third method is shown as an example in fig. 4.17.

A short non-frequency modulated signal whose spectrum is practically constant in the band $(f_0 - \Delta f/2)$, $(f_0 + \Delta f/2)$ and zero outside this band, and which has therefore a duration (at 3 dB) of $1/\Delta f$, enters the network of fig. 4.17 at A. We hence find this signal at A and at D the signal shifted from the delay line Lar by a delay equal to $4/\Delta f$, at E the same signal delayed by $8/\Delta f$ and at B the same signal delayed by $12/\Delta f$.

Filter F_1 is a pass-band filter which transmits the band $(f_0 - \Delta f/2)$, $(f_0 - \Delta f/4)$. Filter F_2 is a pass-band filter $(f_0 - \Delta f/4)$, (f_0), etc.

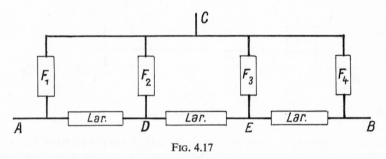

FIG. 4.17

The output of filter F_1 is therefore a signal at $f_0 - 3\Delta f/8$ which lasts for a time $4/\Delta f$.

The output of filter F_2 is a signal of duration $4/\Delta f$ supervening $4/\Delta f$ after the preceding one and at $f_0 - \Delta f/8$, etc. Finally, the signal emerging at C has a duration of $4 \times 4/\Delta f = 16/\Delta f$ and is modulated in frequency by increasing frequencies. This is the transmission signal.

If, at the reception point, this signal enters the same network at B, it emerges at C identical to the incident signal. Indeed, it is clear that on the whole the frequencies of the band $(f_0 - \Delta f/2)$, $(f_0 - \Delta f/4)$ would be delayed by $0 + 12/\Delta f$, the frequencies of the band $(f_0 - \Delta f/4)$, (f_0) by $4/\Delta f + 8/\Delta f$, and so on, all the frequencies being delayed by the same quantity $12/\Delta f$.

We note that an analogous system containing n filters $F_1, F_2, F_3, \ldots, F_n$ and $(n-1)$ delay lines will provide a ratio of lengthening and of compression equal to n^2.

This third method, known as the "parallel method" can be generalised in order to provide the method called Turin's method (shown in fig. 4.18), utilising a delay line with n outputs (separated by a delay τ) and n amplifiers.

Let $G_1(p)$, $G_2(p)$, $G_3(p)$, ..., $G_n(p)$ be the transfer functions of the amplifiers G_1, G_2, ..., G_n. The network crossed from B to C is the filter matched to the signal obtained at C when we feed the network at A with a Dirac pulse $\delta(t)$, on condition that

$$\{G_1(j\omega) + G_2(j\omega) \exp(-\tau j\omega) + \ldots + G_n(j\omega) \exp[-(n-1)\tau j\omega]\}$$

is an imaginary conjugate of

$$\{G_n(j\omega) + G_{n-1}(j\omega) \exp(-\tau j\omega) + \ldots + G_1(j\omega) \exp[-(n-1)\tau j\omega]\}K_2 \exp(T_1 j\omega)$$

K_2 and T_1 being two constants (independent of ω).

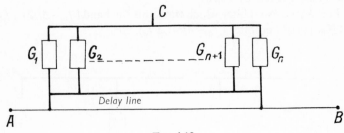

FIG. 4.18

It is evident that if we have preceding (or following) the network $(A \to C)$ of a pass-band filter not modifying the phases in the pass band, the set remains correct providing we add an identical pass-band filter at the reception point. The third method (parallel) hence constitutes only a particular case of Turin's method.

The above relation is verified in particular if all the $G_i(j\omega)$ are real numbers, with $K_2 = 1$ and $T_1 = (n-1)\tau$, i.e. if the amplifiers G_i do not change the phase of the signals crossing them (modulo 180°). Thus the system of fig. 4.17 remains correct if the filters F_i are associated to amplifiers of this type having different gains G_i depending on the number of the filter.

In the particular case where the amplifiers G_i have real gains and a large pass band, the envelope of the output signal at C of the Turin network—when we feed A with a Dirac pulse—is equal to

$$S_1(t) = G_1\delta(t) + G_2\delta(t-\tau) + G_3\delta(t-2\tau) + \ldots \qquad \text{(see fig. 4.19)}$$

The Fourier transform $\Phi_1(f)$ of $S_1(t)$ is periodic of a time $1/\tau$ and it is, modulo a constant factor, equal to

$$\ldots \Phi(f+2/\tau) + \Phi(f+1/\tau) + \Phi(f) + \Phi(f-1/\tau) + \Phi(f-2/\tau) + \ldots$$

where $\Phi(f)$ is the Fourier transform of the envelope $S(t)$ of the signal $S_1(t)$; $\Phi(f)$ being zero outside the frequency interval

$$(-1/2\tau, +1/2\tau).$$

If therefore we feed $S_1(t)$ into a low-pass filter eliminating the frequencies greater then $1/2\tau$ (and not modifying the components less than $1/2\tau$), we will obtain, at the output of this filter, $S(t)$, the envelope of $S_1(t)$, and the filter matched to $S(t)$ will be the cascade of the network in the direction $B \to C$ preceded or followed by a low-pass filter eliminating frequencies above $1/2\tau$.

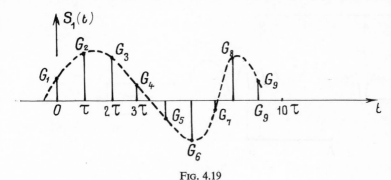

FIG. 4.19

If for example we wish to transmit a signal

$$S(t) = \sin 2\pi \left(F_1 t + \frac{t^2}{2K} \right) \quad \text{for} \quad 0 < t < T$$

and

$$S(t) = 0 \quad \text{for} \quad t > T \quad \text{and} \quad t < 0,$$

i.e. a signal of duration T linearly modulated in frequency between F_1 and $T/K + F_1$ with $T^2/K \gg 1$ and whose spectrum is (practically) lying between F_1 and $T/K + F_1$, we could take

$$\tau = \frac{1}{2(F_1 + T/K)}$$

and

$$G_i = \sin 2\pi \left[F_1(i-1)\tau + \frac{(i-1)^2\tau^2}{2K} \right],$$

and we shall follow the network $A \to C$ (fed at A by a Dirac pulse) with a low-pass filter cutting at $T/K + F_1$.

(In practice and to simplify matters we could content ourselves with taking for G_i, 1 or -1, according to its sign.)

At the reception point we will utilise in cascade the network $B \to C$ and a low-pass filter cutting at $T/K + F_1$ (see fig. 4.20).

This method is very fruitful since it permits us, at least theoretically, to make all conceivable signals $S(t)$ and the relevant matched filter.

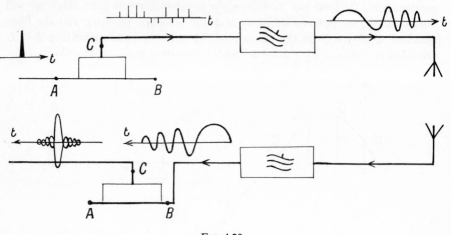

FIG. 4.20

4.5.3   General properties of pulse compression

4.5.3.1   Improvement of the signal-to-noise ratio

The long signal (like the short signal) occupies a spectrum of width Δf and (by assuming it to be of constant level during its duration T) it has a power $P = E/T$, E being its energy.

Before compression, the signal-to-noise ratio in power is hence equal to $P/b\Delta f$, if b is the spectral density (assumed uniform) of the noise, i.e. $E/bT\Delta f$. After compression, the signal-to-noise ratio in power is equal to E/b (see remark at the end of section 3.4).

We see that the operation of compression has multiplied the signal-to-noise ratio in power by $T\Delta f$ (we evidently obtain the same result as in the reception by correlation).

4.5.3.2   Sidelobes

We have seen in the example given of active generation that the compressed signal consisted of a main lobe surrounded by sidelobes at levels from 13 to 14 dB below the main lobe. This is due to the fact that the transmitted spectrum is rectangular.

In the third method described in sub-section 4.5.2.2.3 we find an analogous result because it has been shown that the short compressed signal was identical to the incident signal assumed *a priori* of that form.

In the second method described in sub-section 4.5.2.2.2 theoretically this difficulty (which is not always a difficulty) does not exist because the compressed signal is identical to the incident signal, in which no hypothesis of this type was necessary. But in fact the transmitter which transmits the long signal most of the time will operate a top-limiting in order to provide a signal of constant level during its duration (this is for very valid technological reasons), and, from the time when the long transmitted signal is of a constant level, its spectrum becomes quasi-rectangular, thus giving a signal compressed with sidelobes.

Returning to the third method described in sub-section 4.5.2.2.3, it was noted that we could affect the filters $F_1, \ldots, F_n$ of different gains G_i without modifying the quality of the matching at the reception. As an example, for a number of filters $n = 10$, if the gains of the filters are the following

G_1	G_2	G_3	G_4	G_5	G_6	G_7	G_8	G_9	G_{10}
-7 dB	-4 dB	-2 dB	-1 dB	0	0	-1 dB	-2 dB	-4 dB	-7 dB

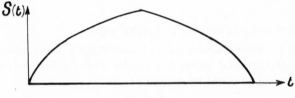

FIG. 4.21

the spectrum of the transmitted signal will be triangular and the compressed signal will this time be composed of:
— a main lobe of total width equal to $4/\Delta f$ (width doubled) and of 3 dB width equal to $1 \cdot 3/\Delta f$ (increased by 30 per cent);
— and of sidelobes, the first of which has a level of 27 dB below the main one. But the transmitted signal will also have a triangular form in power, i.e. rounded in voltage (see fig. 4.21).

If we now assume that the amplifiers of different gains are utilised only at the reception with the following values (in decibels)

G_1	G_2	G_3	G_4	G_5	G_6	G_7	G_8	G_9	G_{10}
-14	-8	-4	-2	0	0	-2	-4	-8	-14

the compressed signal will have the same form, but the reception filter will no longer be matched to the transmitted signal. The result is as if we had used a matched filter followed by a pass-band filter of a triangular characteristic (in voltage). We say that we weighted the sidelobes.

The useful signal has therefore a *level* divided by 2 and the noise has a *power* divided by 3, which renders finally the signal-to-noise ratio divided by 1·33 (a loss of 1·3 dB) (see fig. 4.22).

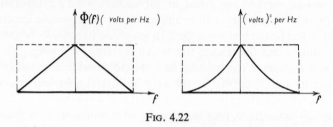

FIG. 4.22

The reduction of the sidelobes has implied (besides an enlargement of the compressed signal) a loss in the signal-to-noise ratio. It is evident that the above example should be considered as such and generalised only with precaution. In particular for the utilisation of the laws of frequency modulation of transmitted signal differing from the linear law (even by only a little) the results could numerically be very different.

4.5.3.3 Ambiguity in the case of CHIRP signals

This name has been given to radars transmitting a rectangular signal linearly frequency modulated and which, historically, were the first pulsed compression radars. Such a signal could be written as:

$$S(t) = \sin\left(\frac{\pi t^2}{K}\right) \quad \text{for} \quad -T/2 < t < T/2$$

$$S(t) = 0 \quad \text{for} \quad t < -T/2 \quad \text{and} \quad t > T/2.$$

The operation of reception in a matched filter is the following operation of correlation, by denoting the received signal by $y(t)$ and by $t = 0$ the instant of arrival of the signal

$$\int_{-\infty}^{+\infty} y(u) \cdot S(u-t) \, du.$$

Neglecting here the effect of noise in order to take into account only the useful signal, the compressed signal, in the absence of Doppler effect, is written as

$$g(t) = \int_{-\infty}^{+\infty} S(u) \cdot S(u-t) \, du,$$

$$g(t) = \int_{-T/2+t}^{+T/2} \sin\left(\frac{\pi u^2}{K}\right) \cdot \sin\left(\frac{\pi(u-t)^2}{K}\right) \, du \quad \text{if} \quad t > 0.$$

In the presence of Doppler effect shifting the received signal by a frequency F_D (assumed negative), the compressed signal is written as

$$g_D(t) = \int_{-T/2+t}^{+T/2} \sin 2\pi \left(F_D u + \frac{u^2}{2K} \right) \cdot \sin \pi \frac{(u-t)^2}{K} \, du.$$

These expressions become

$$g(t) = \frac{1}{2} \int_{-T/2+t}^{+T/2} \cos \frac{2\pi}{K} \left[ut - \frac{t^2}{2} \right] du,$$

$$g_D(t) = \frac{1}{2} \int_{-T/2+t}^{+T/2} \cos \frac{2\pi}{K} \left[u(t + KF_D) - \frac{t^2}{2} \right] du.$$

$g(t)$ is maximal for $t = 0$, which is normal, the maximum being $T/2$; $g_D(t)$ is, if $KF_D^2/2 \ll 1$, no longer maximal for $t = 0$ but it is for $t = -KF_D$, the maximum being practically equal to $T/2$.

The relation $KF_D^2 \ll 1$ can also be written as, since $K\Delta f = T$,

$$F_D \ll 1\cdot4 \frac{\Delta f}{\sqrt{\rho}}$$

(with $\rho = T\Delta f$, the compression ratio).

Numerical applications:

$-\Delta f = 10^6$ Hz, $\qquad\qquad T = 10^{-4}$ s, $\qquad\qquad\qquad \rho = 100,$

$K = 10^{-10}$ s^2, $\qquad\qquad 1\cdot4 \dfrac{\Delta f}{\sqrt{\rho}} = 140$ kHz.

For a Doppler effect of 10 kHz, the compressed signal is shifted by 1 μs

$-\Delta f = 10^5$ Hz, $\qquad\qquad T = 10^{-2}$ s, $\qquad\qquad\qquad \rho = 1000$

$K = 10^{-7}$ s^2, $\qquad\qquad 1\cdot4 \dfrac{\Delta f}{\sqrt{\rho}} = 5$ kHz.

For a Doppler effect of 1 kHz, the compressed signal is shifted by 100 μs

$-\Delta f = 3000$ Hz, $\qquad\qquad T = 10^{-2}$ s, $\qquad\qquad\qquad \rho = 30$

$K = 3 \cdot 10^{-6}$ s^2, $\qquad\qquad 1\cdot4 \dfrac{\Delta f}{\sqrt{\rho}} \approx 1$ kHz.

For a Doppler effect of 50 Hz, the compressed signal is shifted by 150 μs.

REMARKS

(1) We could say (since a signal at $t = 0$ and $F_D = 0$ finally gives the same result as a signal of the same level affected by the Doppler effect F_D at $t = -KF_D$)[1] that the ambiguity between these two signals is close to 1, because it is impossible to distinguish one from the other.

This result is due to the linear law of frequency modulation used (see subsections 3.10.6 and 3.10.4). For another law of modulation of the long signal, we find an ambiguity of a different nature (see Chapter 3).

It is interesting to note that if the sense of the linear frequency modulation is the correct one we measure the radial distance of a target with an error proportional to the radial velocity of the target, i.e. that *we measure the distance which the target would have at a few instants later*, which could not therefore always be an error.

(2) If we top-limit the received signal before passing it into the reception filter, i.e. before compressing it, we obtain a C.F.A.R. reception (see section 4.6).

(3) If a long signal modulated by increasing frequencies passes into a filter intended to compress similar signals but modulated by decreasing frequencies, we could, as a first approximation, say that it is stretched in a ratio 2 and that its level is reduced by 3 dB. In a similar way, a transmitted signal of duration $1/\Delta f$, non-frequency modulated, will have its level reduced by the compression ratio $T\Delta f$. This property is interesting from the viewpoint of anti-jamming.

4.5.4   Calculation of faults due to the imperfection of compression

4.5.4.1   Method of pair-echoes

Besides the sidelobes which are due to the nature of the transmitted signal and which could be reduced by weighting, others appear which are due to the difference between what are practical and theoretical operations.

It is necessary to know in advance the precision with which we must attain theoretical performances on the equipment. For this a method called "pair-echoes" has been developed by numerous authors.[2] Without going into the corresponding numerical calculations, we shall give the general idea.

Let us confine ourselves to the errors introduced by the difference between the law obtained for $|\Phi(f)|$ and the law which should have been obtained for it.

---

[1] Physically speaking, this result is intuitive. The matched filter at the reception point being a delay line whose transmission time increases (or decreases) with the frequency, it is natural that the shifting of the spectrum of frequency received through F_D introduces a shifting in the time of the compressed signal at the output of the delay line.

[2] See, in particular, the reference to Klauder, Price, Darlington and Albersheim given in the Bibliography. See also: C. E. Cook "Transmitter phase modulation errors and pulse compression waveform distortion', *Microwave Journal*, **6**, No. 5 (May 1963), pp. 63-69.

This could always be written in the form of a sum of terms as follows (assuming the central frequency to be zero):

$$A \cos (2\pi T_i f + \varphi).$$

Such a term of error gives *two* parasitic signals situated on both sides of the centre of the useful signal at a distance T_i from this centre, whence the name "method of pair-echoes".

4.5.4.2 Utilisation of dispersive filters with turning of the spectrum

We utilise an all pass-band filter whose phase characteristic as a function of the frequency f is $\varphi(f)$ per cell. The useful signal is centred on the value f_0 such that

$$\frac{d^3\varphi}{df^3} = 0.$$

In these conditions, denoting $(f - f_0)$ by F the phase could be put in the form (by neglecting the terms of the form $A + BF$)

$$\varphi(F) = CF^2 + DF^4 + EF^5 + \ldots$$

(in what follows we neglect the terms of higher order in the development).

In fact the value of f_0 should be chosen and there is no reason why it should be the frequency centrally transmitted. For reasons of convenience it could be greater than or less than this.

If we try to obtain a linear frequency modulation of the long signal, the term CF^2 is hence the useful term and the terms DF^4 and EF^5 are the parasitic terms.

The term DF^4 has two different effects. First, it destroys the perfect linearity of the frequency modulation, which is generally not inconvenient, because in the absence of a Doppler effect the turning of the spectrum has the effect of passing the signal on its return into a filter of characteristic $-\varphi(-F)$. Thus adding, we get:

$$CF^2 + DF^4 - C(-F)^2 - D(-F)^4 = 0.$$

On the other hand, if there is a Doppler effect, the received signal does not correspond to $\varphi(F)$ but to $\varphi(F + F_D)$ and this time we obtain

$$C(F + F_D)^2 + D(F + F_D)^4 - CF^2 - DF^4$$
$$= 2CF_D F + CF_D^2 + 4DF^3 F_D + 6DF^2 F_D^2 + 4DFF_D^3 + DF_D^4,$$

i.e. we do not take into account the constant terms (phase displacement of the carrier) and the terms in KF (displacement of the compressed pulse),

$$4DF^3 F_D + 6DF^2 F_D^2 \qquad \text{instead of zero.}$$

The presence of a Doppler deviation introduces an error of the phase on the edge of the spectrum of the form $\varepsilon_1(F)$

$$\varepsilon_1(F) = 2DF_D F^2 (2F + 3F_D),$$

whose maximal value is equal to $3/2 \ DF_D \Delta f$, if we assume that $F_D \ll \Delta f/2$.

The term EF^5 gives after the two-ways, a phase error on the edge of the spectrum of the form $\varepsilon_2(F)$:

$$\varepsilon_2(F) = EF^5 - E(-F)^5 = 2EF^5$$

whose maximal value is equal to $E\Delta f^5/16$.

It is indispensable to evaluate the effect of these parasitic terms by noting that they are to be multiplied by the number N of filter cells.

When there is no phase error, the useful signal, after compression, is written as:

$$S_u(t) = \int_{\Delta f} \Phi(f)\Phi(-f) \exp(2\pi jft) \, df = \int_{\Delta f} |\Phi(f)|^2 \exp(2\pi jft) \, df.$$

This signal is maximal for $t = 0$ and has an amplitude $S_u(0)$ such that, if we assume $|\Phi(f)|$ to be constant in the band Δf and zero outside it we have

$$|\Phi(f)|^2 = S_u(0)/\Delta f.$$

If there is a phase error $\varepsilon(f)$, we obtain

$$S(t) = \int_{\Delta f} \Phi(f) \cdot \Phi(-f) \exp[j\varepsilon(f)] \exp(2\pi jft) \, df = \frac{S_u(0)}{\Delta f} \int_{\Delta f} \exp\{j[2\pi jft + \varepsilon(f)]\} df$$

$$S(t) = S_1(t) + S_2(t)$$

with

$$S_1(t) = \frac{2S_u(0)}{\Delta f} \int_0^{\Delta f/2} \cos 2\pi ft \cdot \cos \varepsilon(f) \cdot df,$$

$$S_2(t) = \frac{2S_u(0)}{\Delta f} \int_0^{\Delta f/2} \sin 2\pi ft \cdot \sin \varepsilon(f) \cdot df.$$

If $\varepsilon(f)$ is quite negligible, $S_1(t)$ differs very little from $S_u(t)$: it appears that the error $\varepsilon(f)$ implies the existence of a parasitic term $S_2(t)$ of amplitude equal to that of the useful term multiplied by

$$\frac{2}{\Delta f} \int_0^{\Delta f/2} \sin 2\pi ft \cdot \sin \varepsilon(f) \cdot df,$$

a factor which presents a *maximum maximorum* for a certain value of t different from zero (because for $t = 0$, it is zero), which verifies the equation

$$\int_0^{\Delta f/2} f \cdot \cos 2\pi ft \cdot \sin \varepsilon(f) \cdot df = 0.$$

This parasitic term $S_2(t)$ hence behaves like a supplementary sidelobe.

We obtain an increase in the amplitude of this lobe by replacing ($\sin 2\pi ft$) by 1, which gives for its amplitude (with reference to $S_u(0)$)

$$\frac{2}{\Delta f} \int_0^{\Delta f/2} \sin \varepsilon(f) \cdot df$$

i.e. by neglecting the Doppler effect:

$$\frac{2}{\Delta f} \int_0^{\Delta f/2} \sin (2NEF^5) \cdot dF.$$

If we suppose, in order to clarify our ideas, that a level of secondary lobes less than the level of the useful signal by more than 12 dB is acceptable, it is certainly sufficient, when the Doppler effect has a negligible effect, that this expression be less than 0·25—which gives after the calculations,

$$NE\Delta f^5 < 35.$$

However, if we wish to obtain a long signal of duration T occupying a spectrum of width Δf (compression ratio $\rho = T\Delta f$), with $K = T/\Delta f$, it is necessary that the number N of cells of the filter be such that $NC = \pi K$, and, finally, the system be defined, by neglecting the faults due to a Doppler effect, by the two relations

$$NC = \pi K$$

and

$$NE\Delta f^5 < 35$$

(for sidelobes certainly better than 12 dB; or 10, instead of 35, for sidelobes certainly better than 20 dB; or 3, instead of 35, for sidelobes certainly better than 30).

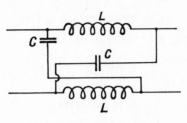

FIG. 4.23

In fact, a family of similar filters could, by means of different choices of the parameters, give laws $\varphi(F)$ such that

$$C = C_1/F_1^2, \qquad D = D_1/F_1^4, \qquad E = E_1/F_1^5$$

C_1, D_1 and E_1 depend solely on the nature of the elementary cell chosen and F_1 depends solely on the choice of the parameters. (In a parallel-tuned circuit, the Q factor is equivalent to C_1, D_1 and E_1, and the resonance frequency is equivalent to F_1.) The relations given above become

$$NE_1\left(\frac{\Delta f}{F_1}\right)^5 = 35, \qquad NC_1 = \pi KF^2,$$

or again

$$\boxed{N = 0\cdot57(E_1^2/C_1^5)^{1/3}\rho^{5/3}} \qquad \text{(with } \rho = T\Delta f\text{)}.$$

The number N of necessary cells increase with the quality of sidelobes desired (the factor $0\cdot57$, which becomes $1\cdot3$ for lobes of -20 dB and $2\cdot9$ for lobes of -30 dB, and it is, for a given quality, proportional to (compression ratio)$^{5/3}$, i.e. $(\rho)^{5/3}$.

N being defined, we could calculate F_1. As an example, if we consider a cell as shown in fig. 4.23 closed on its characteristic impedance

$$Z_C = \sqrt{L/C},$$

providing that we centre the useful spectrum on the frequency

$$f_0 = \frac{1}{2\pi\sqrt{3LC}}$$

we find that the phase can be written as

$$\varphi = 2 \text{ Arc tg } (2\pi f \sqrt{LC}),$$

which gives, by writing $(2\pi F_1)^2 LC = 1,$

$$C_1 = 3\sqrt{3}/8 = 0.65; \quad D_1 = 9\sqrt{3}/64 = 0.24; \quad E_1 = 27/160 = 0.17.$$

$$\boxed{N = 0.37 \rho^{5/3}}$$

Numerical application:

$$\Delta f = 1 \text{ MHz}, \quad T = 100 \text{ } \mu s, \quad \rho = 100, \quad K = 10^{-10} s^2$$

The preceding formula gives $N = 750$. From this, we deduce

$$F_1^2 = \frac{750 \cdot 0.65}{\pi \cdot 10^{-10}} = 1.5 \cdot 10^{12}, \quad F_1 = 1.2 \text{ MHz}$$

$$f_0 \approx 0.7 \text{ MHz}.$$

We could return the influence of a Doppler deviation in the matter of sidelobes and evaluate it in an analogous manner by determining the effect of the term

$$2NDF_D F^2 (2F + 3F_D).$$

In the context of the above numerical example we find that as long as F_D is of the order of few kilohertz and that we accept secondary lobes of -20 dB, this term has a negligible effect.

4.5.5 Practical procedures for dispersive filters and delay lines

It was seen that the operation of radars with matched filters (pulsed compression radars) required non-dispersive delay lines or dispersive delay lines.

The present book is not intended to provide technological information (which the reader could find in the more specialised literature) but to give theoretical ideas which help us to visualise new methods. In this spirit we shall indicate three new tendencies.

4.5.5.1 Utilisation of shift-register as delay lines

If we wish to use either the parallel method or Turin's method we are led to use a delay line giving a delay of the order of the duration of the long pulse T in a frequency band Δf.

For this we could use a shift-register having M cells, the passage from one cell to another being made at a frequency F_R. Such a register normally provides in addition a top-limiting of the incident signal, and the delay which it entails is equal to

$$M/F_R \approx T$$

It is necessary that the sampling of the signal should be carried out at a sufficient rate, i.e. F_R should be greater than twice the highest frequency to be transmitted, which itself should be at least equal to Δf. We have therefore at least $F_R = M/T > 2\Delta f$.

$$M > 2T\Delta f = 2\rho.$$

We see that the limitation to which this expression leads is not excessive and that it could lead to reasonable operations for reasonable compression ratios.

4.5.5.2   Dispersive acoustic lines

We could utilise the characteristics of ultrasonic acoustic wave propagation in certain environments (water columns, wire, metallic films) in order to obtain dispersive delay lines which have the desired qualities for the curves, giving their time propagation as a function of frequency.

This is a very fruitful field.

4.5.5.3   Optical methods

Again this is a very productive method. Here, instead of transforming the electrical signal to be treated into an acoustic one (as in the acoustic lines), we transform it into luminous signal.

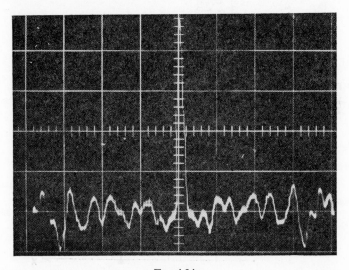

FIG. 4.24

Figure 4.24 gives an example of a compressed signal (in a ratio of 60) obtained by means of optics.[1] Figure 4.25 indicates a simple method of obtaining the

[1] Experiments made in the Laboratories of COTELEC in the Optic and Infrared Section.

M

function of cross-correlation of two functions $f(x)$ and $g(x)$. The functions $f(x)$ and $g(x)$ are represented by two films whose transparencies vary as the functions $f(x)$ and $g(x)$ vary. The light intensity at the focus F of the lens L represents

$$\int_{-\infty}^{+\infty} f(x) \cdot g(x)\, dx.$$

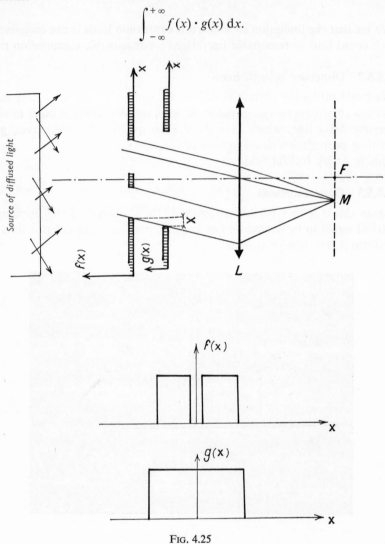

FIG. 4.25

The light intensity at the point M of the focal plane represents

$$\int_{-\infty}^{+\infty} f(x) \cdot g(x - X)\, dx.$$

Hence we see that the measurement of the intensity in the focal plane of the lens gives the cross-correlation function of $f(x)$ and $g(x)$. But, if we know how to calculate the cross-correlation function we also know how to make an ideal receiver.

A whole family of systems, on the other hand, utilise the fact that the diffraction figure of an image $y(x)$ may be in fact its Fourier transform $Y(v)$. Similarly we could obtain the Fourier transform $\Sigma(v)$ of another function $S(x)$ and photograph it (at least, if it is real). Lighting the photograph of $Z(-v)$ with $Y(v)$ and again making the diffraction figure of $Y(v) \cdot \Sigma(-v)$ we obtain the expression

$$\int y(x) \cdot S(x - x_0) \, dx,$$

which an ideal receiver calculates. This implies that the light used is parallel and sufficiently monochromatic and also that the Fourier transform of $S(x)$ is real and positive. If this last condition is not satisfied, we could overcome this difficulty by replacing $\Sigma(v)$ by a hologram of $S(x)$, which allows us to obtain the same result.

4.6 CONSTANT FALSE ALARM RATE RECEPTION

4.6.1 Principles of C.F.A.R. receivers

In a radar, whether it be with a correlation or a matched filter, the noise $C_p(t)$ accompanying the useful signal at the output is subjected to variations of level for various reasons, in particular, as a function of the level of jamming received (voluntary or involuntary jamming).

On the other hand, the extractor which follows the radar (be it a classical scope or a digital extractor) does not easily allow variations in this noise level, which have the effect of changing the false alarm probability. If the noise level has very slow variations, we could, of course, slowly modify the threshold in order to keep the false alarm probability constant. But this becomes very difficult when the noise level variations are very rapid. In this case we utilise receivers called C.F.A.R. receivers.

The property of C.F.A.R. is obtained by top-limiting at a very low constant level the received signal before its passage through the matched filter (or before correlation). The level of top-limiting is chosen in such a way that, even in the absence of a useful signal and for low noise (thermal noise of the receiver itself), the noise is limited.

The top-limiting is carried out on the set (signal + noise) occupying a band greater than or equal to Δf of the spectrum of the transmitted signal, a band $Mf\Delta$ (with $M > 1$). It follows that in the absence of a useful signal we obtain a signal of mean value zero, positive or negative, but of constant level (see fig. 4.26), and therefore absolutely non-gaussian.

This signal is filtered and we thus obtain a non-gaussian signal as shown in a non-continuous line in fig. 4.26, defined in a way necessary and sufficient by its values at consecutive instants $1/M\Delta f$ apart. The operation of passage through a matched filter of reception (or a correlator) has the effect of integrating this non-gaussian noise over a time T such that

$$\frac{T}{1/M\Delta f} = MT\Delta f \text{ is large (at least 10).}$$

We could therefore assume that at the output of the matched filter (or of the correlator) the output noise is the sum of $MT\Delta f$ independent variables and that it is therefore gaussian, with a constant variance (power).

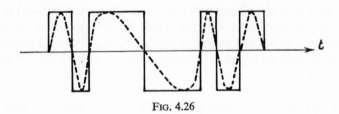

Fig. 4.26

To simplify matters, we could say that the noise has a constant power after limiting (assumed to be unity) divided by the ratio of bands (before limiting and after reception), i.e. a constant power equal to $1/M$.

The useful signal, when it is alone, has its power increased in the ratio $T\Delta f$ (compression ratio in the case of a matched filter radar): it has therefore a power equal to $T\Delta f$.

Thus, it roughly seems that

— in the absence of a useful signal, the noise at the output of the receiver is gaussian with a power equal to $1/M$;

— when the noise is negligible *vis-à-vis* the useful signal (in the absence of noise) the latter possesses at the output of the receiver a constant power $T\Delta f$ and that thus in this case the ratio

$$\frac{\text{power of useful signal when it is high}}{\text{power of the noise in the absence of useful signal}}$$

is also constant and equal to $MT\Delta f$.

In the following sections we shall attempt to describe these general ideas in greater detail.

4.6.2 Output level of the useful signal and of the noise

4.6.2.1 General

Complete results will be given only for the case where the useful signal of transmission is a signal of constant level (of constant power) during its duration T. This is very close to the practical cases. (However, something will be said about the case where the transmitted signal is of non-constant power.)

The hypothesis therefore is that the transmission signal is of the form $\sin (2\pi ft)$, the frequency f possibly varying as a function of time. The useful signal received is hence of the form

$$S \sin (2\pi ft).$$

The noise signal is of the form

$$B(t) \sin [2\pi ft + \varphi(t)],$$

$B(t)$ is a positive variable having a Rayleigh distribution of amplitude and $\varphi(t)$ is equiprobable between 0 and 2π (i.e. the noise is gaussian), such that

$$N = \overline{B^2(t) \sin^2 [2\pi ft + \varphi(t)]} \qquad (N: \text{noise power})$$

and that the probability density of B is written as

$$p(B) = \frac{B}{N} \exp (-B^2/2N) \qquad \text{for} \qquad B > 0$$

and

$$p(B) = 0 \qquad \qquad \text{for} \qquad B < 0.$$

The ratio

$$SB_1 = \frac{\text{power of the signal}}{\text{noise power}}$$

at the input (before top-limiting) is therefore equal to

$$SB_1 = S^2/2N.$$

4.6.2.2 In the absence of top-limiting (non-C.F.A.R. reception)

After correlation over the time T, we find

$$\text{Useful signal} = S \int_T \sin 2\pi ft \cdot \sin 2\pi ft \cdot dt = ST/2$$

$$\text{Noise} = \int_T \sin 2\pi ft \cdot B(t) \cdot \sin [2\pi ft + \varphi(t)] \, dt,$$

a random gaussian variable of mean value zero and of variance

$$\overline{B^2(t) \sin^2 [2\pi ft + \varphi(t)]} \cdot \frac{1}{M \Delta f} \cdot \int_T \sin^2 2\pi ft \, dt,$$

i.e. $TN/2M\Delta f$, which gives at the output of the correlator a signal-to-noise ratio (in power) equal to

$$\frac{S^2T^2}{4} \times \frac{2M\Delta f}{TN} = \frac{S^2}{2N} \times MT\Delta f = \frac{S^2T}{2} \cdot \frac{1}{b} = R$$

(with $b = N/M\Delta f$ spectral density of noise and with $S^2T/2 =$ energy of signal received).

IMPORTANT REMARK

We note that in the absence of top-limiting, *we obtain the same result whatever the width of the band before passing through the matched filter* (or the correlator). In practice, the greater the value of M (large pass-band before filtering through the matched filter) the greater must be the dynamic of the matched filter (or the correlator).

4.6.2.3 In the presence of top-limiting (C.F.A.R. reception)

4.6.2.3.1 *General*

The set (signal + noise) before top-limiting is written as

$$S \sin (2\pi ft) + B(t) [\sin (2\pi ft + \varphi(t)]$$

or again as

$$[\sqrt{S^2 + B^2(t) + 2B(t)S \cos \varphi(t)}] \sin (2\pi ft + \Phi(t)),$$

with

$$\cos \Phi(t) = \frac{S + B(t) \cos \varphi(t)}{\sqrt{S^2 + B^2(t) + 2SB(t) \cos \varphi(t)}}$$

$$\sin \Phi(t) = \frac{B(t) \sin \varphi(t)}{\sqrt{S^2 + B^2(t) + 2SB(t) \cos \varphi(t)}}$$

After top-limiting and filtering, there remains

$$\sin (2\pi ft + \Phi(t)).$$

The correlation of this term with reference $\sin (2\pi ft)$ gives in the absence of noise (or when the noise is negligible compared to the useful signals)

$$\int_T \sin 2\pi ft \cdot \sin 2\pi ft \cdot dt = T/2,$$

in the absence of a useful signal ($\Phi = \varphi$)

$$\int_T \sin 2\pi ft \cdot \sin (2\pi ft + \varphi(t)) \cdot dt,$$

i.e. a gaussian random variable of mean value zero and variance (power):

$$MT\Delta f \cdot \frac{1}{M^2 \Delta f^2} \cdot \overline{\sin^2 2\pi ft} \cdot \overline{\sin^2 (2\pi ft + \varphi(t))}$$

being

$$\frac{T}{4M\Delta f}$$

The ratio

$$\frac{\text{power of the useful signal when it is high}}{\text{power of the noise in the absence of a useful signal}}$$

is hence equal to

$$\frac{T^2}{4} \times \frac{4M\Delta f}{T} = MT\Delta f.$$

In the simultaneous presence of a useful signal and of noise we obtain at the output of the correlator (or of the matched filter)

$$\int_T \sin (2\pi ft) \cdot \sin (2\pi ft + \Phi(t)) \cdot dt,$$

a random gaussian variable whose mean value is equal to

$$\frac{1}{2} \overline{\int_T \cos \Phi(t) \cdot dt} = \frac{T}{2} \overline{\cos \Phi}.$$

This random variable, which constitutes the output signal of the radar, could be considered as a sum

— of the useful signal $\dfrac{T}{2} \overline{\cos \Phi}$

— of a gaussian term due to $\cos \Phi(t)$ not being constant, i.e. the output noise, with a mean value of zero and a certain power (variance): the power of the output noise.

4.6.2.3.2   *Very small signal-to-noise ratio in power SB_1*

If the signal-to-noise ratio at the input is very small, i.e. if $S^2/2N \ll 1$, we could write (by taking the risk of not being rigorous)

$$\cos \Phi \approx \frac{\cos \varphi + S/B}{\sqrt{1 + \dfrac{2S}{B} \cos \varphi}} \approx \left(\cos \varphi + \frac{S}{B} \right) \left(1 - \frac{S}{B} \cos \varphi \right)$$

$$\approx \cos \varphi + \frac{S}{B} \sin^2 \varphi,$$

$$\overline{\cos \Phi} = \frac{S}{2} \cdot \overline{\left(\frac{1}{B}\right)} = \frac{S}{2} \int_0^\infty \frac{1}{N} \exp\left(-B^2/2N\right) dB = \frac{S\sqrt{2\pi}}{2\sqrt{N}} \cdot \frac{1}{\sqrt{2\pi N}} \times$$

$$\int_0^\infty \exp\left(-B^2/2N\right) dB$$

$$= \frac{S}{4} \sqrt{\frac{2\pi}{N}}$$

The useful signal is therefore written as

$$\frac{ST}{8} \sqrt{\frac{2\pi}{N}} = \frac{T}{2} \cdot \sqrt{\frac{\pi}{4}} \cdot SB_1.$$

However, the noise power at the output is very close to the value it has for SB_1 equal to zero, i.e. of $T/4M\Delta f$. Thus the signal-to-noise ratio at the output —SB_2—is equal (at the position of the signal) to

$$SB_2 = \frac{T^2}{4} \cdot \frac{\pi}{4} \cdot SB_1 \times \frac{4M\Delta f}{T} = \frac{\pi}{4} \cdot SB_1 \cdot MT\Delta f$$

$$= \frac{\pi}{4} \cdot \frac{S^2}{2N} \cdot MT\Delta f = \frac{\pi}{4} R.$$

It is identical to the case of the non-C.F.A.R. receiver, multiplied by $\pi/4$ (a loss of 1 dB over the signal-to-noise ratio).

4.6.2.3.3   A very high signal-to-noise ratio SB_1

In the case of $\cos \Phi(t) \approx 1$ the useful signal is close to $T/2$, a result already found, and after top-limiting the signal could be written as

$$\frac{S \sin (2\pi f t)}{\sqrt{S^2 + 2BS \cos \varphi + B^2}} + \frac{B(t) \sin (2\pi f t + \varphi(t))}{\sqrt{S^2 + 2BS \cos \varphi + B^2}}$$

$$\approx \sin (2\pi f t) \left(1 - \frac{B}{S} \cos \varphi\right) + \frac{B}{S} (\sin 2\pi f t \cdot \cos \varphi + \cos 2\pi f t \cdot \sin \varphi)$$

by neglecting the terms in B^2/S^2.

$$\sin 2\pi f t + \frac{B}{S} \cos 2\pi f t \sin \varphi,$$

with $\sin 2\pi f t$ representing the useful signal, $(B/S) \cos 2\pi f t \sin \varphi$ representing the noise after top-limiting, which shows (with the danger of being not rigorous) that the signal-to-noise ratio after top-limiting has become

$$\frac{1/2}{\dfrac{1}{2S^2} \cdot B^2 \sin^2 \varphi} = \frac{S^2}{N} = 2SB_1$$

The top-limiting simply has the effect of doubling the signal-to-noise ratio, a result evidently maintained after correlation (or reception) through a matched filter. We have hence a gain of 3 dB over the signal-to-noise ratio due to the C.F.A.R. reception, for high signal-to-noise ratios at the input (and a loss of 1 dB for low ratios at the input).

This appears a little surprising. It seems at first that the C.F.A.R. receiver improves reception, which is contradictory to the fact that as the C.F.A.R. reception is not optimal, we must lose something, or at least have nothing to gain. We shall see in sub-section 4.6.3 that this contradiction is only an apparent one.

4.6.2.3.3   General case: an arbitrary signal-to-noise ratio SB_1

The useful signal is given by $\overline{\cos \Phi}/2$ and the noise appears to be given by

$$\int_T \{ [\sin 2\pi ft \cdot (\sin 2\pi ft + \Phi(t))] - \tfrac{1}{2} \overline{\cos \Phi} \} \, dt$$

or as

$$\frac{1}{M\Delta f} \sum [f(t_i) - \overline{f(t)}]$$

t_i being the instants of sampling $1/M\Delta f$ apart, and with

$$f(t) = \sin 2\pi ft \cdot \sin (2\pi ft + \Phi(t)),$$

the noise power is the variance of this term, i.e.

$$\frac{1}{M^2 \Delta f^2} \sum \overline{[f(t_i) - \overline{f(t)}]^2} = \frac{1}{M^2 \Delta f^2} \sum [\overline{f(t_i)}^2 - (\overline{f(t)})^2]$$

$$= \frac{1}{M\Delta f} \left[\int f^2(t) \, dt - \left(\frac{\overline{\cos \Phi}}{2} \right)^2 T \right]$$

$$= \frac{T}{4M\Delta f} [1 - (\overline{\cos \Phi})^2]$$

The signal-to-noise ratio at the position of the signal is hence given by

$$SB_2 = \frac{T^2}{[4} \times \frac{4M\Delta f}{T} \times \frac{(\overline{\cos \Phi})^2}{1 - (\overline{\cos \Phi})^2},$$

$$SB_2 = MT\Delta f \frac{(\overline{\cos \Phi})^2}{1 - (\overline{\cos \Phi})^2}$$

If the signal-to-noise ratio (SB_1) is very small, we obtain

$$\overline{(\cos \Phi)^2} \approx \frac{S^2}{8} \cdot \frac{\pi}{N},$$

$$SB_2 \approx \frac{S^2}{2N} \cdot \frac{\pi}{4} \cdot \left(1 + \frac{S^2}{2N} \cdot \frac{\pi}{4}\right) \cdot MT\Delta f,$$

$$SB_2 \approx \frac{\pi}{4} SB_1 \left(1 + \frac{\pi}{4} SB_1\right) \cdot MT\Delta f,$$

$$SB_2 \approx \frac{\pi}{4} R \left(1 + \frac{\pi}{4} \cdot \frac{R}{MT\Delta f}\right).$$

If SB_1 is very large,

$$\cos \Phi = \sqrt{1 - \sin^2 \Phi} \approx 1 - \frac{\sin^2 \Phi}{2},$$

$$\cos \Phi \approx 1 - \frac{B^2 \sin^2 \Phi}{2S^2},$$

$$\overline{\cos \Phi} \approx 1 - \frac{N}{2S^2} = 1 - \frac{MT\Delta f}{4R},$$

$$SB_2 \approx \frac{MT\Delta f}{MT\Delta f / 2R} \approx 2R.$$

We obtain the preceding results.

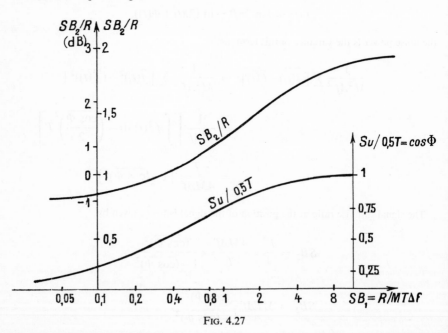

FIG. 4.27

All the results are reproduced in fig. 4.27, giving as a function of $R/MT\Delta f$ the variations of SB_2/R and of the signal (divided by $0\cdot5T$), i.e. $\overline{\cos\Phi}$.

They are shown in more expressive way in fig. 4.28 which shows as a function of time t the output signal of a C.F.A.R. receiver for $MT\Delta f = 60$, $T\Delta f = 10$, $M = 6$, when there is useful signal at t_1 corresponding to $R = 10$ dB (fig. 4.28(a)) or $R = 30$ dB (fig. 4.28(b)). The power is reduced on both sides of the signal,

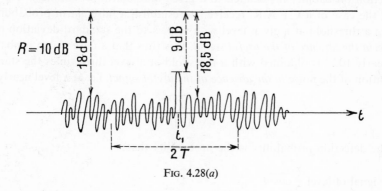

FIG. 4.28(a)

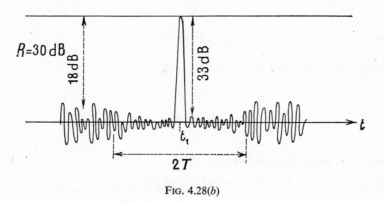

FIG. 4.28(b)

over a total width of $2T$, passing progressively for $R = 30$ dB $(R/MT\Delta f = 12$ dB$)$ from the value -33 dB at the position of the signal $(-R-3$ dB$)$ to the value -18 dB outside the interval $(1/MT\Delta f)$, while for $R = 10$ dB $(R/MT\Delta f = -8$ dB$)$, it passes progressively from $-18\cdot5$ dB at the position of the signal whose level is -9 dB $(-9-10+0\cdot5)$ always to -18 dB on the exterior of the interval $2T$.

It must hence be noted that if $T\Delta f$ were equal to 1 (classical radar) the weakening of the noise at the position of the signal will not be seen on the figures.

4.6.3 Detection probability

4.6.3.1 General

We have seen in sub-section 4.6.2 that when the signal of transmission had a constant power during its duration, the signal-to-noise ratio at the output of a C.F.A.R. receiver was equal to R diminished by 1 dB if $R/MT\Delta f$ were small, and was equal to $2R$ if $R/MT\Delta f$ were large. But what is really important is the detection probability (associated to a given false alarm probability).

In the case of a C.F.A.R. receiver we establish a false alarm probability by fixing a threshold at a given level with respect to the standard deviation of the noise *in the absence of the useful signal*. It is thus that a false alarm probability of nearly 10^{-3} is obtained with a threshold at a level three times the standard deviation of the noise *in the absence of the useful signal*, i.e. at a level nearly

$$\frac{3}{2}\sqrt{\frac{T}{M\Delta f}}$$

The detection probability is the probability that:

a signal of level $\dfrac{T}{2}\overline{\cos \Phi}$

$+$ a gaussian noise of mean value zero and variance equal to

$$\frac{T}{4M\Delta f}[1-\overline{(\cos \Phi)^2}],$$

be greater than this level of threshold

$$\frac{3}{2}\sqrt{\frac{T}{M\Delta f}}.$$

4.6.3.2 A probability of detection of 0·5

We thus obtain a detection probability of 0·5 if

$$\frac{T}{2}\overline{\cos \Phi} = \frac{3}{2}\sqrt{\frac{T}{M\Delta f}}$$

$$\frac{S_u}{0·5T} = \overline{\cos \Phi} = \sqrt{\frac{9}{MT\Delta f}}$$

If $MT\Delta f$ is large:

$$\overline{\cos \Phi} \sim \sqrt{\frac{\pi}{4}SB_1} \sim \sqrt{\frac{\pi}{4}\frac{R}{MT\Delta f}}$$

and we obtain

$$\sqrt{\frac{\pi}{4}} R = \sqrt{9},$$

$$R = 9 \times \frac{4}{\pi},$$

while for the non-C.F.A.R. receiver we found $R = 9$.

More generally, for any false alarm probability we have to put the threshold at a level equal to K times the standard deviation of the noise in the absence of the signal, and we find that the probability of detection of 0·5 is obtained (when $MT\Delta f$ is sufficient) for $A = 4K^2/\pi$ with the C.F.A.R., instead of K^2 with the matched receiver. This corresponds to a loss of 1 dB for $MT\Delta f$ fairly large and for a probability of detection of 0·5.

If $MT\Delta f$ is not large, the loss due to C.F.A.R. for a probability of detection of 0·5 increases and the following table gives in terms of $MT\Delta f$ the loss introduced by the C.F.A.R. receiver for a probability of detection of 0·5 and a false alarm probability of nearly 10^{-3}.

$MT\Delta f$	100	50	20	15	10	9
Loss in dB for $P_1 = 0\cdot5$ $P_f \sim 10^{-3}$	1	1·3	2·2	3	7	∞

REMARK

This assumes that the detection is made over a single measurement of duration T. If we use n identical measurements (particularly with coherent integration) the results are better, and the losses are fewer (in the coherent integration events occur as if $MT\Delta f$ were multiplied by n).

4.6.3.3 The general case

We could calculate the detection probability as a function of R for a given value of $MT\Delta f$ by utilising the relation given at the end of sub-section 4.6.3.1.

Thus was calculated the curve given in fig. 4.29 (for $MT\Delta f = 50$ and $P_f = 10^{-3}$). We see in the figure that for reasonable values of the probability of detection (less than 0·999) the C.F.A.R. receiver introduces in fact a loss of the order of 1·3 dB, although the signal-to-noise ratio (at the position of the signal) is, for a probability of detection of 0·999, 1 dB higher with the C.F.A.R. receiver.

If we find sometimes that the C.F.A.R. improves the signal-to-noise ratio, this is due to the fact that the signal-to-noise ratio at the position of the signal does not have, by itself, a physical meaning. The probability of detection, which is related in a simple and known way to the signal-to-noise ratio only if the noise has the same characteristics in the presence or absence of the useful

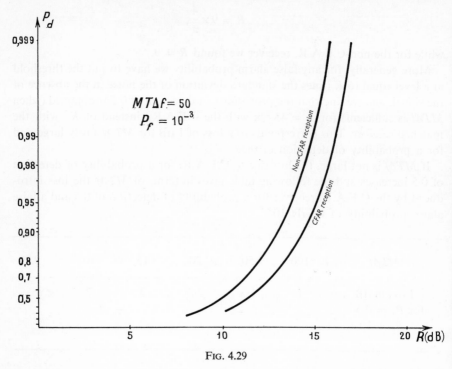

FIG. 4.29

signal, is the only interesting thing. And in fact the probability of detection depends simultaneously on the signal-to-noise ratio at the position of the signal and on the ratio

$$\frac{\text{Signal}}{\text{Signal-to-noise outside the signal}}.$$

REMARK

The hypothesis that $MT\Delta f$ is sufficiently large for the noise to be gaussian is valid only if we do not consider the probabilities of detection very close to 1 or the false alarm probabilities that are very small.

4.6.4 Examples of application

4.6.4.1 Classical radar

When $T\Delta f \simeq 1$, the preceding applies to the case of classical radar. $MT\Delta f$ is then equal to M, the ratio between the bandwidth before limitation and the matched band. The receiver thus made is commonly known as the Dicke-fix receiver (see fig. 4.30).

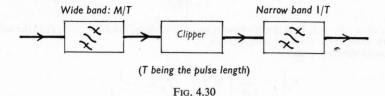

Wide band: M/T   Narrow band 1/T

Clipper

(T being the pulse length)

Fig. 4.30

4.6.4.2 Pulse compression radar

When $M = 1$ and $T\Delta f$ is large, the preceding applies (practically) to pulse compression radar with limitation, at the normal bandwidth, before compression (see fig. 4.31).

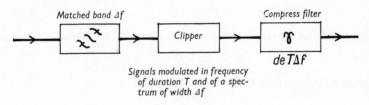

Matched band Δf Compress filter

Clipper

$de\,T\Delta f$

Signals modulated in frequency
of duration T and of a spectrum of width Δf

Fig. 4.31

In this case, however, a certain difficulty appears that does not exist in the case of a Dicke-fix receiver.

Let us suppose that we are *in the presence of two identical targets* very close to each other but separable (a radial distance of the order of $1/\Delta f$), each giving a value R. We could— without making rigorous calculations—consider that the power of each signal at the output is equal to half of that of a unique target twice as powerful, while the noise power at the output at the position of the signals is practically unchanged if R is small and divided by 2 if R is very large. We find this by the following approximations.

Because of top-limiting, the sum of the noise power P_B and the power of the signal P_S corresponding to a target is equal to 1

$$P_B + P_S = 1$$

and since we have

$$P_S = P_B \times SB_1$$

we deduce

$$P_B[1 + SB_1] = 1, \qquad P_B = \frac{1}{1 + SB_1}.$$

In the case where we are in the presence of two targets, we find

$$P_B = \frac{1}{1 + 2SB_1}.$$

If therefore $SB_1 \ll 1$, P_B in the two cases is equal to 1 nearly. But if $SB_1 \gg 1$, P_B in the second is half its value in the case of a unique target.

We could similarly write

$$P_u \left[1 + \frac{1}{SB_1} \right] = 1, \qquad P_u = \frac{1}{1 + \dfrac{1}{SB_1}}$$

in the case of one target and

$$P_u = \frac{1}{1 + \dfrac{1}{2SB_1}}$$

in the case of two targets, which gives, if SB_1 is small,

$$P_u = SB_1$$

for one target, $2SB_1$ for two targets, SB_1 for each of them, and, if SB_1 is large,

$$P_u = 1$$

for one target, 1 for two targets, 0·5 for each of them.

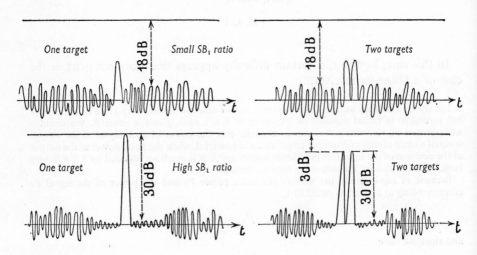

FIG. 4.32

These results are shown in fig. 4.32.

It follows that the losses due to C.F.A.R. for a probability of detection of 0·5 are, when we are in the presence of two close targets, given by the following table (false alarm probability of the order of 10):

$T\Delta f$	100	50	30	20	18
Loss in dB	1·3	1·7	3	7	∞

In other respects, when the targets become farther away the loss due to C.F.A.R. decreases.

If we consider *two* very close *targets* but *of different levels*, one of them very powerful and the other B^2 times less powerful ($B \gg 1$), the very powerful target will give a signal of maximal amplitude ($T/2$), the less powerful signal will give a signal of amplitude limited to $T/2B$, while the noise power will be weaker at the position of the targets than it would have been in the absence of the large target.

The same approximate reasoning proves this. Denoting by SB_1 the signal-to-noise ratio due to the small target before top-limiting; by P_B the noise power after top-limiting; by P_{u1} the power of the signal of the large target after top-limiting; and by P_{u2} the power of the signal of the small target after top-limiting; we have

$$P_{u1} = B^2 SB_1 P_B, \qquad P_{u2} = SB_1 P_B,$$

$$P_B[1 + (B^2+1)SB_1] = 1, \qquad P_B = \frac{1}{1+(B^2+1)SB_1}$$

$$P_{u2}\left[1 + \frac{1}{SB_1} + B^2\right] = 1, \qquad P_{u2} = \frac{1}{1 + \dfrac{1}{SB_1} + B^2}$$

By assuming the large target to be of sufficient size, we have

$$B^2 SB_1 \gg 1$$

and hence

$$P_B = \frac{1}{B^2 SB_1},$$

$$P_{u2} = \frac{1}{B^2},$$

while in the absence of the large target, we would have

$$P_B = \frac{1}{1+SB_1}, \qquad P_{u2} = \frac{SB_1}{1+SB_1}$$

Then a detection probability of 0·5 of the small target is possible for $P_f \approx 10^{-3}$ only if

$$\frac{T}{2B} > \frac{3}{2}\sqrt{\frac{T}{\Delta f}}$$

$$\frac{1}{B^2} > \frac{9}{T\Delta f}, \qquad B^2 < \frac{T\Delta f}{9}$$

(a formula valid if $B^2 \gg 1$).

N

The following table gives the maximal value of B^2 (in decibels):

$T\Delta f$	100	50	30
B^2	10·5	7·5	6

If the targets are no longer very close to each other the results improve. Thus if their distance is equal to $T/2$, even if the large target is very large, it will be always possible to obtain a probability of detection of 0·5 over the small target providing that the value of R for this small target is at least equal to the value given (in decibels) by the table below (for a false alarm probability of 10^{-3}), which corresponds to a loss of 3 dB with respect to the value necessary for obtaining the same result for two identical targets.

$T\Delta f$	100	50	30	20
R	14·5	15	15·5	20·0

4.6.4.3   General case

When M and $T\Delta f$ are both greater than 1, the preceding applies to the case of a pulse compression radar with a Dicke-fix receiver.

Obviously, all the preceding remarks apply to correlation radars.

REMARK

All the preceding remarks apply exclusively to radars transmitting a signal of constant power during its duration. If the transmitted signal is modulated in amplitude, the top-limiting of C.F.A.R. causes the loss of information contained in the amplitude, and the losses over the detector probabilities are thereby increased. Thus, as an example, if we consider that a useful transmitted signal to have random amplitude following a gaussian law (analogous to a thermal noise), we find a loss of the order of 5 dB, instead of 1 dB.

CHAPTER 5

BEHAVIOUR OF REAL TARGETS:
TARGET FLUCTUATION

5.1 GENERAL

The preceding chapters have dealt with the simple problem where the target was assumed to behave in a manner convenient at least for the various calculations.

We admitted that if a radar transmitted a certain signal $S(t)$ whose spectrum was $\Phi(f)$, then it received in return, by reflection against a target, a signal (weakened in a given known ratio) obtained by displacing $S(t)$

— by t_{01} in time,
— by f_D in frequency

(at least in the general case, where the width of the spectrum $\Phi(f)$ was small compared to the carrier frequency).

When we started, in a general way, to write the radar equations to determine the energy to be transmitted, we found ourselves obliged to use the term "equivalent echoing area", defined as follows.

If at the position of the target the density of power (W/m^2) is p and if the target re-radiates in the direction of the radar a certain density of power (of W/m^2) it would seem for the radar as if the target radiated a power $p\sigma_e$ in an omnidirectional way, σ_e being the "equivalent area" of the target by definition.

In other words, we replace the target by a kind of a punctual target which is designated by "centre of reflection" which is capable of absorbing a density of energy $p\sigma_e$ and radiating it in an omnidirectional way, the centre of reflection being given the coordinates x, y, z.

This concept of a centre of reflection is valid on the condition that we admit that it has a position variable versus time and that it is not closely attached to the target, sometimes to the right, sometimes to the left, and even sometimes to the gravity centre of the target.

In the same way, the concept of "equivalent echoing area" is valid if we admit that it has a very poor relation with the surface area of the target and that it is variable versus time.

179

This is normal if we realise that the targets are very large when compared to the wavelength (1,000 times larger), are of very unusual shape, and do not in any way resemble a punctual target absorbing $p\sigma_e$.

However, we now know that this pessimistic picture has an encouraging aspect, namely, that if the equivalent echoing area is a random variable and if, on the other hand, the position of the centre of reflection is also a random variable, then these two variables are not independent of each other. They are correlated between themselves in a certain way and we shall try to analyse this relation in the rest of this chapter.

5.2 EQUIVALENT ECHOING AREA OF A FLAT PLATE

Let us consider a target consisting of a plane circular mirror. It is common knowledge that this mirror reflects fairly well the wave that is received in the direction of the incident ray if it is perpendicular to it and rather poorly otherwise.

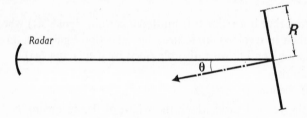

FIG. 5.1

In other words, its equivalent echoing area is very large if the angle θ between the normal and the radar-target direction is zero or very small. But it is very low when θ is rather large (see fig. 5.1).

If $\theta = 0$, all the points of the plate are illuminated by electrical fields of the same phase, the power picked up by the mirror being

$$\pi R^2 \times p$$

This power is re-radiated with different gains varying with the directions, and in particular, in the direction of the radar we have

$$G = \frac{4\pi}{\lambda^2}(\pi R^2)$$

The equivalent echoing area of the plate when $\theta = 0$ is, therefore,

$$\boxed{\frac{4\pi S^2}{\lambda^2} = \sigma_e}$$

where S denotes the surface area of the plate.

Numerical application:

$$R = 1 \text{ m} \qquad S = 3 \text{ m}^2$$
$$\lambda = 0\cdot03 \text{ m} \qquad \sigma_e = 100,000 \text{ m}^2$$

(the centre of reflection being the centre of the plate).

If $\theta = \lambda/4R$, the gain of the plate in the direction of the radar is zero, the equivalent area is zero, and the illuminated centre of reflection does not exist.

Numerical example (application):

$$R = 1 \text{ m}; \qquad \lambda = 0\cdot03 \text{ m}; \qquad \theta = \lambda/4R = 0\cdot008 \text{ rd} = 0\cdot5°$$

Hence, if the plate considered is a target moving in the space more or less in a direction perpendicular to that of the radar-target (if the plate is subject to small rotational movements of the type that θ varies through a few degrees around a mean value $\theta = 0$, what is quite difficult to avoid), then we find ourselves in the presence of a target whose equivalent echoing area varies between 0 and 100,000 m^2.

We note that if the same plate is used in front of a radar of wavelength 10 cm, then this time it has an equivalent echoing area of 10,000 m^2 for $\theta = 0$, and that for identical (similar) movements in the space ($\theta = \lambda/4R = 0\cdot025$ rd $= 1\cdot5°$) the equivalent echoing area varies on average three times more slowly.

It is usual to represent in polar coordinates the variation of the equivalent area as a function of the angle θ between the normal to the plate and the direction of the radar. We obtain thus a radiation pattern of the target very analogous to that of the classical diagrams in the case of an aerial (this analogy should not be extended too far: a radar-target is not an aerial but a moving reflector with respect to the primary source which is the radar situated at a great distance).

Figure 5.2 represents the radiation pattern at a flat plate.

FIG. 5.2

5.3 EQUIVALENT ECHOING AREA OF A METALLIC SPHERE

Let us consider a target consisting of a metallic sphere of radius R much greater than the wavelength λ used. It is assumed that the part of the sphere normal to the radar-target direction radiates mostly (the angle of incidence being in the neighbourhood of zero) in the direction of the radar, while the other portions of the sphere mostly radiate in different directions.

It is therefore usual to admit that the part of the sphere which contributes the maximum is that which is closest to the radar, i.e. the centre of reflection is in some way the point of the sphere closest to the radar.

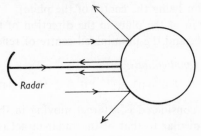

FIG. 5.3

It is evident that we can show that the equivalent echoing area of the entire sphere is finally not greater than that of a portion of the sphere centred on the centre of reflection once the maximum dimension of the portion, α, is greater than $\sqrt{2\lambda R}$.

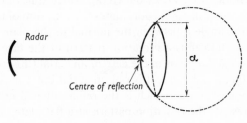

FIG. 5.4

If this condition is fulfilled, the portion of the sphere in fig. 5.4 has the same equivalent echoing area as the entire sphere in fig. 5.3, i.e. πR^2.

Numerical example:

$$R = 20 \text{ m}; \qquad \lambda = 0\cdot1 \text{ m}$$

$$\sqrt{2\lambda R} = 2 \text{ m}$$

The entire sphere has an equivalent echoing area of 1,200 m².

A portion of the sphere of 3m aperture has also an equivalent echoing area of 1,200 m² even if it has a surface area of the order of 10 m².

This property could be generalised as follows. If we have a portion of sufficient dimension of a convex metallic surface normal to the radar-target direction at one point, then, the centre of reflection is the point that is the closest to the radar and the equivalent echoing area of the object considered is equal to

$$\pi R_1 R_2$$

where R_1 and R_2 are the radii of the principal curves in this point.

It is evident from this case that the equivalent echoing area has very little relation with the surface area of the object.

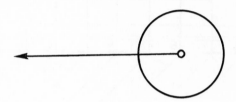

FIG. 5.5

REMARK

It is evident that, the sphere being isotropic, its equivalent echoing area does not depend on its orientation.

Figure 5.5 represents, therefore, the radiation pattern of a metallic sphere.

5.4 PASSIVE RESPONDERS

We have seen that a flat plate had an equivalent echoing area which varied greatly as a function of the angle between the normal to the surface and the radar-plate direction, but that if this angle was zero the corresponding equivalent area could be very large.

The metallic sphere has an equivalent echoing area independent of its orientation but relatively small.

Certain systems have the two properties of having an equivalent echoing area quite significant when compared to their real surface area, and of having a constant or almost constant equivalent echoing area as their orientation changes.

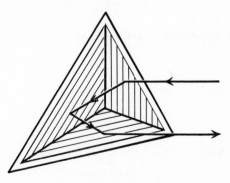

FIG. 5.6

We usually call these passive responders. For example:
— a corner (see fig. 5.6),
— the Luneberg lens,
— the Van Atta responder (see fig. 5.7).

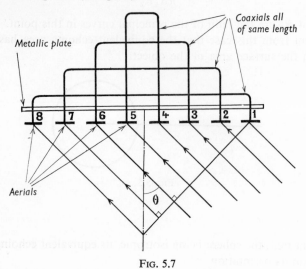

Fig. 5.7

The Luneberg lens consists of a sphere which is metallised over half of its surface, itself being made up of concentric layers of diaelectric constant variable materials which returns the power in the direction of incidence.

In the Van Atta responder which is shown in fig. 5.7 the radiation that reaches 1 has a certain phase, say, Φ_0:

that reaching 2 has a phase

$$\Phi_0 - \frac{2\pi d \sin \theta}{\lambda}$$

and that reaching 8 has a phase

$$\Phi_0 - \frac{14\pi d \sin \theta}{\lambda}$$

(if d denotes the distance between two consecutive aerials).

The radiation fed into 1 emerges from 8 with a phase

$$\Phi_0 - \Phi_1.$$

The radiation fed into 2 emerges from 7 with a phase

$$\Phi_0 - \frac{2\pi d \sin \theta}{\lambda} - \Phi_1.$$

The radiation which emerges from 1 (fed into 8) has a phase

$$\Phi_0 - \frac{14\pi d \sin \theta}{\lambda} - \Phi_1.$$

Finally, the radiation which emerges from the passive responder is that of a plane wave propagating in the direction opposite to that of incidence. The description that is given in the plan (in two dimensions) can be generalised to three dimensions and we finally obtain (at least for θ less than 20 or 30°) a responder having almost the same equivalent area as that of the plate which supports it.

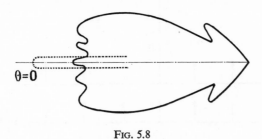

FIG. 5.8

Figure 5.8 gives the radiation pattern of a passive responder (in dotted lines) and the radiation pattern of a flat plate of equal surface.

5.5 A FIELD RADIATED BY AN OMNIDIRECTIONAL HYPOTHETICAL TARGET

In order to analyse correctly the essential differences between real targets and hypothetical targets it is necessary to review the properties that an ideal target possesses, i.e. a punctual target situated at O which deducts from the radiation of the radar a power $p\sigma_e$ and re-radiates it in an omnidirectional manner.

In this case, if we consider all the points of the sphere situated at a distance D from the target O, the amplitude of the field (electrical) is the same at every point of the sphere and the phase of the field is also the same. We say that a sphere centred at O is an equiphase surface.

Once we place ourselves at a distance D from the target sufficiently large in relation to the dimensions of the radar aerials used, we could consider, for all practical purposes, that the portion of the equiphase surface is a plane along the length of which the electrical field has a constant amplitude.

Two equiphase surfaces π_1 and π_2 placed at a distance d (d is small in relation to the wavelength λ) between each other correspond to the phases Φ_1 and Φ_2 such that

$$\Phi_2 = \Phi_1 - \frac{4\pi d}{\lambda}.$$

Because D is assumed to be very large in relation to λ and hence in relation to d, the amplitude of the field along π_1 is the same as that along π_2 $\left(\text{since } \frac{1}{D^4} \approx \frac{1}{(D+d)^4}\right)$ (see fig. 5.9).

In other words, we could affirm that the normal to the equiphase surface is directed towards the hypothetical, punctual and omnidirectional target.

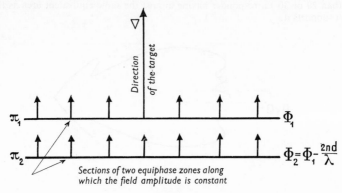

Sections of two equiphase zones along which the field amplitude is constant

FIG. 5.9

5.6 A TARGET CONSISTING OF TWO IDENTICAL PUNCTUAL TARGETS

Let us consider a target diagrammatically constituted by two identical punctual sources situated at O_1 and O_2, such that the distance O_1O_2 is fixed and equal to r (r being very small in relation to the distance D of the target from the radar and very large in relation to the wavelength λ).

We also assume that the bisecting plane of O_1O_2 makes an angle θ with the radar-target direction (see fig. 5.10).

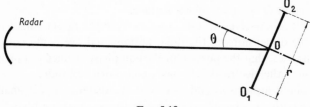

FIG. 5.10

Denoting the distance radar-O_1 by d_1 and the distance radar-O_2 by d_2, the wave coming from O_1 could be written in the form

$$A \exp\left(-4\pi j d_1/\lambda\right)$$

the wave coming from O_2 could be written in the form

$$A \exp\left(-4\pi j d_2/\lambda\right)$$

and this gives for the resultant wave

$$E = A[\exp(-4\pi j d_1/\lambda) + \exp(-4\pi j d_2/\lambda)]$$

$$E = 2A \exp[-2\pi j(d_1+d_2)/\lambda] \cos\left(\frac{2\pi(d_1-d_2)}{\lambda}\right)$$

i.e. by denoting the distance radar-O by D:

$$D \approx \left(\frac{d_1+d_2}{2}\right)$$

$$E = 2A \exp(-4\pi j D/\lambda) \cos\left(\frac{2\pi r \sin\theta}{\lambda}\right)$$

When the target is fixed and the radar moves along a sphere of centre O, the phase of the wave received by the radar is constant and equal to Φ_0 when

$$-\frac{\pi}{2} < \frac{2\pi r \sin\theta}{\lambda} < \frac{\pi}{2} \quad \text{(mod. } 2\pi\text{),}$$

$$\frac{k\lambda}{r} - \frac{\lambda}{4r} < \sin\theta = \theta < \frac{\lambda}{4r} + \frac{k\lambda}{r} \quad (k = \text{integer}),$$

and the phase of the wave received by the radar is constant and equal to $\Phi_0 + \pi$ when

$$k\frac{\lambda}{r} + \frac{\lambda}{4r} < \sin\theta = \theta < \frac{3\lambda}{4r} + \frac{k\lambda}{r},$$

the amplitude of the signal received varying as

$$\left|\cos\frac{2\pi r \sin\theta}{\lambda}\right| = \left|\cos\frac{2\pi r\theta}{\lambda}\right|.$$

Hence the spheres of centre O are no longer equiphase surfaces: along the length of these surfaces the phase is constant mod. π, and elsewhere the amplitude of the field received on these spheres is not constant (see fig. 5.11).

It would be useful to give the order of size of the parameters in fig. 5.11.

Let us assume a target equivalent to two atomic sources separated by a distance $r = 5$ m (grosso-modo a twin-engined aircraft going away from a radar could be considered as corresponding to this definition). Also let $\lambda = 0.1$ m and $D = 200$ km.

We find that $D\lambda/2r = 2,000$ m and that $\lambda/2r = 10^{-2}$ rd $\approx 0.6°$.

In the light of the dimensions of the classical wave collectors which are of the order of 10 m at the considered wavelength, we are justified in considering that the amplitude of the field received is constant at all the points of the wave collector if the target is fixed.

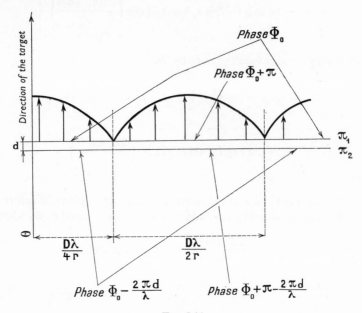

FIG. 5.11

On the other hand, if the target is subject to small random movements (inevitable) the amplitude of the field received (the same at all points of the wave collector) also becomes random, varying between the limits 0 and $2A$: the receiver does not receive the signal $kS(t-t_0)$—if $S(t)$ is the signal transmitted—but a signal $aS(t-t_0)$ with $|a| = |B \sin \varphi|$ and all the values of φ between 0 and π are equally probable since no value of θ is *a priori* most likely.

In other words, a is a random variable whose amplitude distribution is characterised by a density probability $p_1(|a|)$ such that

$$p_1(|a|)\, \mathrm{d}a = p(\varphi)\, \mathrm{d}\varphi,$$

with

$$\varphi = \arc \sin \frac{a}{B},$$

$$\mathrm{d}\varphi = \frac{1}{B} \frac{\mathrm{d}a}{\sqrt{1 - a^2/B^2}} = \frac{\mathrm{d}a}{\sqrt{B^2 - a^2}}$$

and

$$p(\varphi) = 2/\pi,$$

i.e.

$$p_1(|a|) = \frac{2}{\pi\sqrt{B^2 - a^2}}$$

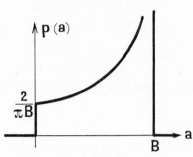

FIG. 5.12

The velocity with which a varies in time depends essentially on the velocity of rotation of the target with respect to the radar. As an example and as a way of obtaining the order of size, it is useful to consider two main cases:

(a) The target is an aircraft flying at 300 m/s and executing a turn with an acceleration of $2g$ (20 m/s^2). The angular velocity of rotation is therefore $6 \cdot 10^{-2}$ rd/s. If $r = 5$ and $\lambda = 0.1$ m, the aircraft turns by $\lambda/2r = 10^{-2}$ rd in 0.16 sec. In this case we could say that a passes from one maximum to another in a time of the order of 0.15 s. Generally, this time is significantly larger than the time of the radar's measurement, i.e. we could consider that the signal received is constant during the time measurement of the radar.

(b) The target is given to be an aircraft which moves in a direction perpendicular to that of the radar-target with a velocity of 300 m/s and at a distance of 5 km. In this case the velocity of rotation of the straight line radar-target with respect to the target is equal to $300/5 \cdot 10^3$, i.e. again $6 \cdot 10^{-2}$ rd/s.

a characterises (modulus a factor) the amplitude of the signal which will be sent into the radar's receiver (expressed in volts).

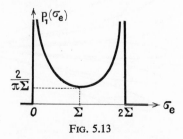

FIG. 5.13

One remaining important consideration is the energy received, i.e. the value of a^2 (modulus a factor) whose mean value characterises the mean value of the power received from the target. The value of a^2 (modulus a factor) is the equivalent echoing area of the target which is therefore a random parameter whose mean value has a physical sense, and which has a certain probability distribution characterised by its density $p_2(a^2)$, with

$$p_2(a^2) \, da^2 = p_1(|a|) \, da,$$

$$2p_2(a^2)a \, da = p_1(|a|) \, da,$$

$$p_2(a^2) = \frac{1}{\pi \sqrt{B^2 - a^2} \cdot \sqrt{a^2}}.$$

The density probability of the equivalent echoing area σ_e can therefore be written as

$$\boxed{p_2(\sigma_e) = \frac{1}{\pi \sqrt{2\Sigma - \sigma_e} \cdot \sqrt{\sigma_e}}}$$

where Σ denotes the mean value of σ_e (see fig. 5.13).

To conclude the study of the two-point target we could note that the corresponding equiphase surfaces have the aspect of a step-function as shown in fig. 5.14 (the equiphase surface being at the points where at a given time the field has the same phase).

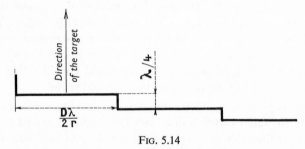

FIG. 5.14

Figure 5.15 represents the radiation pattern of such a two-point target.

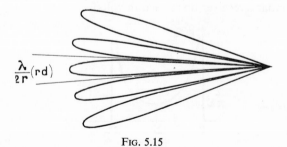

FIG. 5.15

We see that it has the petal form of the marguerite; hence the name "marguerite effect" given to the phenomena of the fluctuations of radar targets.

5.7 A TARGET CONSISTING OF TWO DIFFERENT PUNCTUAL TARGETS

Let us now consider a target diagrammatically constituted by two punctual sources situated at O_1 and O_2 (the notations are the same as those used in section 5.6), but the source O_1 having an equivalent echoing area four times that of O_2.

The wave coming from O_1 could be written as

$$A \exp\left(-4\pi j d_1/\lambda\right)$$

The wave coming from O_2:

$$0{\cdot}5A \exp\left(-4\pi j d_2/\lambda\right)$$

which gives for the resultant wave

$$A[\exp\left(-4\pi j d_1/\lambda\right) + 0{\cdot}5 \exp\left(-4\pi j d_2/\lambda\right)]$$

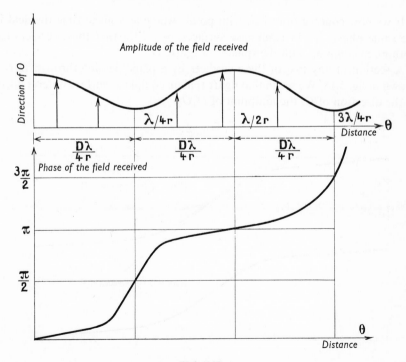

Fig. 5.16

When the target is fixed and the radar moves over a sphere of centre O, the phase of the received wave varies constantly and the amplitude of the signal received varies as

$$\sqrt{1\cdot25+\cos\frac{4\pi r\theta}{\lambda}}$$

Hence the spheres of centre O are no longer equiphase surfaces and the amplitude of the field received over these spheres is not constant either (see fig. 5.16). Figure 5.17 represents the radiation pattern of the target.

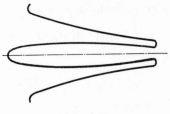

FIG. 5.17

If we now concern ourselves with points where at a given time the field has the same phase, i.e. in equiphase surfaces, we realise that these surfaces have nothing in common with the spheres of centre O.

A section of any two of these surfaces by a plane passing through O_1O_2 is shown in fig. 5.18. We see in that figure that an equiphase surface is never normal to the direction of O, the midpoint of O_1O_2.

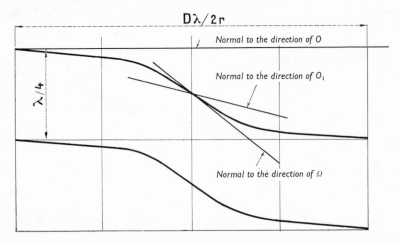

FIG. 5.18

In half the number of cases the normal to the equiphase surfaces is directed towards a point outside O_1O_2, possibly Ω symmetrical to O_2 with respect to O_1 (see fig. 5.19).

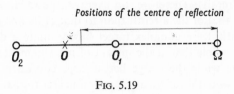

FIG. 5.19

In the other cases it is directed towards a point situated between O and O_1. As we shall see in Chapter 6, when a radar has to locate the direction of a target, it identifies precisely the direction normal to that equiphase surface, and it seems as if the target were equivalent to a centre of reflection possibly between O_1 and Ω.

Once we admit that the target is subject to small random movements, we could conclude that in the case analysed:

— the position of the centre of reflection has a 50 per cent chance of being outside the real target;

— the equivalent echoing area of the target could vary between a certain value Σ and 9Σ (the ratio of the amplitudes of the field at $\theta = 0$ and at $\theta = \lambda/Ar$ being equal to 3, the ratio of the corresponding powers fed into the radar being equal to 9);

— the centre of reflection is as much outside the target as the equivalent echoing area is low.

REMARK

We have already noted that the diagram of the target studied in section 5.6 represented to a large extent that of a twin-engined aircraft going away from a radar.

We could also note here that the diagram of the target studied in the present section (two different targets but analogous) explains to a large extent what happens when an aircraft is at a low altitude over a reflecting surface (for example, over the sea when the wave beamed by the radar has a horizontal polarisation) (see fig. 5.20).

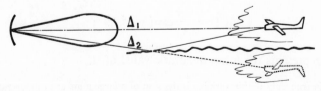

FIG. 5.20

Let us suppose, for example, that the coefficient of reflection over the sea is 0·5: on average, the signal received along the trajectory Δ_1 (coming from the aircraft) is twice the signal received along the trajectory Δ_2 (coming from the reflection of the aircraft). Therefore, on average, the radar would measure an elevation nearer to that of the aircraft than to that of its image. But in fact, the aircraft alone constitutes a complex target having quite a distorted radiation pattern, and it is possible that at the instant of measurement it had a low equivalent echoing area while the image had a large equivalent echoing area. In this case the radar would measure an elevation nearer to that of the image. The result is that it is not really possible, in this case, to expect an accurate measurement of the elevation of the target by radar.

5.8 FLUCTUATIONS IN RAYLEIGH'S LAW

All that has been said so far shows clearly that a target has a very badly defined equivalent echoing area and that it fluctuates in time with quite a low velocity (the equivalent area remaining constant during the measurement by a radar).

The equivalent echoing area is therefore a random variable characterised, we may say, by:

— a fairly narrow spectrum of frequencies (or a fairly large diameter of correlation);

— an amplitude distribution (an example of which was given in section 5.6).

Just as when there is a random variable the distribution of which is ignored, we say that its distribution is gaussian,[1] so we are led to define a very random target in the following way.

At any given time we could always consider the field received to have two components:

— a component 1 in phase (or in phase opposition) with a certain phase reference,

— and a component 2 in phase quadrature with this reference.

We admit that for a very random target component 1 has a mean value of zero and a gaussian distribution, and that component 2 has the same distribution.

With these hypotheses we deduce that the amplitude A of the field received has a Rayleigh distribution, i.e. that the density probability of A is given by

$$p_1(A) = \frac{2A}{A_0^2} \exp(-A^2 A_0^2) \qquad (1)$$

where A_0^2 represents the mean quadratic value of A.

---

[1] Which is true only if this variable is the sum of a large number of independent random variables.

This means (cf. the calculations in section 5.6) that the density probability of the equivalent area of a random target can be written as

$$p_2(\sigma) = \frac{1}{\sigma_0} \exp(-\sigma/\sigma_0)$$

where σ_0 represents the mean value of σ (σ is proportional to A^2).

This mean value σ_0 has a physical meaning because it represents the average power radiated by the target in the direction of the radar. It could therefore characterise the target in a valid way and we could compare:

— a non-fluctuating target (metallic sphere) having a constant equivalent echoing area σ_0;

— and a very random target having an average equivalent echoing area σ_0.

In particular, it is very advantageous to compare the curves of the detection probability as functions of R in the two cases.

In the case of a non-fluctuating target the value of R depends only on the distance of the target from the radar: at a given distance (assuming that the target is in a direction of maximum radiation by the radar) the value of R is known.

In the case of a complex target, we only know the mean value R_0 of R, under the same conditions.

In practice, the receiver of an ideal radar whether it correlates during the time T the signal received with a fraction of the transmitted signal with a delay $kS(t-t_0)$, or filters the received signal with a filter of characteristic $k\Phi(-f)$ or $k\Phi(f-f_0)$, delivers at the output in the absence of a target (at a good distance) a gaussian noise $b(t)$ of zero mean value having a certain variance which could be taken as unity for simplifying the arguments.

In this case it also delivers the useful signal, whose amplitude is $\sqrt{R} = s$.

We now define a threshold such that in the absence of a useful signal the probability that the noise shall exceed this given level is given (probability of false alarm Pf being equal to, for example, 10^{-3}). A target is detected only if the amplitude of "the useful signal + noise" is greater than this threshold, the probability of such an event being the detection probability Pd.

Figure 3.4 (Chapter 3) represents the variation of Pd as a function of R in the case of a non-fluctuating target.

If the target is fluctuating, it may happen that at the time of measurement, the value of R (proportional to σ) is very high, and hence the probability of detection is nearer to 1, but it could also happen that the value of R is very low and that there is little chance of detecting the target.

Mathematically we could write

$$p_2(R) = \frac{1}{R_0} \exp\left(-R/R_0\right)$$

and

$$p_1(s) = \frac{2s}{R_0} \exp\left(-s^2/R_0\right)$$

and, for $P_f = 10^{-3}$ (the threshold being approximately equal to 3),

$$P_d = \frac{1}{\sqrt{2\pi}}\left[\int_0^\infty \frac{2s}{R_0} \exp\left(-s^2/R_0\right) ds \int_{3-s}^\infty \exp\left(-b^2/2\right) db\right]$$

i.e. the probability of detection Pd is the mean value of the probability that at a given time we have the relation $s+b > 3$ (useful signal + noise is greater than the threshold) or $b > 3-s$.

R_0 (dB)	P_d complex target	P_d non-fluctuating
3	0·07	0·05
6	0·18	0·15
9·5	0·40	0·50
12	0·58	0·85
14	0·69	0·98
17	0·83	≈ 1·00

After all these calculations, we find the results shown in the above table, that give as a function of R_0 (mean value of R, obtained by replacing σ by its mean value σ_0 in the radar equations), the value of the probability of detection P_d of an ideal radar in the case of a non-fluctuating target (on the right) and in the case of a target fluctuating according to the Rayleigh law (on the left), whilst the threshold is adjusted so that the probability of false alarm P_f is around 10^{-3}.

Figure 5.21[1] gives the graphs corresponding to this table.

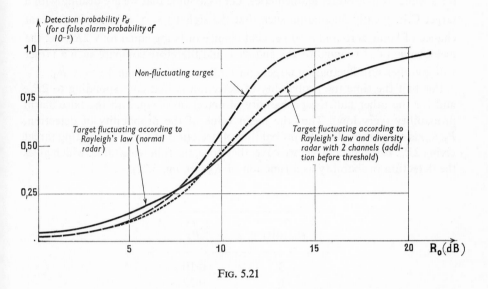

FIG. 5.21

A study of this figure shows that in order to obtain 90 per cent probability of detection of a complex target with an equivalent area σ_0, it is necessary to transmit, other things being equal, an energy greater by 7–8 dB than the energy necessary for detecting with a 90 per cent probability a non-fluctuating target of the same (average) equivalent echoing area σ_0, i.e. an energy multiplied by 5 or 6. On the other hand, if we aim at a 50 per cent detection probability then it is necessary to transmit more or less the same energy whether the target be a sphere or complex.

---

[1] P_d is generally written, after the calculations, as

$$P_d = P_f + \left\{ \exp\left[-A^2/2 + R_0\right] \right\} \left[2\pi(1 + 2/R_0)\right]^{-1/2} \int_{-A/\sqrt{1+2/R_0}}^{\infty} \exp\left(-v^2/2\right) \, dv$$

with

$$P_f = \frac{1}{\sqrt{2\pi}} \int_{A}^{\infty} \exp\left(-v^2/2\right) \, dv$$

when $P_f < 10^{-2}$ and that $P_d > 0.10$, the expression simplifies itself into

$$P_d = \frac{\exp\left[-A^2/(2 + R_0)\right]}{\sqrt{1 + 2/R_0}}$$

which allows the calculation of P_d for all useful values of P_f and of R_0 (see the figures at the end of the text).

In order to understand these phenomena better, it is useful to try to escape for a while from abstract mathematics. Let us assume that we are dealing with a target C.E. greatly fluctuating such that the signal $s = \sqrt{R}$ has a 50 per cent chance of being zero and a 50 per cent chance of being equal to $\sqrt{2R_0}$, i.e. the mean value of s^2 is equal to R_0, and we could therefore compare such a target with another non-fluctuating target constantly emitting a signal $s = \sqrt{R_0}$.

For half the time the probability of detection is that corresponding to $2R_0$, and for the other half the probability of detection is equal to the false alarm probability (very low). Thus the mean value of the probability of detection, $P_d(R_0)$ is equal to half of the probability of detection of a non-fluctuating target giving $2R_0$. For such a target we have, therefore, the following table, which gives the detection probability as a function of R_0 (see fig. 5.22).

R_0 (dB)	P_d
3	0·10
6	0·22
9	0·42
12	0·5
20	0·5

(P_d can never exceed 0·5).

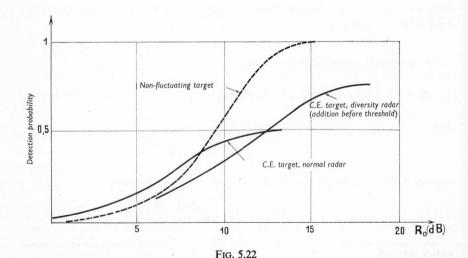

FIG. 5.22

We obtain from this simple example (which is not very different from the target studied in section 5.6) the result that for low values of R_0 the detection of a fluctuating target is better than that of a non-fluctuating target, while for high values of R_0 the probability of detection of a fluctuating target is very poor and we can physically understand the reasons for this.

5.9 FREQUENCY DIVERSITY, FREQUENCY AGILITY

Let us now assume that we work in the following way. The transmitted power is divided into two, such that we have two identical transmitters except that they have different frequencies: we also have two different receivers, which finally give at the output

— a signal s_1 corresponding to $R_0/2$ and submerged in a gaussian noise of standard deviation 1;

— a signal s_2 corresponding to $R_0/2$ and submerged in a gaussian noise of standard deviation 1,

the signals s_1 and s_2 having respectively the same probability distribution (the probability that s_1 or $s_2 = 0$ being 0·5 and that s_1 or $s_2 = \sqrt{R_0}$ being 0·5), but, fluctuating in an independent way if the frequencies of transmission used are fairly different[1] and the two noises are independent.

Since if we add the signals at each receiver's output we could have

— a noise of standard deviation $\sqrt{2}$

— a signal $s_3 = s_1 + s_2$

or again

— a noise of standard deviation 1

— and a signal $s = s_1/\sqrt{2} + s_2/\sqrt{2}$.

We could then carry out the usual operations on the set (s+noise) (with a threshold such that $P_f = 10^{-3}$): what do we obtain in this case?

— the probability that $s_1/\sqrt{2} = 0$ is 0·5

— the probability that $s_1/\sqrt{2} = \sqrt{R_0/2}$ is 0·5

— the probability that $s_2/\sqrt{2} = 0$ is 0·5

— the probability that $s_2/\sqrt{2} = \sqrt{R_0/2}$ is 0·5

[1] Consider a target whose largest dimension is d. The number of petals (the marguerite effect) of its radiation pattern is of the order of $5d/\lambda$, i.e. $(5d/c)F$, where F is the frequency used and c the speed of light. We could consider, *grosso modo*, that if the frequency had changed by a quantity ΔF such that this number is increased by 1, the pattern has completely changed. This happens for $\Delta F \approx c/5d$. We could consider that this gives the order of size of the frequency jump that is necessary to obtain an equivalent echoing area independent of the first.
Numerical application: $d = 10$ m, $\Delta F \approx 10$ MHz.

in other words

— the probability that $s = 0$ is 0·25
— the probability that $s = \sqrt{R_0/2}$ is 0·5
— the probability that $s = \sqrt{2R_0}$ is 0·25.

The mean detection probability associated with such a radar is therefore equal to

0·50 × probability of detection of a non-fluctuating target for $R_0/2$
+0·25 × probability of detection of a non-fluctuating target for $2R_0$.

And we get the final results as shown in the following table (see fig. 5.22).

R_0 (dB)	P_d
3	0·05
6	0·14
9	0·29
12	0·47
15	0·67
18	0·75
20	0·75

With the same transmitted power, the use of a *diversity* radar (with two channels and addition before threshold) has enabled us to improve considerably the detection probability for relatively high values of R_0.

Figure 5.23 shows the distribution of amplitude of s in the case of classical radar (fig. 5.23(a)) and in the case of a diversity radar (fig. 5.23(b)).

If we now return to the case of a complex target it is logical to expect that the use of a diversity radar modifies to a good measure the curve drawn with a continuous line in fig. 5.21, showing the variation of the detection probability of a complex target as a function of R_0.

We see this if we compare

— the distribution of the amplitude of the useful signal (the noise being kept at a level such that its standard deviation is 1) in the case of a complex target and a normal radar:

$$p_1(s) = \frac{2s}{R_0} \exp\left(-s^2/R_0\right)$$

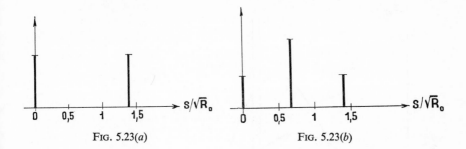

FIG. 5.23(a)   FIG. 5.23(b)

— the distribution of amplitude $p_1(s)$ in the case of a complex target and a diversity radar with two channels (addition before threshold):

$$p_1(s) = 2 \exp\left(-2s^2/R_0\right)\left[2\frac{s}{R_0}\exp\left(-2s^2/R_0\right) + \Theta\left(\frac{s\sqrt{2}}{\sqrt{R_0}}\right) \times \sqrt{\frac{\pi}{2}}\left(\frac{4s^2}{R_0} - 1\right)\frac{1}{\sqrt{R_0}}\right]$$

$$\left[\text{where } \Theta(x) = \frac{2}{\sqrt{\pi}}\int_0^x \exp\left(-t^2\right)\mathrm{d}t\right]^1$$

Figure 5.24 shows the curves giving $p_1(s)\sqrt{R_0}$ as a function of $s/\sqrt{R_0}$ in these three cases. We see that the distribution of amplitude of s with a diversity radar is closer to the distribution of a non-fluctuating target.

The calculation of the detection probability corresponding to the diversity radar follows from the curves of fig. 5.24 and the result is shown in fig. 5.21 (the curve in dotted lines). We see here that

— if we were interested in a detection probability of 0·5 the diversity radar does not practically give any advantage;

— if we were interested in a detection probability of 0·9, in the case of very complex target, the diversity radar with two channels permits an economy of nearly 3 dB over the transmitted power (we could transmit 50 per cent of the power required while it is not the diversity radar).

If we use a diversity radar with a large number of channels, say n, the result is as if we had a constant useful signal s_0 equal to $\sqrt{n}$ times the mean value of s corresponding to R_0/n, accompanied by a noise of unit standard deviation, with

$$s_0 = \sqrt{n}\int_0^\infty \frac{2ns^2}{R_0}\exp\left(-ns^2/R_0\right)\mathrm{d}s,$$

$$s_0 = \sqrt{R_0\frac{\pi}{4}}.$$

---

[1] The calculation leading to this formula is classical, relatively complicated, and does not have any interest in itself, not more than the formula itself: only the curve in dotted lines of fig. 5.24 is interesting.

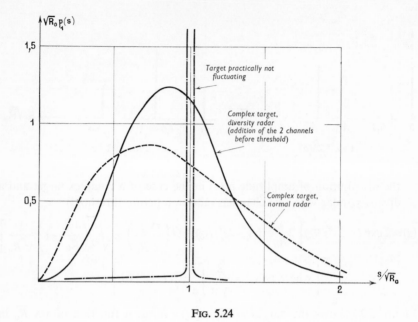

FIG. 5.24

We obtain a result as if we had a non-fluctuating target having an equivalent echoing area equal to 0·79 times its mean value. Finally we could consider that the noise fluctuation causes a loss of 1 dB.

In practice, if we are interested in detection probabilities less than 0·9 and also in false alarm probabilities greater than 10^{-10}, we could consider (modulo 0·5 dB) that n is large if it is at least equal to 4.

Figure 5.25 gives the possible diagram of a pulsed diversity radar with two channels.

Transmitter 1 transmits pulses of 4 μs, 1 MW of peak power at 3,000 MHz at instants 0·4 ms, 8 ms, 12 ms . . .

Transmitter 2 transmits pulses of 4 μs, 1 MW of peak power at 3,100 MHz at the instants 8 μs, 4,008 μs, 8,008 μs, 12,008 μs.

Therefore the duplexor, the antenna and the whole microfrequency guidance system never have to support peak powers greater than 1 MW while if transmitters 1 and 2 transmitted simultaneously, the peak power in these elements could at times attain 4 MW.

This situation causes the received signal at 3,000 MHz to be delayed by 8 μs before combining the signals at the output of the two receivers.

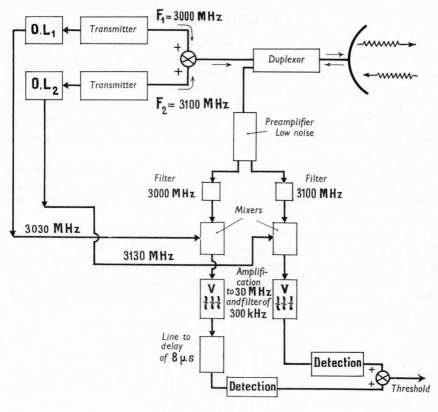

FIG. 5.25

Frequency agility radars

We obtain an analogous effect of reduction in target fluctuation, when in the course of radar measurement we change a certain number n times the central frequency of transmission (for example, by transmitting each time with a central frequency chosen arbitrarily in a given frequency band, thus obtaining a radar called a random frequency radar). In this case, we could obtain in some way the equivalent of what we would obtain with a diversity radar of n channels. Hence, for a frequency agility radar transmitting more than four different frequencies during radar measurement, a target could be considered non-fluctuating.[1]

---

[1] With a constant equivalent echoing area, slightly less than the average equivalent echoing area (of 1 dB for a very fluctuating target, of 0 to 2 dB in the general case).

5.10 CONCLUSIONS

When we are in the presence of a target we could define in a valid way its mean equivalent echoing area at a given frequency, for a given presentation, for a given polarisation, and in a free space.

This signifies, in fact, that the equivalent echoing area of the target fluctuates about this mean value, in general slowly in comparison with the time of the measurement of a radar (which rarely exceeds a few tenths of a millisecond, except in tracking radar, whose antenna remains permanently directed towards the objective).

The direction Δ of the centre of reflection fluctuates at the same time, generally around a mean direction Δ_m, passing near the target's centre of gravity, such that Δ is near to Δ_m when the equivalent echoing area is large and is far away from Δ_m when the equivalent echoing area is small.

This correlation between the direction of the centre of reflection and the level of the signal received by the radar could, on the other hand, allow the elimination of the wrong angular measurements. The effects of the fluctuations of the target are minimised when, during the measurement, we use many central frequencies which are quite different, and are practically cancelled when the number of these frequencies exceeds 4.

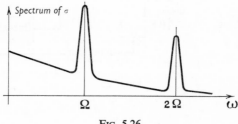

FIG. 5.26

It is to be noted that since the equivalent echoing area of a target is a random function of time, there is a spectrum which corresponds to it. This spectrum is normally simple, its amplitude gradually decreasing with frequency. However, if the target contains objects rotating with a certain velocity Ω (expressed in radians per second), e.g. helices, compressor blades, etc., the spectrum generally possesses at the frequency Ω and its harmonics 2Ω, 3Ω . . ., points which could be very high (see fig. 5.26).

All this is true only in an infinite free space, for a given presentation, and with a given polarisation of waves. In reality, there are at least two restrictions to be noted:

— First, that the ground could give to the equivalent echoing area of a low flying target a behaviour pattern very different due to the reflection on the ground;

— Second, that the atmosphere could lead to an absorption more or less significant of the powers in question (of which it is necessary to take account in the radar equation).

It must not be forgotten also that the atmosphere could, in certain cases, reflect the waves. It is thus that some clouds behave as targets of very high equivalent echoing area in rectilinear polarisation such that the targets located inside them become indistinguishable. This effect is generally less seen in circular polarisation (hence the use of these to eliminate clouds). When the targets are not clouds but metallic targets (aircraft, etc.) it is interesting to know the behaviour of the target for different polarisations used. This problem has not been studied in great detail.

It seems, however, that in general, the mean equivalent echoing area of an aircraft is practically the same (to within 50 per cent) whether the used wave is horizontal or vertical or circular polarisation.

In fact the "radarists" should not forget that the propagation of waves is not always carried out in a straight line, they should take account of the phenomena of tropospheric refraction, ionospheric reflection,[1] etc.

IMPORTANT REMARK

If the equivalent echoing area of a target varies with the central frequency of transmission we easily conceive that the position of the centre of reflection also varies with frequency. This signifies that when the radar changes its central transmission frequency during the time necessary for the measurement of the radial velocity of the targets, we often measure the velocity of the centre of reflection during the same time. This speed could be very high.

We cannot therefore eliminate the fixed echoes with a radar transmission whose central frequency varies during the time of the measurement (for example, by more than $3 \cdot 10^{-3}$).

---

[1] Cf. in particular to the course by Mirbeck at Ecole Supérieure d'Electricité and the course by M. Thourel at Ecole Nationale Supérieure de l'Aéronautique.

CHAPTER 6

MEASUREMENT OF ANGLES WITH
A RADAR

6.1 GENERAL

If a radar, by definition, is an instrument designed to measure the distance between itself and a target (even though some of them serve only to measure the radial speed of targets) it is evident that by itself this information is not enough to locate the target.

Moreover, at least in an approximate way, the determination of the target's direction has been made by radar since the beginning.

In any case, in order to avoid transmission of a very high power, we need to concentrate the transmission in a chosen direction or a chosen plane.

Historically, we were thus led to make radars which used directional antennae transmitting at a given time mainly in a vertical half-plane and regularly rotating about a vertical axis. These radars, called panoramic radars, receive a significant signal from the target only when the antenna is directed towards it, thus permitting an approximate measurement of the target's bearing.

An approximate measurement of the target's altitude was easily made in an analogous way with the help of an aerial concentrating its transmission in a plane but nodding round an horizontal axis contained in this plane and perpendicular to the direction of the target. As the aerial of such a height-finding radar is nodding the signal received is normally maximal while the target is in the plane of maximal radiation, which thus allows us to determine the target's elevation and hence its altitude (since the radial distance is known).

For tracking radars which are meant to locate the direction of a unique target, the panoramic and height-finding functions were obtained simultaneously with the same aerial. This aerial, transmitting mainly in one direction, was capable of rotating round a direction Δ (generating a cone of revolution with Δ as the axis). The final aim of this operation was to force Δ to be directed towards the target, which normally happens when the signal received is constant during the rotation of the aerial. In practice, in such a radar (called a scanning radar) the movement of the radar's beam round Δ was obtained by placing before the

207

reflector a primary feed in the focal plane but offset the axis $\varDelta$, the rotation of this primary feed round the axis $\varDelta$ assuring the scanning required.

Then, over a period of time, the angular measurements have been improved in many ways:

— by the use of digital systems of extraction associated, for example, with panoramic radars;

— by the use of procedures called "monopulse" intended to measure the bearing or the elevation of targets and also permitting their simultaneous measurement when their value is known approximately.

6.2   PANORAMIC RADAR [1]

6.2.1   Functioning over cooperative targets in continuous waves (16)

Let us consider a panoramic radar which has to measure the bearing of a target called "cooperative" because it transmits a signal, which we assume to be continuous and of a constant level, very much higher than the level of the naturally reflected signal against the target (skin-return), the target being equipped with a transponder.

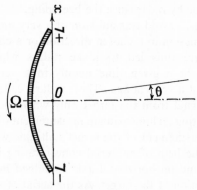

Fig. 6.1

The radar antenna is assumed to rotate round a vertical axis at an angular speed Ω (rd/S). The gain (in tension) of this antenna in the considered elevation, at a given time, is a function of its bearing θ, i.e. $g(\theta)$.

Let us suppose, in order to make things easier, that the cross-section of the antenna is rectangular and such that every section by a horizontal plane is illuminated (by a primary feed, if it is a reflector) in the same way. There

---

[1] The paper of S. Drabovitch cited in the Bibliography is highly recommended. It would usefully complement the notions given in Section 6.2.1 and more generally, those given in this chapter.

exists a simple relation between this gain $g(\theta)$ and the illumination $A(v)$ of the antenna, $A(v)$ being expressed as a function of spatial frequency $x/\lambda = v$ of the antenna (see fig. 6.1). $A(v)$ is zero if $|v| > L/\lambda$, where $2L$ is the span of the antenna.

In effect, $g(\theta)$ is the Fourier transform of $A(v)$.

When the antenna rotates, the signal received (or resulting) from a target placed at the bearing θ_0 varies according to the expression

$$Kg(\Omega t - \theta_0)$$

To locate the bearing θ_0 of the target would imply the determination of the time t_0 when the signal $Kg(\Omega t - \theta_0)$ is maximal.

The problem is similar to that already discussed in Chapter 3. The error with which we could measure this time is gaussian random variable of zero mean value and standard deviation

$$\frac{1}{2\pi B \sqrt{R}}$$

where $R = E/b$. E is the energy of the signal received, b the spectral density of the accompanying noise, and B is the second order moment of the spectrum of $Kg(\Omega t)$. S. Drabovitch has shown:

(a) That the energy E of the signal was only a function of the variation of the gain of the antenna versus elevation (and also of the transponder's power and aerial-target distance) and of the time T (at least if this time were large enough), but it was not a function of the pattern $g(\theta)$ of the antenna in bearing—and this by definition itself of the antenna gain.

(b) That the value of B could be evaluated in a simple way. Since the Fourier transform of $Kg(\Omega t)$ is equal to $A(f/\Omega)$ (modulo a factor) we have,

$$B^2 = \frac{\displaystyle\int_{-\infty}^{+\infty} f^2 \, |A^2(f/\Omega)| \, \mathrm{d}f}{\displaystyle\int_{-\infty}^{+\infty} |A^2(f/\Omega)| \, \mathrm{d}f},$$

$$B^2 = \Omega^2 \frac{\displaystyle\int_{-v_0}^{+v_0} v^2 \, |A^2(v)| \, \mathrm{d}v}{\displaystyle\int_{-v_0}^{+v_0} |A^2(v)| \, \mathrm{d}v} = \Omega^2 B_v^2,$$

with

$$B_v^2 = \frac{\displaystyle\int_{-v_0}^{+v_0} v^2 \, |A^2(v)| \, \mathrm{d}v}{\displaystyle\int_{-v_0}^{+v_0} |A^2(v)| \, \mathrm{d}v}$$

P

where $v_0 = L/\lambda$ is the close-out frequency (spatial) of the antenna and B_v is the moment of the second order of $|A(v)|$. (For uniformly illuminated antenna, $B_v = L/\lambda\sqrt{3}$.)

Thus the standard deviation of the error committed while measuring t_0 can be written as

$$\frac{1}{2\pi\Omega B_v\sqrt{R}}$$

and the standard deviation of the error committed over the measurement of θ_0 can be written as

$$\frac{1}{2\pi B_v\sqrt{R}}.$$

This is an expression completely analogous to Woodward's formula where R—at least under certain conditions—does not depend on the pattern in bearing but on the time of measurement and $A(v)$ performs the same role for the angular measurement as $\Phi(f)$, the Fourier transform of the transmitted signal, does for the measurement of the distance.

In particular, the quality of the angular measurement depends on $|A(v)|$ and not on the phase of $A(v)$.

All this is true only under the condition that the work at the receiving end is done well.

We could deduce that the discriminating power in the plane depends, with the reservations made in sub-section 3.6.3.1, only on the form of the function $|A(v)|$ and that it could not be better than

$$\frac{1}{2v_0} = \frac{\lambda}{2L}.$$

6.2.2   Functioning over a cooperative target in pulse conditions

If the transponder transmits a periodic train of pulses we could no longer say that we continuously receive a signal $Kg(\Omega t - \theta_0)$. We have only a sampling of this signal. In this case, the determination of the most probable position of the maximum could be made theoretically if the sampling frequency is greater than $2\Omega v_0 = 2L\Omega/\lambda$, on condition that the calculator is highly sophisticated—which is rarely the case.

6.2.3   Functioning over a non-cooperative target

In this case the problem is different for two reasons:

— first the signal received varies as $K|g^2(\Omega t - \theta_0)|$;

— and second in certain cases, the target fluctuates in such a way that K is no longer a constant.

The occurrence of this second characteristic will be examined in part later.

The first characteristic leads us to the fact that $|A(v)|$ is no longer the key curve but the autocorrelation function of $A(v)$, say $\rho_A(v)$. It follows that the extreme limit of the resolution could not be better than $1/4v_0$ (instead of $1/2v_0$), i.e. $\lambda/4L$, and this under the same reservations as those made in sub-section 3.6.3.1.

But the general behaviour remains almost the same (the standard deviation of the error committed over the measurement of θ_0 is inversely proportional to the square root of the ratio R).

REMARK

In practice, the signal received from a target could very often be written as

$$y(\theta) = K \exp(-2 \cdot 8\theta^2/\alpha^2)$$

where α is the 3 dB width of the beam (of transmission or of reception, in the case where the same antenna serves for both transmission and reception) for at least all weak enough values of θ/α.

It could therefore be written as a function of time in the form

$$y(t) = K \exp(-2 \cdot 8\Omega^2 t^2/\alpha^2)$$

If we use formula (22) of sub-section 3.6.4 to determine the time which would separate two signals so that we may distinguish them, then with these hypotheses we find a time interval equal to

$$0 \cdot 75 \, \frac{\alpha}{\Omega}$$

i.e. an angular resolution equal to $0 \cdot 75 \, \alpha$.

We could distinguish between two targets by the difference in their bearings with a panoramic radar only if their bearings differ by more than three-quarters of the beamwidth in bearing when the same antenna is used at the transmission side and the reception side.

(It goes without saying that if we could distinguish the targets by the difference in their radial speeds or radial distances, then the fact that they have the same bearing does not prevent us from distinguishing them. This commonsense remark has some relevance.)

6.3 GENERAL PRINCIPLE OF MONOPULSE RADARS

Figure 6.2 shows the radiation pattern in the vertical plane of maximal radiation of the antenna of a panoramic radar.

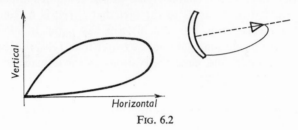

FIG. 6.2

Such a pattern is generally obtained by placing a unique primary feed in the focus of the parabolic reflector (slightly deformed in order to obtain the cosecant square).

Let us suppose that the antenna is composed of a parabolic reflector and two horns situated in the same vertical plane on the two sides of the focus (see fig. 6.3).

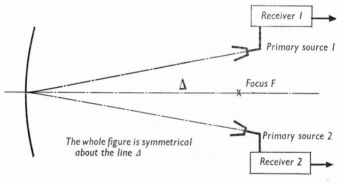

FIG. 6.3

It is clear that if the two primary feeds transmit, for example, identical radiations, receivers 1 and 2 would receive, from a target situated on the axis Δ, two signals of the same amplitude and in phase.

On the other hand, from a target which is not on the axis, receivers 1 and 2 would generally each receive a signal 1 and a signal 2, these signals being in general of different amplitudes and not in phase.

The comparison—either in phase or in amplitude—of the signals simultaneously received[1] by receivers 1 and 2 could therefore, in a certain way, allow us

---

[1] The expression "monopulse" comes precisely from the fact that the measurement is made over the signals received simultaneously coming from the same unique transmitted signal.

to determine the position of the target. In this case the radiation pattern of the antenna is that shown by fig. 6.4.

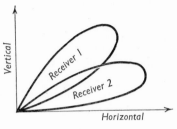

FIG. 6.4

In this way at each period of recurrence during the passing of the antenna over the target we could proceed to determine the target's elevation. It is evident that such a determination is possible only when the signals received by the two receivers are of a sufficiently high level; otherwise we would be led to compare either the phases or the amplitudes of the noises of each receiver, which normally have only a distant relation with the elevation of the target.

A priori, therefore, the determination of the elevations by such procedures called "monopulse" are valid only when the value of R for every reception channel is sufficient, i.e. when the antenna passes over the target.

Nothing prevents us from introducing n horns over the focal line of the reflector in such a way as to have n reception channels, the comparison being made at the same time between channels 1 and 2, between channels 2 and 3, . . ., between channels $(n-1)$ and n.

In such a case, if the highest level signal received is in channel 4, for example,

— the signal received in channel 3 is quite strong,

— the signal received in channel 5 is weak,

— and the signal received in the other channels are very weak.

We deduce from this that the elevation of the target is not far from the axis Δ_{34} of the two beams 3 and 4, and the comparison of signals 3 and 4 gives us the exact elevation of the target.

But let us suppose that we have two targets and that they cannot be distinguished either by their radial distances or by their radial speeds or by their bearings, and that one of them, A, is almost on the axis Δ_{23} and the other, B, on the axis Δ_{45}.

Receiver 2 receives a significant signal coming from A.

Receiver 3 receives a significant signal coming from A.

Receiver 4 receives a significant signal coming from B.

Receiver 5 receives a significant signal coming from B.

Comparison 2–3 has a meaning (or interpolation 2–3).

Comparison 4–5 has a meaning.

Comparison 3–4 has no meaning.

But, in fact, it is very difficult to know in this case which interpolations have a meaning and which do not. We could also say, in a way, that resolution in elevation is less fine than the difference of elevations between the two axes $\Delta_{j-1, j}$ and $\Delta_{j+1, j+2}$.

Finally, we see that in this case we are led to consider a zone of confusion (or of ambiguity) in a plane of four dimensions:

— radial distance,

— radial speed,

— bearing,

— elevation,

inside which it is not possible to separate targets.

6.4 ANGULAR FLUCTUATIONS OF TARGETS

As the procedures of angular measurements by means of radars have become more and more exact, we have begun to observe certain strange phenomena. For example, in one case, with an aircraft flying along a straight line in the direction of the radar the angle being measured by the radar was subject to arbitrary changes. On average, the radar determined the direction of the aircraft but from time to time it indicated quite astonishing directions.

We knew, of course, that the direction of an aircraft with a wing span of 20 m situated at a distance of 10,000 m from the radar could only be determined to within an error of 2 mrads. This is because in physics we are always taught not to seek a solution with an error of less than E to a problem whose size is defined to within an error of E (we learn this, but seldom remember it)! But we certainly did not ever expect to see such an accurate and expensive radar committing such crucial mistakes.

It was only after finding out that the instants of aberrations of the radar corresponded to the instants when the signal received from the target was minimal that we knew that the radar did not, in fact, determine the direction of the target but only that of the normal to the equiphase surface of the re-radiation of the target (called the direction of the centre of reflection), and that this direction could be different from that of the target when the signal received was minimal (see Chapter 5).

Let us consider the angular measurement by means of a radar. We recall (Chapter 5) that if the amplitude of the field varies along the equiphase surface, then this variation is slow, i.e. at every point of the antenna (of the wave collector) we could consider the field received to be constant. Now, when an antenna rotates round a fixed point, the signal received by it is maximal when every point of the antenna is illuminated by fields in phase, i.e. when the antenna

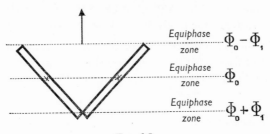

Fig. 6.5

is in the plane tangent to the equiphase surface of re-radiation of the target. When the antenna of a panoramic radar rotates round a vertical axis, the maximum of the signal received is obtained when its principal plane of radiation has the bearing of the direction of the centre of reflection (normal to the equiphase zone, etc.).

Moreover, since the equiphase surfaces are parallel, when the antenna generates a cone of revolution (scanning radar), the level received during the period of revolution is constant (if this period is small in relation to the speed of the target's fluctuation) when the axis of the cone is the direction of the centre of reflection.

In the case of a monopulse radar with two receivers, the result obtained is as if it possessed two identical antennae whose centres are either coinciding or parallel.

When the bisecting plane of these two antennae contains the direction of the centre of reflection, on the one hand the signal received by the two antennae have the same levels, and on the other hand they are in phase (see fig. 6.5).

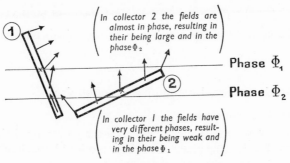

Fig. 6.6

But, in the general case, if the bisecting plane does not contain the direction of the centre of reflection, the signals received by each of the antennae have different levels and different phases (see fig. 6.6).

We thus see that we have two different methods of determining the direction of the centre of reflection:

— either by equality of phases of the signals received by the two antennae;

— or by the equality of the levels received by the two antennae.

In any event, in the general case (where the antenna's dimension is small in relation to the irregularities of the equiphase surfaces of re-radiation), a mono-pulse radar also determines the direction of the centre of reflection.

Errors in angle measurement by radar

The errors in angle measurement by radars come mainly from four different sources:

1. The fluctuation of the centre of reflection, which we could reduce by using a diversity radar or a frequency agile radar.

2. The difference between theory and practice (faults of aerial diagrams, receivers, etc.).

3. The parameters of the measurement (beamwidth, extraction criteria).

4. The noise which accompanies the useful information.

In the following paragraphs, 1 will not be studied, 2 will be partially studied, while 3 and 4 will be studied in detail by means of examples.

6.5 DESCRIPTION OF MONOPULSE RADARS

We have seen that in a monopulse radar we obtain a result as if we have two identical antennae whose centres are either coincident or not and which are either parallel or not, and that we could use two different means to locate the direction of the centre of reflection,

— either by equality of phases of the signals received by the two antennae;

— or by the equality of the amplitudes of the signals received by the two antennae.

6.5.1 Amplitude monopulse and phase monopulse

6.5.1.1 Amplitude monopulse

In amplitude monopulse, the two antennae are so arranged that, whatever the direction of the bisecting plane, the signals received by each of the antennae have the same phase (as shown in fig. 6.7).

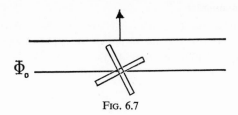

FIG. 6.7

In other words, the two antennae have the same phase centre. Figure 6.8 shows the process most commonly used to obtain in a practical way two antennae which are at a certain angle to each other and which have almost the same phase centre.

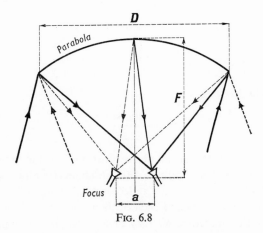

FIG. 6.8

From this process we obtain the equivalent of two antennae which are at an angle a/F to each other (a being the distance of the primary feeds and F the focal distance of the parabola) and whose phase centres are at a distance a approximately between each other. (They are not entirely coincident.)

Numerical example:

Let

— S Band (10 cm),

— $D = 7$ metres,

— $F = 5$ metres,

— $a = 0 \cdot 1$ metres,

— $a/F = 1°$,

be the equivalent of two antennae with an aperture of 7 m, at an angle of 1° to each other, with their phase centres being nearly 0·1 m apart.

6.5.1.2 Phase monopulse

In phase monopulse the two antennae are so arranged that, whatever the orientation of the set, the signals received by each antenna have the same amplitude (and phases different from $\Delta\Phi$).

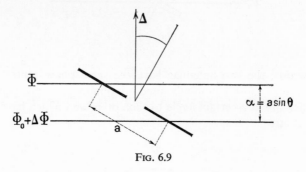

FIG. 6.9

This is represented in fig. 6.9.

We see in this figure that

$$\Delta\Phi = \frac{2\pi a \sin\theta}{\lambda},$$

where a is the distance between the phase centres of the antennae.

We obtain the equivalent of these two antennae (parallel) by the process shown in fig. 6.10 by using a single reflector and two primary feeds, both of which are situated at the focus and each of them illuminating only a part of the reflector (the two illuminated zones may or may not be overlapping).

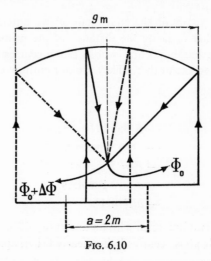

FIG. 6.10

For example, in order to obtain two phase centres at 2 m apart and with the same lobe aperture as in the preceding case (with the same frequency) we will be led to use an antenna whose aperture is nearly $7+2 = 9$ m.

6.5.2 Processing of R.F. signals in monopulse radars

Thus, at least diagrammatically, we find that we have two types of monopulse radars, each very different from the other: i.e.

— the amplitude monopulse, in which the two signals coming from a target are in phase but have different amplitudes;

— the phase monopulse, in which the two signals coming from a target have the same amplitude but a difference in phase.

6.5.2.1 Amplitude monopulse

Let us denote by $G_1(\theta)$ the expression giving the amplitude of one of the signals S_1 received, versus the angle θ (the angle between the target's bearing and the plane of symmetry of the antenna), and by $G_2(\theta)$ the corresponding expression for the other signal S_2.

If the antenna is symmetrical, we could write

$$G_1(\theta) = G_2(-\theta).$$

If θ remains constant (a given direction of the target) but with the target being more or less near or more or less powerful, the levels of the signals S_1 and S_2 are both multiplied by the same coefficient.

The problem consists in obtaining from S_1 and S_2 a signal E which is zero for $\theta = 0$ and a linear function of (approximately) θ.

There are many known solutions to this problem.

6.5.2.1.1 *Processing in amplitude*: Radars called "amplitude–amplitude monopulse".

The two solutions most used are to form either

$$E = \log \frac{S_1}{S_2} \quad \text{or} \quad E = \frac{S_1 - S_2}{S_1 + S_2}$$

For most radars, the function $G(\theta)$ could be written as

$$G_1(\theta) = G_0 \exp\left[-k(\theta - \theta_0)^2\right]$$

(and often one of the difficulties in constructing amplitude monopulse radars is to obtain the most precision with this law).

Under these conditions:

$$E = \log \frac{S_1}{S_2} = \log \frac{G_1}{G_2}$$

becomes

$$E = k[(\theta+\theta_0)^2 - (\theta-\theta_2)^2] = 4k\theta\theta_0.$$

We thus have a signal E which vanishes with θ and is a linear function of θ. In this expression k characterises the width of a lobe and $2\theta_0$ the distance between the lobes (see fig. 6.11).

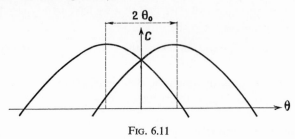

FIG. 6.11

The larger k is, the narrower are the lobes.

In practice, signals S_1 and S_2 are amplified in logarithmic amplifiers as identically as possible, then the signals at the output of these logarithmic amplifiers are subtracted from each other (in video, for example). We easily understand that the difficulty in constructing these radars is found here. If we assume, for example, that the two amplifiers are quite logarithmic but have different gains we no longer get $E = k\theta\theta_0$ but $E = 4k\theta\theta_0 + E_0$ (see fig. 6.12).

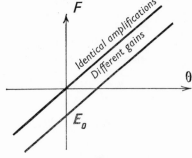

FIG. 6.12

If we form the expression

$$E = \frac{S_1 - S_2}{S_1 + S_2} = \frac{G_1 - G_2}{G_1 + G_2}$$

we also obtain an expression which becomes zero for $\theta = 0$ and which can be written as

$$E = \text{th}\,(2k\theta\theta_0)$$

i.e. an increasing function of θ whose central part (θ weak) is linear.

In practice, we form in microwave (with the help of 3 dB couplers or magic T's) the sum $\Sigma = S_1 + S_2$ and the difference $\Delta = S_1 - S_2$. We amplify Σ and Δ independently and we take the quotient at the end of the channel of reception (in video, for example).

What happens if the two reception channels have different gains after this? Such an event would mean no longer determining E, but kE. The signal obtained vanishes for $\theta = 0$ but the inclination $dE/d\theta$ is no longer true (see fig. 6.13).

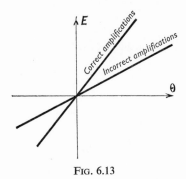

FIG. 6.13

We thus see that the two processes are not to be arbitrarily used.

In the case of a tracking radar, it is necessary for the signal of error E to be zero for $\theta = 0$, but the inclination $dE/d\theta$ could vary a little without being very problematical.

On the contrary, in the case of a volumetric radar, it matters little that, for $\theta = 0$, E is not zero; but it is desirable that $d\theta/dE$ be constant in relation to time, and it is very useful that if it is versus θ.

In the case of a tracking radar we shall very often prefer the solution

$$E = \frac{S_1 - S_2}{S_1 + S_2}$$

and in the case of a volumetric radar we could prefer

$$E = \log \frac{S_1}{S_2}$$

6.5.2.1.2 *Processing in phase*: Radars called "amplitude-phase monopulse".

The main difficulty of the process which we have just described is that it requires the different channels to have exactly the same gain. We could moderate this fault by using, for example, the following procedure:

We form, firstly, the sum $\Sigma = S_1 + S_2$ and the difference $\Delta = S_1 - S_2$ in microwave before any amplification or change in frequency. We thus obtain two signals in phase (or in opposite phase if $S_1 - S_2 < 0$).

With the help of 3 dB couplers we form again in microwave

$$\Sigma + j\Delta \quad \text{and} \quad \Sigma - j\Delta.$$

We thus obtain two signals in phase if $\Delta = 0$ and, if Δ is different from zero, two signals whose difference in phase Φ is given by

$$\Phi = 2 \text{ Arc tan } \frac{\Delta}{\Sigma}$$

(see fig. 6.14), i.e. with the hypothesis of the preceding paragraph,

$$\tan \frac{\Phi}{2} = \text{th} (2k\theta\theta_0)$$

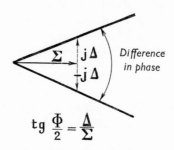

FIG. 6.14

This difference in phase Φ is measured in intermediary frequency by a known method and constitutes the measure of θ. The curve giving Φ versus θ passes through the origin ($\Phi = 0$ for $\theta = 0$) and it is linear around the value $\theta = 0$. We note that if the gains of the two channels are different, then this does not have any incidence over the measure of Φ.

On the contrary, if one of the channels dephases a signal with respect to the other, this will have the effect of translating the curve $\Phi = f(\theta)$, which will no

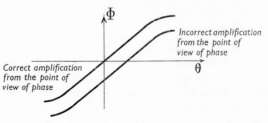

FIG. 6.15

longer pass through the origin (see fig. 6.15). However, it seems from this point of view that it would be technologically easier to obtain two amplification channels correct in this respect than to obtain two channels having the same gain.

6.5.2.2 Phase monopulse

Our aim here is to measure the difference in phase between the signals S_1 and S_2 (of the same amplitude). This difference in phase Φ being proportional to the sine of the angle θ:

$$\Phi = k \sin \theta$$

The simplest method that comes to mind is to measure Φ. The two reception channels need not have the same gain but they should not dephase each other. We could call such a radar "phase–phase monopulse".

But we could also form the difference $\Delta = S_1 - S_2$ and the sum $\Sigma = S_1 + S_2$. Since

$$S_1 = S_2 \exp(-j\Phi)$$

we obtain

$$\Delta = S_2[1 - \exp(-j\Phi)]$$

$$\Sigma = S_2[1 + \exp(-j\Phi)]$$

and if we form the quotient Δ/Σ, we obtain a purely imaginary number

$$\frac{\Delta}{\Sigma} = \frac{1 - \exp(-j\Phi)}{1 + \exp(-j\Phi)} = j \tan\left(\frac{\Phi}{2}\right)$$

whose absolute value is

$$\left|\frac{\Delta}{\Sigma}\right| = \tan\frac{\Phi}{2}$$

Since the absolute value of a quotient is the quotient of the absolute values, we could measure Φ by measuring the ratio between the amplitudes of the signals Δ and Σ.

In principle, the signals Σ and Δ are directly obtained in microwave and we are referred back to the explanations in sub-section 6.5.2.1.1. In particular, it is essential that the gains of the two channels be the same, in order to prevent $dE/d\theta$ from being incorrect.

(It is clear that before the combination which provides Δ and Σ, it is necessary that the signals S_1 and S_2 have the same delay in order to be sure that E will vanish with θ, the contrary being harmful in the case of a tracking radar.)

6.5.3 Influence of receiver noise on the precision of angular measurements by a monopulse radar

6.5.3.1 Phase monopulse radar

In a phase monopulse radar we are led to measure the difference in phase Φ between the two signals each received by an antenna followed by a receiver, this difference in phase Φ being related to the angle θ to be determined by the relation

$$\Phi = k\theta.$$

The problem is to know how precisely we could define this difference in phase, taking into account the fact that each of the signals is constituted by a useful signal accompanied by a noise.

To simplify the reasoning we could assume (this often corresponds to a practical method) that the useful signal is one of constant amplitude S whose pulsation ω is fixed or variable versus time (classical radars or pulse compression radar), and to find, as simply as possible, how precisely we could define the phase of such a signal when it is accompanied by noise.

Let us therefore consider a signal $S \sin \omega t$ of duration T, having by definition the zero phase, accompanied by a gaussian noise occupying a spectrum of width Δf. It is to be noted that ω is to be considered as the instantaneous pulsation of the signal and could vary versus time during the period T of the measurement. The power of the signal is therefore represented by $S^2/2$ and the energy of the signal during this time of measurement is represented by $S^2 T/2$.

The noise could be written in the form

$$b(t) \sin [\omega t + \varphi(t)],$$

where $b(t)$ and $\varphi(t)$ are random functions of time.

It is to be noted that the mean value of $b^2(t) \sin^2 [\omega t + \varphi(t)]$ represents the mean power of the noise and that the mean value of

$$\frac{b^2(t) [\sin^2 \omega t + \varphi(t)]}{\Delta f}$$

represents the spectral density of the noise.

We also assume that the noise is quite low with respect to the useful signal (R being quite high), which is justified by what we saw in Chapter 3. Under these conditions, the set (signal + noise) can be written as

$$S \sin \omega t + b(t)[\sin \omega t + \varphi(t)] = \sin \omega t(S + b \cos \varphi) + \cos \omega t(b \sin \varphi).$$

At a given time the apparent phase Φ_a of the set (signal + noise) is not generally zero, and it is given by

$$\tan \Phi_a = \frac{b \sin \varphi}{S + b \cos \varphi}$$

$$\Phi_a \approx \frac{b(t) \sin \varphi(t)}{S}$$

This measurement of Φ_a could be repeated a certain number of times and we could take the average of the values obtained. However, it has been indicated that we can only make $T\Delta f$ independent measurements.

Therefore, the value of Φ measured appears as a random gaussian variable whose variance is given by

$$\frac{\overline{b^2 \sin \varphi}}{S^2 T \Delta f} = \frac{1}{2R}$$

Instead of measuring a phase zero, the presence of noise leads us to find a value different from zero, this error appearing as a gaussian variable of zero mean value and of standard deviation equal to $1/\sqrt{2R}$.

When we wish to measure the phase of a useful signal accompanied by a noise, we make an error which is gaussian, of standard deviation equal to $1/\sqrt{2R}$ (in radians).

Thus, in a phase monopulse radar, when we receive two signals of the same power in each of the reception channels accompanied by noises (independent) of the same characteristics, we make an error in the measurement of the difference in phase between these two signals, whose standard deviation is equal to $1/\sqrt{R}$ (in radians), R characterising the ratio

$$\frac{\text{Energy received over the duration of the measurement}}{\text{Spectral density of the noise}}$$

for one or other of the signals.

The error due to the noise in the measurement of the angle therefore appears to have a standard deviation inversely proportional to $\sqrt{R}$. We thus find again a result analogous to that already obtained for the error in the measurement of the distance or radial speed by means of a radar.

6.5.3.2 Amplitude monopulse radar

Let us place ourselves in the situation where the measurement of θ is made by the calculation of

$$E = \log \left(\frac{S_1}{S_2}\right) = \log S_1 - \log S_2$$

Q

with

$$S_1 = S_0 \exp[-k(\theta - \theta_0)^2]$$

and

$$S_2 = S_0 \exp[-k(\theta + \theta_0)^2]$$

assuming that S_1 is accompanied by a noise b_1 and S_2 by a noise b_2 (independent gaussian noises occupying a spectrum of width Δf while the useful signals last for a period T).

Instead of measuring $E = \log S_1 - \log S_2$, we shall measure in fact

$$E + dE = \log (S_1 + b_1) - \log (S_2 + b_2)$$

with

$$dE = \frac{b_1}{S_1} - \frac{b_2}{S_2}$$

Since we can make $T\Delta f$ independent measurements, it finally comes that the variance of the ultimate error that we commit on the measurement of E can be written in the form

$$\frac{1}{2R_1} + \frac{1}{2R_2}$$

For $\theta = 0$ the two signals received (S_1 and S_2) are, on average, equal if they are conveyed in analogous receivers (i.e. having same characteristics for the noises in the two receivers). We therefore have

$$R_1 = R_2 = R$$

and the standard deviation of the error committed in the measurement of E is $1/\sqrt{R}$.

We therefore get a result very similar to that already obtained for phase monopulse.

6.5.4 Uniqueness of monopulse procedures

We have made the customary distinction between amplitude monopulse and phase monopulse. This section aims to show that these two kinds of monopulse are not in fact different, but two different methods of doing the same thing.

6.5.4.1 Amplitude-phase monopulse and phase monopulse

Figure 6.16 represents diagrammatically a complete amplitude monopulse antenna in a field of equiphases.

We denote by M_1 and M_2 respectively the points on antennae 1 and 2 and by l_1 and l_2 the lengths OM_1 and OM_2 (ordinates of M_1 and M_2: Z_1 and Z_2).

The field of the wave collected by antenna 1 could be written as

$$A_1 = \bar{a} \int_{-L}^{+L} \exp\left(2\pi j Z_1/\lambda\right) dl_1,$$

$2L$ being the span of any one of the two antennae and λ the wavelength used, with

$$Z_1 = l_1 \cos\left(\pi/2 - \alpha - \theta\right) = l_1 \sin\left(\alpha + \theta\right).$$

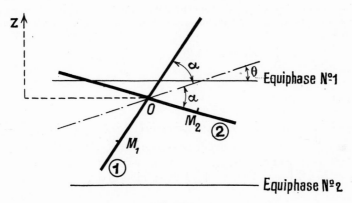

FIG. 6.16

The field of the wave collected by antenna 2 can be written as

$$\bar{A}_2 = \bar{a} \int_{-L}^{+L} \exp\left(2\pi j Z_2/\lambda\right) dl_2,$$

with

$$Z_2 = l_2 \sin\left(\theta - \alpha\right).$$

By replacing Z_1 and Z_2 in terms of l_1 and l_2 and integrating, we obtain

$$\bar{A}_1 = \bar{a}\,\frac{\lambda}{\pi \sin\left(\alpha + \theta\right)} \sin\left\{\frac{2\pi L}{\lambda}\left[\sin\left(\alpha + \theta\right)\right]\right\},$$

$$\bar{A}_2 = \bar{a}\,\frac{\lambda}{\pi \sin\left(\theta - \alpha\right)} \sin\left\{\frac{2\pi L}{\lambda}\left[\sin\left(\theta - \alpha\right)\right]\right\}.$$

It is clear that $\bar{A}_1$ and $\bar{A}_2$ are in phase, equal for $\theta = 0$, and their absolute values are maximal for $\theta = -\alpha$ and $\theta = \alpha$ respectively.

Let us now assume that these signals are processed in phase, as described in sub-section 6.5.2.1.2. Since we form

$$\bar{\Sigma} = \bar{A}_1 + \bar{A}_2 \qquad \text{and} \qquad \bar{\Delta} = \bar{A}_1 - \bar{A}_2,$$

and then

$$\mathscr{X}_1 = \bar{\Sigma} + j\bar{\Delta} \qquad \text{and} \qquad \mathscr{X}_2 = \bar{\Sigma} - j\bar{\Delta},$$

we obtain

$$\mathscr{X}_1 = \bar{a}\left\{\int_{-L}^{+L} \exp\,(2\pi jZ_1/\lambda)(1+j)\mathrm{d}l_1 + \int_{-L}^{+L} \exp\,(2\pi jZ_2/\lambda)(1-j)\mathrm{d}l_2\right\}$$

$$\mathscr{X}_2 = \bar{a}\left\{\int_{-L}^{+L} \exp\,(2\pi jZ_1/\lambda)(1-j)\mathrm{d}l_1 + \int_{-L}^{+L} \exp\,(2\pi jZ_2/\lambda)(1+j)\mathrm{d}l_2\right\}$$

Denoting by x the algebraic distance of O from the variable point of the bisector represented by the dotted line in fig. 6.16 and assuming that α and θ are small, which is the case always, we can write

$$Z_1 = x(\alpha+\theta), \qquad l_1 = x,$$
$$Z_2\dot{} = x(\theta-\alpha), \qquad l_2 = x,$$

and becomes

$$\overline{\mathscr{X}}_1 = \bar{a}\int_{-L}^{+L} \exp\,(2\pi jx\theta/\lambda)\,[\exp\,(2\pi jx\alpha/\lambda)\,(1+j)+\exp\,(2\pi jx\alpha/\lambda)\,(1-j)]\mathrm{d}x,$$

$$\overline{\mathscr{X}}_1 = 2\bar{a}\sqrt{2}\int_{-L}^{+L}\cos\,\left(\frac{2\pi\alpha x}{\lambda}+\frac{\pi}{2}\right)\,\exp\,(2\pi jx\theta/\lambda)\,\mathrm{d}x,$$

and also,

$$\overline{\mathscr{X}}_2 = 2\bar{a}\sqrt{2}\int_{-L}^{+L}\cos\,\left(\frac{2\pi\alpha x}{\lambda}-\frac{\pi}{4}\right)\,\exp\,(2\pi jx\theta/\lambda)\,\mathrm{d}x,$$

where $x\theta$ is the ordinate of the variable point of the dotted line.

The result is as if we had two antennae parallel or coincident, illuminated in a non-uniform way: the signal $\overline{\mathscr{X}}_1$ being received by one of the antennae illuminated mostly on its left, and the signal $\overline{\mathscr{X}}_2$ being received by the other antenna illuminated mostly on its right.

Figure 6.17 shows this result for $L = \lambda/4\alpha$.

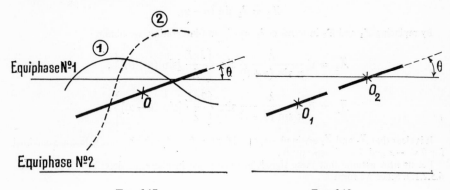

FIG. 6.17   FIG. 6.18

Figure 6.18 shows a set of two antennae for phase monopulse giving a very similar result with the phase centres O_1 and O_2 respectively.

6.5.4.2 Amplitude monopulse and phase-amplitude monopulse

Returning to fig. 6.16, we could now consider the process in which we form

$$\overline{\Sigma} = \overline{A}_1 + \overline{A}_2$$

and

$$\overline{\Delta} = \overline{A}_1 - \overline{A}_2.$$

Similarly, we find that

$$\overline{\Sigma} = \overline{A}_1 + \overline{A}_2 = 2\bar{a} \int_{-L}^{+L} \cos \frac{2\pi\alpha x}{\lambda} \cdot \exp\left(2\pi j x\theta/\lambda\right) dx$$

$$\overline{\Delta} = \overline{A}_1 - \overline{A}_2 = 2\bar{a} \int_{-L}^{+L} j \sin \frac{2\pi\alpha x}{\lambda} \cdot \exp\left(2\pi j x\theta/\lambda\right) dx$$

Figure 6.19(a) shows a method of obtaining $\overline{\Sigma}$ with a single antenna illuminated in a non-uniform way.

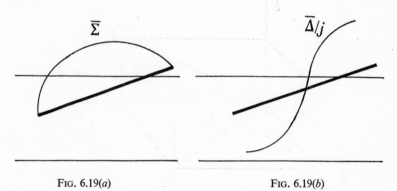

FIG. 6.19(a)   FIG. 6.19(b)

Figure 6.19(b) shows a way of obtaining $\overline{\Delta}/j$ with the same antenna but illuminated in a different way (the two figures for $L = \lambda/4\alpha$).

If we consider the set of antennae for phase monopulse in fig. 6.18 and we assume that we also form $\overline{\Sigma} = \overline{A}_1 + \overline{A}_2$ and $\overline{\Delta} = \overline{A}_1 - \overline{A}_2$ with uniformly illuminated aerials, it is clear that the result obtained is that in figs. 6.20(a) and 6.20(b), whose analogy with figs. 6.19(a) and 619(b) is evident.

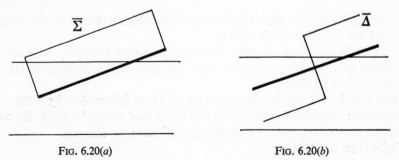

FIG. 6.20(a)   FIG. 6.20(b)

6.5.4.3 Conclusions

Thus this rapid survey has enabled us to understand that all monopulses are in fact systems which process the difference in phase between fields received in different points of space, according to the old principle of interferometers, and that amplitude monopulses are only a way of realising phase monopulses.

6.6 SCANNING RADAR

In such a radar (generally intended for the purpose of tracking), we try to determine the three coordinates of the target with respect to a trihedral of reference attached to the radar's aerial. For this, we first determine the distance by one of the methods already described. At the same time, we determine

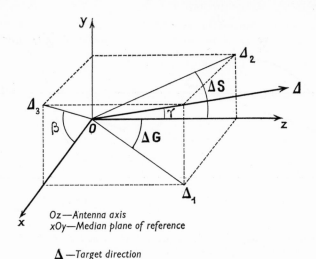

Oz—Antenna axis
xOy—Median plane of reference

Δ—Target direction

FIG. 6.21

— the angle γ between the axis of the antenna (which is that of the revolution) and the direction of the target;
— the angle β between the plane antenna axis, target direction and a certain plane of reference passing through the axis of the antenna (meridian plane) (see fig. 6.21).

The method of measuring the angles γ and β is as follows (see fig. 6.22).

A rotating aerial is illuminated by a primary feed situated outside the axis, and rotates round this axis at a certain speed f (turns per second).

Under these conditions:

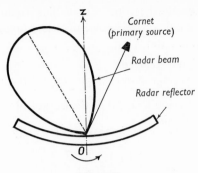

FIG. 6.22

— if the target is found on the axis of the reflector, the signal received has a constant amplitude (fig. 6.23(a));

— if the target is not on the axis of the reflector, the amplitude of the signal received varies as a function of time, as shown in fig. 6.23(b).

It is almost a sinusoidal signal with a frequency f, whose phase with respect to a sinusoidal wave of reference (with frequency f) gives the angle β of the plane of the antenna-target axis with respect to a plane of reference.

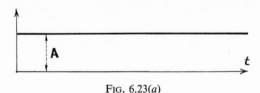

FIG. 6.23(a)

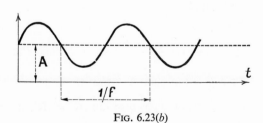

FIG. 6.23(b)

Moreover, the closer is the direction of the target to the axis of the reflector, the more the amplitude of the sinusoidal signal decreases (this is valid only for directions of the target near to the axis of the reflector). In other words, the signal received could be approximately written as

$$S = A[1 + k\gamma \sin(2\pi f t + \beta)] \qquad (1)$$

In fact, the received signal is one with a high frequency F (for example, 10,000 MHz) (see fig. 6.24), and the value of A is a function of the distance of the target from the radar. But

— if we detect the signal received

— if an appropriate system of automatic gain control is used,

we obtain after amplification a signal at the output of the receiver represented by (1) where A is a constant.

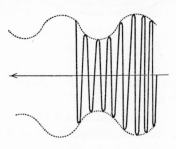

FIG. 6.24

After the passage of this signal through a high-pass filter designed to eliminate the continuous component, we obtain a signal S'

$$S' = k\gamma \sin (2\pi ft + \beta) \tag{2}$$

When γ and β vary (slowly) the signal at the output of the receiver presents itself as a signal with a frequency f,

— modulated in amplitude by γ

— modulated in phase by β.

The important thing is to extract from the signal S' the values γ and β, more precisely the values

$$\gamma \sin \beta \approx \tan \gamma \sin \beta = \tan \varDelta S \approx \varDelta S,$$

$$\gamma \cos \beta \approx \tan \gamma \cos \beta = \tan \varDelta G \approx \varDelta G,$$

which represent

— the angle between the planes XOZ and XOA

— and the angle between the planes YOZ and YOA (see fig. 6.21) respectively.

(These values $\gamma \sin \beta$ and $\gamma \cos \beta$ are usually signals of error that two servo-mechanisms try to neutralise by classical procedures so that OZ is led to coincide with OA when the radar is a tracking radar.)

Now let us suppose that we multiply S' by $\sin 2\pi ft$ (in other words, the demodulation of S' by a signal in phase with the reference). We obtain

$$S' \sin 2\pi ft = \frac{K\gamma}{2} [\cos \beta - \cos (4\pi ft + \beta)].$$

If this demodulation (or multiplication) is followed by a filtering through a low-pass filter which eliminates the frequency $2f$ (a filtering usually carried out by the servomechanism) we obtain finally,

$$\boxed{\frac{K}{2} \gamma \cos \beta}$$

Similarly, the multiplication of S' by $\cos 2\pi ft$ (a demodulation of S' by a signal in quadrature with the reference) followed by a filtering through a low-pass filter gives us

$$\boxed{\frac{K}{2} \gamma \sin \beta}$$

6.7 INCIDENCES OF TARGET FLUCTUATION ON THE PRECISION OF RADAR MEASUREMENTS

Besides the fact that the fluctuation of targets in amplitude is inevitably accompanied by a fluctuation of the centre of reflection, which gives in turn a fluctuation in angular measurement, whatever the procedure used, the fluctuation of amplitude by itself gives rise to problems, which we consider here through two examples.

6.7.1 Radar scanning

If a target is on the axis of the radar ($\beta = 0$ and $\gamma = 0$) but fluctuates in amplitude at the scanning frequency, this signifies that the S of formula (1) varies according to the form

$$S = S_0 \sin (2\pi ft + \beta)$$

from which we deduce that the target is not on the axis.

This remains true if the target fluctuates at a frequency close to the scanning frequency, from the moment the difference between these two frequencies remains less than the bandwidth of the servomechanism of the radar.

On the other hand, even if the fluctuation in amplitude of S is negligible, the fluctuation of the coordinates β and γ of the target could, if the utilisation (of modulation) is imperfect (which is true in most cases), introduce undesirable effects of the same nature.

6.7.2 General case

We have seen that a radar's measurements of distances, of radial speeds and of angles were normally falsified by the presence of noise, and that these corresponding errors were mostly gaussian with a standard deviation $K/\sqrt{R}$, where R is the ratio

$$\frac{\text{Energy received during the time of measurement}}{\text{Spectral density of the noise}}$$

If the target does not fluctuate, then this implies that R is independent of time and that it is equal to its mean value R_0.

We are justified in saying that the measurement is falsified—because of the noise—by a gaussian error ε of standard deviation equal to $K/\sqrt{R_0}$ and whose density probability is hence

$$p_1(\varepsilon) = \frac{1}{K}\sqrt{\frac{R_0}{2\pi}}\exp\left(-\varepsilon^2 R_0/2K^2\right)$$

But suppose that the target fluctuates, for example, in such a way that there is a 50 per cent chance of having $R = 0{\cdot}1R_0$ and a 50 per cent chance of having $R = 1{\cdot}9R_0$ (the mean value of R being, therefore, equal to R_0). The density probability of ε is then written as

$$p_2(\varepsilon) = \frac{0{\cdot}5}{K}\sqrt{\frac{R_0}{2\pi}}\left[0{\cdot}32\exp\left(-\varepsilon^2 R_0/20K^2\right)+1{\cdot}38\exp\left(0{\cdot}95\varepsilon^2 R_0/K^2\right)\right]$$

It is no longer gaussian.

As an example,

— in the first case (with R non-fluctuating)

the probability that $|\varepsilon| < 0{\cdot}5K/\sqrt{R_0}$ is $0{\cdot}38$;

the probability that $|\varepsilon| < K/\sqrt{R_0}$ is $0{\cdot}68$;

the probability that $|\varepsilon| < 2K/\sqrt{R_0}$ is $0{\cdot}95$;

the probability that $|\varepsilon| < 3K/\sqrt{R_0}$ is $0{\cdot}997$;

— in the second case ($R = 1{\cdot}9R_0$ 50 per cent of the time

$R = 0{\cdot}1R_0$ 50 per cent of the time)

the probability that $|\varepsilon| < 0{\cdot}5K/\sqrt{R_0}$ is $0{\cdot}31$;

the probability that $|\varepsilon| < K/\sqrt{R_0}$ is $0{\cdot}53$;

the probability that $|\varepsilon| < 2K/\sqrt{R_0}$ is $0{\cdot}73$;

the probability that $|\varepsilon| < 3K/\sqrt{R_0}$ is $0{\cdot}83$.

In other words, in this example chosen, the fact that the target fluctuates has multiplied

— the errors of low probability by 15 per cent,

— the errors of 70 per cent probability by 2,

— the errors of 95 per cent probability by more than 5.

In the case of a very complex target, i.e. a target which fluctuates according to Rayleigh's law, we could show that the density probability of the error has a Student distribution[1] and that (if R_0 is the mean value of R)

— the probability that $\varepsilon < 0.5K/\sqrt{R_0}$ is 0.34;

— the probability that $\varepsilon < K/\sqrt{R_0}$ is 0.58;

— the probability that $\varepsilon < 2K/\sqrt{R_0}$ is 0.81;

— the probability that $\varepsilon < 3K/\sqrt{R_0}$ is 0.90.

When the target fluctuates, it is therefore incorrect to say that the error due to noise in the measurement of a parameter is gaussian. The errors are greater in the case of fluctuating targets than in the case of non-fluctuating targets of the same equivalent echoing area. And they are as much greater as the probabilities are higher.

6.7.3 Precision of a radar making several consecutive measurements

Here we ask ourselves how we can improve radar measurements by making n consecutive measurements: the answer is not unique.

6.7.3.1 If the target does not fluctuate during these n measurements and if the measurements are identical, i.e. if the value of R is the same for all the measurements, we divide the errors by $\sqrt{n}$.

6.7.3.2 If the target does not fluctuate during these n measurements, but if—as in the case of a panoramic radar—the values of R vary during a series of n measurements, the result is no longer true. Thus, in a panoramic radar, we

---

[1] We find that it can be written as:

$$p_3(\varepsilon) = \frac{1}{K\sqrt{2\pi R_0}} \int_0^\infty \exp\left(-R/R_0\right) \sqrt{R} \exp\left(-\varepsilon^2 R/2K\right) \mathrm{d}R$$

$$p_3(\varepsilon) = \frac{\sqrt{R_0}}{K} \times \frac{1}{[2 + R_0\varepsilon^2/K^2]^{3/2}}$$

This calculation is due to M. Gerardin, Engineer at the Compagnie Française Thomson-Houston, who was among the first to have studied the effects of target fluctuations on the precision of radar measurements.

should take the average of measurements over only a number less than $\alpha f/V$ (α being the 3 dB beamwidth in bearing, f being the recurrence of the radar and V the rotation speed of the antenna), and that under these conditions, the errors are divided by approximately $\sqrt{\alpha f/2V}$.

6.7.3.3 If the target fluctuates between one measurement and another, as in the case of a frequency agile radar, we can no longer consider that we have n measurements, each affected by a gaussian error, and therefore we can no longer say that the final variance is equal to

$$\frac{\text{the sum of the elementary variances}}{n^2}$$

If the target fluctuates, for example, according to Rayleigh's law, each measurement is affected by an error having a Student distribution and, taking the average of measurements, is of little use in improving their accuracy.

6.8 A RETURN TO THE FLUCTUATION OF THE CENTRE OF REFLECTION: ANGULAR TARGET SIGNATURE

We explained in section 6.4 that in the presence of a non-punctual target, with the normal to the equiphase surface not being generally directed towards the centre of the target but in the direction of a point called centre of reflection (of a mobile nature) and the radar in fact determining only the direction of this normal, we could make very incorrect measurements. This is due to the fact that a radar determines only this direction.

When the antenna, assumed to be plane and of span $2L$, is found in the radiation field of a target, we could, by definition, by denoting $E(x)$ to be the field at a varying point x of the antenna, write (an expression valid only for $-L < x < L$)

$$E(x) = E_0$$
$$+ E_1 \sin\left(2\pi \frac{x}{2L}\right) + E_1' \cos\left(2\pi \frac{x}{2L}\right)$$
$$+ E_2 \sin\left(2\pi \frac{x}{L}\right) + E_2' \cos\left(2\pi \frac{x}{L}\right)$$
$$+ \ldots$$

The knowledge and measurement of E_0 and its variation during time enables us to determine two independent parameters of the target. The knowledge and measurement of E_0 and E_1, at a given time, give the same result. But the measurement of more than these parameters enables us to learn more about the target.

As an example, if we know that a target is a double-sphere target, then it depends on four independent parameters which are,

— the amplitude of the signal received from the first sphere,
— the amplitude of the signal received from the second sphere,
— the bearing of the first sphere,
— the bearing of the second sphere (we restrict ourselves to working in the horizontal plane).

The knowledge of

$$E_0 = \frac{1}{2L} \int_{-L}^{+L} E(x)\,dx$$

enables us to know the amplitude of the signal received from the two spheres.

The knowledge of

$$E_1 = \frac{1}{L} \int_{-L}^{+L} E(x) \sin\left(2\pi\,\frac{x}{2L}\right) dx$$

enables us to know the direction of the centre of reflection.

In an amplitude monopulse radar, E_0 is determined by the sum signal and E_1 by the difference signal (very closely).

But nothing prevents us from also measuring[1]

$$E_1' = \frac{1}{L} \int_{-L}^{+L} E(x) \cos\left(2\pi\,\frac{x}{2L}\right) dx,$$

the signal which we often call "écart" signal, nor measuring

$$E_2 = \frac{1}{L} \int_{-L}^{+L} E(x) \sin\left(2\pi\,\frac{x}{L}\right) dx,$$

which would allow us to know completely the double-sphere target considered.

Thus the possibility is found of knowing the targets better[2] (and some say of improving the angular resolution of the antenna), thus giving at least an answer to the reservations formulated in sub-section 3.6.3.1.

It must be noted that in order to obtain valid information from the measurements of E_2, E_2', ... there must be a sufficient signal-to-noise ratio, from which it is evident that angular resolution depends on the signal-to-noise ratio.

Thus we go farther and farther away from the initial ideas on angular resolution in optics.

---

[1] S. Drabovitch, Engineer at the Compagnie Française Thomson-Houston was, to our best knowledge, the first to suggest this measurement and to give the method to do it by utilising feeds called "multimodes".

[2] To obtain a target signature.

CHAPTER 7

PROCESSING OF RADAR INFORMATION
RADAR COVERAGE

7.1 COHERENT INTEGRATION

Let us assume, in order to simplify matters, that the radar makes on the whole n identical measurements (i.e. in particular, that the gain of the aerial in the direction of the target does not vary during these n measurements), each of the elementary measurements lasting a time T' and corresponding to a value of R. This signifies that during a measurement we receive

— a useful signal of amplitude $\sqrt{R}$

— together with a gaussian noise of standard deviation equal to 1.

If the total time T of the measurement is less than $1/f_D$ (f_D being the uncertainty over the Doppler frequency of the target, or the Doppler frequency of the centre of reflection of the target assumed to be, due to lack of information, of zero speed), we could add up the n signals received and thus obtain a useful signal of amplitude $n\sqrt{R}$ together with a gaussian noise of standard deviation equal to $\sqrt{n}$, i.e. the result is as if we had received a useful signal of height $\sqrt{nR}$ together with a gaussian noise of standard deviation equal to 1; or again that the result is as if the received energy to be considered were the total energy received during the total time of the measurement. The results of Chapter 4 therefore remain valid without having to know if the measurements had been made in a permanent way during the time T or, on the contrary, during a certain number n of intervals of time of duration T' such that $nT' < T$.

We should not fail to notice that if we are concerned with a classical pulsed radar, we assume

— that the frequency difference between the local oscillator and the transmitter is extremely constant during the total period T of the measurement, i.e. constant within a range less than $1/T$.

— that the addition takes place in a correct way before detection (we say that the radar makes a coherent integration and the classical radars satisfying the first of these two conditions are called coherent).

In the case of correlation radars as described in section 4.1 no other complementary conditions have to be assumed.

7.2 NON-COHERENT INTEGRATION

We assume that the radar is coherent, that the gain of the aerial in the direction of the target does not vary during the total period T of the measurement, and that the target does not fluctuate during this time T. On the contrary, the target is assumed to have zero radial speed but in fact presents a Doppler frequency f_D (we commit an error f_D due to knowing the Doppler frequency).

If we consider, in order to simplify matters, that the radar transmits during every elementary measurement of duration T a signal of constant amplitude and frequency f, and that every elementary measurement has a duration T' much less than $1/f_D$

$$T' \ll \frac{1}{f_D}$$

The first measurement is made between $t = 0$ and $t = T'$.
The second measurement is made between $t = t_1$ and $t = t_1 + T'$.
. . . .
The kth measurement is made between $t = t_{k-1}$ and $t = t_{k-1} + T'$.
The nth measurement is made between $t = t_{n-1}$ and $t = t_{n-1} + T'$.

The output signal is therefore, modulo a factor, the integral over the duration of an elementary measurement of the product of

$$\cos (2\pi f t) \,^1$$

by

$$A \cos [2\pi(f+f_D)t] + \text{a noise},$$

i.e. we obtain the useful signal

$$\int_{t_{k-1}}^{t_{k+1}+T'} A \cos [2\pi(f+f_D)]t \cdot \cos 2\pi f t \; \mathrm{d}t = B \cos (2\pi f_D t_{k-1})$$

and the output noise.
The useful signal is therefore written as

$$\sqrt{R} \cos (2\pi f_D t_{k-1})$$

which gives $\sqrt{R}$ if $f_D = 0$, and it is accompanied by a gaussian noise of standard deviation 1 (see fig. 7.1).

---

[1] f being, in the failing case, slowly variable; we neglect the case, little used in reality, of amplitude modulation inside a signal.

We see that if the total duration of n elementary measurements is large with respect to $1/f_D$ ($T > 1/f_D$), the addition of n useful signals will be an addition of values, some of which are positive while others are negative, and that generally this addition gives a value which is quasi-zero when the addition of the noises would give a noise with a standard deviation $\sqrt{n}$.

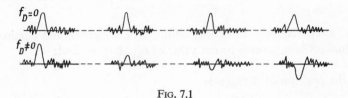

FIG. 7.1

If, therefore, the total duration T of the measurement is greater than $1/f_D$, we gain nothing, on the contrary, by carrying out what is called coherent integration over n elementary measurements contained in the duration T. In this case, it is customary to detect the elementary signals and to add them up after detection: we say that we effect a "non-coherent integration after detection".

The detection is made on the signal at an intermediate frequency[1], i.e. instead of working on

$$\sqrt{R} \cos (2\pi f_D t_{k-1})C(t) + b_{k-1}(t) \qquad (\text{with } \overline{b_{k-1}^2(t)} = 1)$$

during the kth measurement ($C(t)$ being equal to 1 at the position of the signal and zero elsewhere), the receiver provides

$$\sqrt{R} \cos [2\pi(f_i+f_D)t_{k-1}]C(t) + b_{k-1}(t) \cos (2\pi f_i t),$$

f_i being the intermediate frequency.

It is this signal which is detected: the characteristic of detection is not, in general, very simple but by assuming it to be quadratic

— we are not very far from practicality,

— and we simplify the calculations.

We shall assume, therefore, that when $T > 1/f_D$ the elementary signals are raised to the square (the components with high frequency being eliminated) and then added up.

After quadratic detection and elimination of the components at high frequency, we obtain

$$\boxed{RC^2(t) + 2C(t)\sqrt{R}b_{k-1}(t) \cos (2\pi f_D t_{k-1}) + b_{k-1}^2(t)}$$

[1] If not, we lose 3 dB, by detecting over a signal at zero intermediary frequency.

R

where

— $RC^2(t)$ is equal to R at the position of the signal and zero elsewhere,
— $2C(t)\sqrt{R}b_{k-1}(t) \cos (2\pi f_D t_{k-1})$ is a random term of mean value zero and standard deviation $\sqrt{2R}$ at the position of the signal and zero elsewhere.
— $b_{k-1}^2(t)$ is a random variable whose mean value is 1 but which is not gaussian.

Hence, after quadratic detection, addition of n signals, and elimination of the continuous components (mean value of $b_{k-1}^2(t)$), we find:

1. at the position of the signal:

— a term of value nR,
— a random term of mean value zero and standard deviation $\sqrt{2nR}$,
— a random term of mean value zero but non-gaussian $D(t)$;

2. and elsewhere this last term $D(t)$.

The study of the properties of this term $D(t)$ becomes simplified if we assume that the number of measurement n is sufficiently large. In fact, when n is small, the term $D(t)$ is a random variable of mean value zero but which is not gaussian at all. Its moments have the following values when $n = 1$ (cf. sub-section 1.2.4):

Moment of order 2 : 2
Moment of order 3 : 8
Moment of order 4 : 60.

While if the variable were gaussian with the same moment of order 2, the third order moment would be zero and the fourth would be equal to 12.

But, when n increases, the amplitude distribution of $D(t)$ tends to a gaussian distribution of standard deviation $\sqrt{2n}$.

We therefore conclude that if n is sufficiently large,[1] the result is as if we had

1. at the position of signal

— a term of value $R\sqrt{n}/\sqrt{2}$,
— a random gaussian variable of mean value zero and standard deviation $\sqrt{R}$ if R is large compared to 1, and 1 if R is small compared to 1 (generally equal to $\sqrt{R+1}$).

---

[1] We could, in practice, consider that it is a case

for $n > 5$ when $P_f \approx 10^{-3}$
for $n > 10$ when $P_f \approx 10^{-5}$
for $n > 20$ when $P \approx 10^{-10}$

2. Elsewhere

— a random gaussian term of mean value zero and standard deviation 1.

To attain a false alarm probability equal to 10^{-3}, we shall put a threshold approximately at the level 3·1 (we shall take into consideration only signals of amplitude greater than 3·1).[1] This means that the detection probability is the probability that a random gaussian term of mean value zero and standard deviation $\sqrt{R+1}$ is greater than

$$3\cdot1 - \frac{R\sqrt{n}}{\sqrt{2}}$$

We therefore obtain a detection probability equal to 0·5, when

$$3\cdot1 - \frac{R\sqrt{n}}{\sqrt{2}} = 0$$

i.e.

$$R = \frac{3\cdot1\sqrt{2}}{\sqrt{n}} = \boxed{\frac{4\cdot5}{\sqrt{n}} = R} \qquad (1)$$

We shall note that if the false alarm probability had been different from 10^{-3}, we would in any case have found a law in $R = K/\sqrt{n}$. For example, for a false alarm probability of 10^{-2}, we find

$$\boxed{R \approx \frac{3\cdot3}{\sqrt{n}}} \qquad (2)$$

We must recall (Chapter 3) the case where the threshold was effected before detection and where we worked on only one measurement: we found there that the detection probability for a false alarm probability of 10^{-3} was the probability that a random term of mean value zero and standard deviation 1 is greater than $3\cdot1 - \sqrt{R}$.

A detection probability of 0·5 is obtained in this case for

$$3\cdot1 = \sqrt{R} \qquad \boxed{R = 10}$$

We see that, within 0·4 dB, it is twice that which we obtain by assuming $n = 1$ in formula (1).

---

[1] If we were satisfied with a false alarm probability of 10^{-2}, the level of threshold has to be around 2·3 nearly.

If we had considered the detection probability of 0·5 to be associated with a false alarm probability of 10^{-2}, we would have found that it corresponds to $2·3 \approx \sqrt{R}$, $R = 5·6$, i.e. within 0·7 dB, twice that given by formula (2).

In conclusion we have shown the following theorems:

I — When the integration over a sufficiently large number n of elementary measurements is made after quadratic detection, the energy received during an elementary measurement necessary to obtain a detection probability of 0·5 decreases in a manner inversely proportional to $\sqrt{n}$.

II — When the radar is coherent and the uncertainty over the Doppler frequency of the target is greater than the reciprocal of the time of the total measurement, and when we are interested in a false alarm probability of 10^{-3}, when we make a sufficiently large number n of elementary measurements (with integration after quadratic detection) the energy received during the time of an elementary measurement necessary to obtain a detection probability of 0·5 is approximately equal to the energy necessary when the radar makes only one elementary measurement (entirely coherent) divided by $2\sqrt{n}$.[1]

III — The preceding law remains true for practically all detection probabilities around 0·5 (lying between 0·3 and 0·9)—within a range of 1 or 2 dB. This can be easily proved.

REMARKS

— It is easy to understand that non-coherent classical radar verifies the preceding laws, whatever the error made by knowing the target's Doppler deviation.

— If the target is greatly fluctuating during the period of total measurement a supplementary gain due to the fact that the radar functions as a diversity radar or a frequency agile radar (see Chapter 5) is added to the gain due to integration.

[1] As was noted above, this is valid only for $n > 5$. Otherwise, for P_f of the order of 10^{-5}, $2\sqrt{n}$ is to be replaced by $3\sqrt{n}$ (and n must be greater than 10).

Summary

In short, the fact either that the radar is coherent or that the Doppler frequency is not properly known does not permit coherent integration. Coherent integration enables us to divide the power to be transmitted by the number of elementary measurements.

When this is not possible, we must detect (in intermediate frequency) before integrating the elementary measurements. If this detection is quadratic and the number of elementary measurements large enough, integration after detection allows the division of the power to be transmitted by two or three times the square root of the number of elementary measurements. This result becomes null and void

— if we are interested in very low or very high false alarm probabilities (very different from 10);

— if we are interested in very low or very high detection probabilities (very different from 0·5).

For more precise calculations, we could either consult the curves calculated by J. Marcum (published in 1948 and 1952) or make rigorous calculations in the following way (which is valid only if n is sufficiently large). (See fig. 7.2.)

The false alarm probability being related to K by formula (14) of Chapter 3, the detection probability is obtained, according to what has been described above, by the expression

$$P_d = \frac{1}{\sqrt{2\pi}} \int_{(K-R\sqrt{n}/\sqrt{2})/\sqrt{1+R}}^{+\infty} \exp\left(-v^2/2\right) dv.$$

It is thus that the curves in fig. 7.2 were obtained. They show for $n = 10$ and $n = 100$ $(P_f = 10^{-3})$ in the case of coherent integration and non-coherent integration, the ratio R_2 equivalent to the final detection probability versus the ratio R_1 of an elementary measurement $(R_2 - R_1)$ shows the gain due to integration in dB).

As a first approximation, when n is low, the integration after detection of n pulses is equivalent to a coherent integration.[1]

7.3 INTEGRATION IN A PANORAMIC RADAR

Let us consider a panoramic radar rotating at a speed V, using the same antenna for transmission and reception, the 3 dB beamwidth in bearing of the antenna being α, and making short measurements (microseconds) at a frequency of recurrence f (of the order of 100 to 1,000 Hz). We say that the radar makes $f\alpha/V$ measurements during the passage of its 3 dB beam over the target.

[1] See also the article by W. M. Hall in *Space Aeronautics*, July 1962.

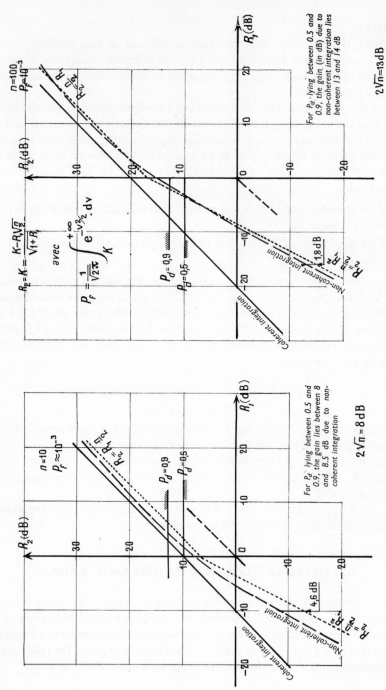

$$P_F = \frac{1}{\sqrt{2\pi}} \int_{K}^{+\infty} e^{-v^2/2} \, dv$$

$$avec \quad K = \frac{K - R\sqrt{2}}{\sqrt{1 + R_1}}$$

$R_2 = K$

$2\sqrt{n} = 13 \, dB$

For P_d, lying between 0.5 and 0.9, the gain (in dB) due to non-coherent integration lies between 13 and 14 dB

$2\sqrt{n} = 8 \, dB$

For P_d, lying between 0.5 and 0.9, the gain lies between 8 and 8.5 dB due to non-coherent integration

Fig. 7.2

Numerical application:

$$f = 250 \text{ Hz},$$

$$\alpha = 1°,$$

$$V = 36°/\text{s},$$

$$f\alpha/V = 7.$$

Thus when the antenna rotates we make a measurement every $1/f$ sec, but as long as the direction of the maximal radiation is not in the neighbourhood of the target's bearing, we make the measurements with low values of R.

On the contrary, when the direction of maximal radiation of the antenna is in the neighbourhood of that of the target, we make the measurements with values of R which are high, whose maximum value is, for example, R_M; and we could calculate precisely that at every rotation of the antenna the value of R is not greater than $R_M/4$ for only $f\alpha/V$ consecutive measurements (with a non-fluctuating target).

7.3.1 Under these conditions, let us assume

— that the radar is a coherent radar

— that the target is not affected by the Doppler effect (or by a negligible or known Doppler deviation)

— that the target fluctuated in a negligible way during the period of passage of the beam over the target

— and that we make a coherent integration over the n pulses (including the most powerful pulse).

If $f\alpha/V$ is sufficiently large and n is small (for example, $f\alpha/V = 10$ and $n = 3$), all the three measurements used correspond to the same value of R, i.e. R_M, events occur (see section 7.1) as if R_M were multiplied by n, i.e. as if we had made only one measurement with a value of R equal to nR_M.

On the contrary, if n is not small in comparison to $f\alpha/V$ (for example, $f\alpha/V = 10$ and $n = 100$), a coherent integration would make

— the addition of n gaussian noise of standard deviation 1, thus giving a noise of standard deviation $\sqrt{n}$;

— and the addition of n useful signals of which a few are high (nearer to $\sqrt{R_M}$) and the rest are weak.

If we admit that a signal received from a target can be written as shown in sub-section 6.2.3

$$\sqrt{R} = \sqrt{R_M} \exp(-2·8\theta^2/\alpha^2)$$

we find, after all the calculations have been made (as soon as $\alpha f/V$ is of the order of a few units), that the addition of n useful signals gives

$$1{\cdot}06 \frac{\alpha f}{V} \sqrt{R_M}\, \theta(x), \qquad \text{with } x = \frac{0{\cdot}83n}{\alpha f/V},$$

i.e. events occur finally as if we had found

— a gaussian noise of standard deviation 1;
— a useful signal of amplitude equal to

$$1{\cdot}06 \frac{\alpha f}{V} \sqrt{\frac{R_M}{n}}\, \theta(x).$$

For $n = 1$, we find that this useful signal is $\sqrt{R_M}$.

For n small with respect to $\alpha f/V$, we find this useful signal to be equal to $\sqrt{nR_M}$.

For n sufficiently large, we find that this useful signal tends to zero, which is normal. And the final result of this calculation is that the useful signal in question is maximal when $n \approx \alpha f/V$.

Hence, we should logically integrate a number of measurements equal to $\alpha f/V$ and under these conditions events occur as if we had only one measurement with a value of R equal to

$$\boxed{0{\cdot}65 \frac{\alpha f}{V} R_M}$$

7.3.2 Let us assume now (which corresponds to numerous applications) that the radar cannot make coherent integration and that as a result we make the integration over n measurements after quadratic detection. In addition, let us assume that the target does not fluctuate during the total duration of the n measurements (which is generally the case).

Under these conditions, the calculations made in sections 7.2 and 7.3.1 result in the following conditions:

If we are interested in a detection probability of the order of 0·5 and in false alarm probabilities (probability of false plots) of the order of 10^{-3}, which is generally the case, when we carry out the integration after quadratic detection in a coherent or non-coherent radar, but in the front of targets of unknown radial speed,

— the integration over a number of n measurements (pulsed), weak with respect to f/V, has the effect of multiplying R_M by $2\sqrt{n}$ if $n > 5$.

— the optimal number of measurements (pulsed) that are to be integrated is of the order of $\alpha f/V$ (a little weaker, in fact, around $0{\cdot}8\ \alpha f/V$, but the difference between $n \approx \alpha f/V$ and $n \approx 0{\cdot}8\ \alpha f/V$ is not large) and, under these conditions, the result is as if we had made a single measurement with

$$R = 1 \cdot 4 \sqrt{\frac{\alpha f}{V}} \times R_M \quad \text{(if } \alpha f/V > 5\text{).}$$

The integration has the effect of multiplying R_M by $1 \cdot 4 \sqrt{\alpha f/V}$.[1]

N.B. With the hypothesis made in section 7.2, this result is valid only if $\alpha f/V > 5$.

7.4 UTILISATION OF DIGITAL EXTRACTORS

The procedure of integration which we have just analysed consists of making the sum of the signals obtained at every elementary measurement (after detection) and then to put a threshold over the sum obtained. It is such a procedure that led us to the most simple fixes and, due to these, this was the procedure most used. But we must note that this is not the only possible procedure. We could envisage

— detection of the signals made from elementary measurements

— making a threshold

— and finally applying a rule of the game, more or less complicated, with the help of a computer (for example, digital).

As an example, let us assume that we are dealing with a radar making fifteen consecutive measurements. We could group them into three blocks of five consecutive measurements, each of the blocks giving rise to an intermediate measurement, i.e. a detection (quadratic), followed by an analogic addition of three signals, and threshold. After this the rule of the game with the computer would be as follows.

For a target to exist, we admit that it is necessary that each of the three intermediate measurements be given a positive result at the same range (a signal above the threshold level).

After that, to obtain a detection probability of 0·5 with the system, it is necessary that each intermediate measurement should give a detection probability of $(0·5)^{1/3}$, i.e. 0·8.

---

[1] For any n, the integration has the effect of multiplying R_M by:

$$\frac{\alpha f}{V} \times \frac{1 \cdot 5}{\sqrt{n}} \times \Theta(\gamma), \quad \text{with} \quad \gamma = \frac{1 \cdot 18 \, n}{\alpha f/V}$$

Coefficient 1·4 represents, with respect to 2, the loss due to the fact that the radar beam is gaussian and not rectangular: the loss of 1·5 dB is called the "lobe effect".

1st signal—detection ⎫
. . . . ⎬ addition—threshold
5th signal—detection ⎭
6th signal—detection ⎫
. . . . ⎬ addition—threshold
10th signal—detection ⎭
11th signal—detection ⎫
. . . . ⎬ addition—threshold
15th signal—detection ⎭

Rule of the game: we say that a target exists when each of the three intermediate measurements gives a signal at the same range.

And the final false alarm probability (we also call it the probability of false plot) is equal to the cube of the false alarm probability of the intermediate measurement. If, therefore, we require a false alarm probability of 10^{-3}, we are led to place the threshold level in such a way that the intermediate measurement gives a false alarm probability of 0·1.

Finally the value of R (for an elementary measurement) must be such that we obtain over five measurements a detection probability of 0·8 for a false alarm probability of 0·1 in order finally to obtain over the fifteen measurements a detection probability of 0·5 for a false alarm probability of 10^{-3}.

We find that this result is obtained for $R = 1·8$ (2·5 dB) while if we had made the integration directly by addition of the n measurements before threshold the application of formula (1) shows that we would have needed

$$R = 4·5/\sqrt{15} = 1·10 \ (0·6 \text{ dB}).$$

The procedure which we have just described results in a loss of 1·9 dB for a detection probability of 0·5 associated with a false alarm probability of 10^{-3}. The chosen rule of the game (the extraction criterion) does not seem to be useful.

Let us now assume that the extraction criterion (rule of the game) is modified, and becomes

— to decide that there is a target, it is necessary and sufficient that one of the groups of the five measurements has given a positive result.

Hence, to have a detection probability of 0·5 with this system, it is necessary that each intermediate measurement gives a detection probability P_{d_i} such that

$$0·5 = 1-(1-P_{d_i})^3$$

$$P_{d_i} = 0·2.$$

And to have a false alarm probability of 10^{-3} with this system, it is necessary that each intermediate measurement gives a false alarm probability P_{f_i} such that

$$10^{-3} = 1-(1-P_{f_i})^3$$

$$P_{f_i} = 0·3 \times 10^{-3}.$$

The new rule of the game leads us, therefore, to find the value of R (for an elementary measurement) such that

— over five measurements we obtain a detection probability of 0·2 for a false alarm probability of 0.3×10^{-3},

— to finally obtain over fifteen measurements a detection probability of 0·5 associated with a false alarm probability of 10^{-3}.

We find that this result is obtained for $R = 1.3$ (1 dB), i.e. that the extraction criterion used results only in a loss of 0·5 dB with respect to an analogical integration before the threshold.

We therefore see that the use of an extraction criterion permitting an integration by logical operations (utilisation of digital computers called extractors) could, when the extraction criterion is well chosen, provide practically the same result as analogical integration (before the threshold).[1]

Let us consider, for example, a panoramic radar working with a useful spectrum of width Δf. This means that the range discrimination is of the order of $1/\Delta f$ (in seconds, or $150 \cdot 10^{-6}/\Delta f$ in metres with Δf in Hz). This means also that the noise signals have, on the average, the same duration. We are, therefore, led to quantify the range into sections of $1/\Delta f$ duration. We could then proceed in the following way.

The signals received at each recurrence are, after detection, fed through a threshold to obtain a certain elementary false alarm probability Pf_e. This means that in the absence of a target we have, after the threshold, a probability of Pf_e to find, in the range quantum, a signal exceeding the threshold.

Let us assume that a calculator works in the following way. It decides on a "target" if, during three successive scans, we find a signal exceeding the threshold on each scan. The probability that we find a false plot at a certain range (in the given quantum) is therefore equal to $(Pf_e)^3$. The probability of false plot is $(Pf_e)^3$, and the most probable number of false plots per antenna rotation is given by the product

— of the probability of false plot $(Pf_e)^3$ by

— the number Q of sections of range

— by the number of measurements per antenna rotation $360 f/V$.

Numerical application:

$$f = 500 \text{ kHz}, \qquad 1/\Delta f = 2 \ \mu\text{s} \rightarrow 300 \text{ m},$$

$$Q = 2,000 \text{ (useful range 600 km)},$$

$$f = 250 \text{ Hz} \qquad V = 36°/\text{s} \qquad Pf_e = 10^{-2}.$$

---

[1] Quite often the integration and threshold are naturally obtained in the sensitive layer of the panoramic indicator (P.P.I. scope).

Probability of false plot $= 10^{-6}$.
The most number of false plots per antenna rotation $= 5$.

Such a criterion for pulse counting is effectively used in simple extractors (called "parasitic eliminators"). With such extractors for obtaining a detection probability of a plot of 0·5 it is necessary that at each scan we have a detection probability of the order of 0·8. (We have seen above that such a criterion was not very helpful from the point of view of target detection in the absence of jamming or in the presence of white noise jamming. Nevertheless it has the advantage of eliminating certain simple jammings and of being inexpensive.)

Thus in such a parasitic eliminator, more generally the detection of a target requires during at least N successive scans (here $N = 3$) that we find a signal exceeding the threshold level in the same range quantum.

If we find, for example, five such successive signals, we are led to admit that the target direction was that of the maximal radiation of the antenna during the reception of the third signal, thus obtaining a close measurement of the target's bearing.

But we could use better and more complicated criteria when we have more complete computers (extractors). An example of such a criterion is as follows.

This is characterised by two parameters N and n. We denote by a train of pulses the sequence of results obtained in the given range quantum. A pulse train is thus constituted by a sequence of signals which either are present (i.e. exceeding the threshold) or absent (i.e. lower than the threshold).

This corresponds to a target when there are at least N pulses present which are not separated by more than n successive absent pulses. If this condition is satisfied, the pulse train starts from the instant when there are no more n consecutive absent pulses and ends when there are n consecutive absent pulses by definition. The direction of the target is assumed to be that which the antenna had located in the middle of the train pulse.

The following diagram shows this definition for $N = 3$ and $n = 1$ (0 indicates the absent pulses, 1 indicates the present pulses).

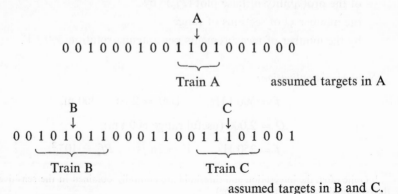

It is shown that with such criterion if we impose a false plot probability of the order of 10^{-3} to 10^{-5}, the parameters N and n (and Pf_e, which fixes the threshold level) should not be chosen in any way. This is logical if we wish to obtain the best results.

We show that[1]

— if $\alpha f/V = 4$, it is necessary to assume $Pf_e \approx 10^{-2}$, $N = 2$, $n = 2$ or 3.

— if $\alpha f/V = 8$, it is necessary to assume $Pf_e \approx 10^{-1}$ to 10^{-2}, $N = 3$, $n = 3$ or 4.

We also prove two important results:

— first, that such an extractor criterion gives practically (within 2 dB nearly) the same result as an analogical integration (after detection over a number of pulses close to $\alpha f/V$), when we choose the best value of N and n;

— second, that when the detection probability obtained is greater than 0·1 or 0·2 (i.e. in all the interesting cases), by assuming for the azimuth (bearing) of the target the bearing of the middle of the pulse train, we never commit an error, over the target's bearing, greater than V/f (at least when $\alpha f/V = 10$).

Numerical application:

$$\alpha = 1°, \quad f = 250 \text{ Hz}, \quad V = 36°/\text{s}, \quad \alpha f/V = 7;$$

$V/f = 0·14°$. The error committed over the measurement of the bearing is always less than $0·14°$.

REMARK

It goes without saying that the errors in the target's bearing due to the fluctuations of the centre of reflection have to be considered elsewhere.

7.5 AN EXAMPLE OF A PRELIMINARY PLAN OF A CLASSICAL PANORAMIC RADAR

7.5.1 Coverage of a classical panoramic radar in the absence of jamming

Let us consider a classical panoramic pulse radar constituted of a transmitter, a duplexer, a unique antenna and a unique receiver. The transmitter sends a signal of wavelength close to $\lambda = 10$ cm, but it is frequency agile and changes its transmission frequency at each period of recurrence. Its frequency of recurrence is 250 Hz $= f$. The speed of the antenna's rotation is $18°/\text{s}$. The 3 dB beamwidth in bearing is 10^{-2} radian ($\alpha = 100$ mrad $= 0·57°$).

---

[1] By assuming the lobe to be gaussian, which is close to reality. By assuming the lobe to be rectangular, which is not realistic, we find results which are very different and which are not valid.

We wish, with such a radar, to ensure a coverage of 500 km in range and 100 km in altitude with a detection probability of 90 per cent over a (fluctuating) target, 10 m² of mean equivalent echoing area, for a false alarm probability of 10^{-3}. The noise temperature T_B of the receiver is assumed to be 1,000°K. We seek to calculate the order of size of the mean power to be transmitted (and in a wish to simplify matters, we neglect the atmospheric and other miscellaneous losses). The calculation of f/V gives here

$$\frac{0\cdot57\times250}{18} = 8.$$

From sub-section 7.3.2 integration has to be made over six elementary measurements (six pulses) and it enables us to divide R by $1\cdot4\sqrt{8} = 4$ (a gain of 6 dB).

The graphs at the end of the book show that it is necessary to consider finally one value of R of the order of 13 dB$-$6 dB, or nearly 7 dB.[1] To which we must add 1 dB of loss due to fluctuations, which gives $R = 8$ dB.

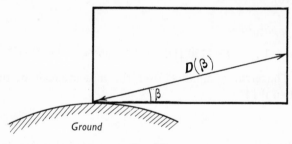

FIG. 7.3

Denote by $G(\beta)$ the antenna gain (which is the same at the transmission as well as at the reception) at the elevation β, and by $D(\beta)$ the range of the radar at the same elevation (see fig. 7.3).

The energy transmitted during the duration of a measurement being E_e, we know that the density of the transmitted energy at the elevation β is given at the range $D(\beta)$ by

$$\frac{E_e G(\beta)}{4\pi D^2(\beta)}$$

The target is assumed, by the definition of σ_e, to re-radiate in the direction of the radar a density of energy at the radar site equal to

$$\frac{E_e G(\beta)}{4\pi D^2(\beta)}\times\frac{\sigma_e}{4\pi D^2(\beta)}$$

[1] The radar being frequency agile, we assume that the target does not fluctuate.

And the antenna therefore collects this density, multiplied by its efficient surface in the direction:

$$\frac{\lambda^2 G(\beta)}{4\pi}$$

We find, therefore, that the energy received from the target at the elevation β and at a range $D(\beta)$ during the duration of the measurement can be written as

$$\frac{\lambda^2}{4\pi} \times \frac{E_e G^2(\beta)\sigma_e}{16\pi^2 D^4(\beta)} = E$$

The noise of the radar receiver being independent of β, the radar should receive the same value of E whatever the elevation considered β. Thus $D^2(\beta)/G(\beta)$ must be independent of β.

The spectral density of the noise is equal to kT_B, and finally we must write

$$\frac{2E}{kT_B} = 6 \qquad \text{(or 8 dB).}$$

Therefore,

$$\boxed{\frac{2E_e\sigma_e\lambda^2}{(16\pi^2)\,(4\pi)} \times \frac{G^2(\beta)}{D^4(\beta)} \times \frac{1}{kT_B} = 6}$$

$$G(\beta) = D^2(\beta)\sqrt{\frac{3kT_B\,(16\pi^2)\,(4\pi)}{E_e\sigma_e\lambda^2}}$$

$$\int_0^{\pi/2} G(\beta)\ \mathrm{d}\beta = \sqrt{\frac{3kT_B\,(16\pi^2)\,(4\pi)}{E_e\sigma_e\lambda^2}} \int_0^{\pi/2} D^2(\beta)\ \mathrm{d}\beta.$$

Since we have

$$\int_0^{\pi/2} G(\beta)\ \mathrm{d}\beta = \frac{4\pi}{\alpha} \qquad (\alpha \text{ in radians})$$

$$\int_0^{\pi/2} D^2(\beta)\ \mathrm{d}\beta = 2S$$

we finally find that

$$\frac{16\pi^2}{\alpha^2} = \frac{3kT_B\,(16\pi^2)\,(4\pi)}{E_e\sigma_e\lambda^2} \cdot (4S^2)$$

$$\boxed{E_e = \frac{150kT_B\alpha^2}{\sigma_e\lambda^2} \cdot S^2}$$

we find the following very interesting result:

— for a given α,

— for given λ,

— for given σ_e,

— for given T_B,

the energy to be transmitted during the duration of the measurement is proportional to the square of the radar coverage area required.

After the calculations are made, we find that

$$E_e = 8 \text{ J}.$$

The radar has to transmit 8 J, 250 times per second: its mean power will therefore be 2 kW.

Assume now that the radar is constituted in a slightly different way:

It utilises two sets of transmitter receivers,

— the first being connected to a primary feed such that its power is radiated only in lower coverage (see fig. 7.4),

— the second being connected to a primary feed such that its power is radiated only in the upper coverage (see fig. 7.4).

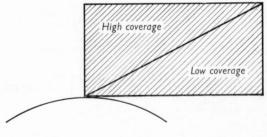

FIG. 7.4

Finally, except that the reflector is unique, we have in fact two radars, each assuring a coverage area of $S/2$.

The two transmitters will hence be identical and each will transmit a power of 0·5 kW (in practice, it is necessary to have a little more). The total power to be transmitted is hence divided by 2, because we use two distinct receivers (for the transmitter could be unique on condition that its power is divided into two equal parts).

7.5.2 Coverage of a classical panoramic radar over a plane, carrier of jamming (self-screening jamming)

We suppose now that we need to obtain the same coverage, with the target transmitting white noise jamming of density 10^{-6} W/Hz $= P$ with an omnidirectional antenna. In this case the energy re-radiated by the target is equal to

$$\frac{E_e G(\beta)}{4\pi D^2(\beta)} \sigma_e$$

Finally, hence, we must have

$$\frac{2E_e G(\beta)\sigma_e}{4\pi D^2(\beta) \cdot P} = 6.$$

Here we see that $G(\beta)/D^2(\beta)$ is independent of β. We could therefore write

$$\int_0^{\pi/2} G(\beta) \, d\beta = \frac{12\pi P}{E_e \sigma_e} \int_0^{\pi/2} D^2(\beta) \, d\beta$$

$$\frac{4\pi}{\alpha} = \frac{12\pi P}{E_e \sigma_e} \cdot 2S$$

$$\boxed{E_e = \frac{6 \cdot P\alpha}{\sigma_e} S}$$

This time we find the interesting result that the energy to be transmitted during the duration of the measurement depends only on α and σ_e and that, these parameters being fixed, it is proportional to the radar coverage required.

After the calculations we find that $E_e = 250$ J for $P = 10^{-6}$.

The radar must therefore transmit 250 J, 250 times per second: its mean power will hence be 65 kW.

This time we gain nothing by using many receivers, each having a partial coverage.

APPENDIX

PROBLEMS

DETECTION PROBABILITIES

1. Detect a non-fluctuating target by means of a radar. We find at the output of the receiver:

— in the absence of a target a gaussian noise of mean value zero and standard deviation equal to 1;

— in the presence of a target at the useful range a useful signal of amplitude $s = \sqrt{R_0}$, plus the noise.

Trace the curve of the variations of the probabilities of detection P_d versus R_0 for a false alarm probability $P_f = 5 \cdot 10^{-5}$.

2. We now assume that the target fluctuates in such a way that the useful signal $s = \sqrt{R}$ delivered at the output of the receiver has

1 chance in 3 to be equal to zero,

1 chance in 3 to be equal to $\sqrt{R_0}$,

1 chance in 3 to be equal to $\sqrt{2R_0}$.

Trace the curve of the variations of P_d versus the mean value of the signal-to-noise ratio in energy for a false alarm probability $P_f = 5 \cdot 10^{-5}$.

3. The total power is now assumed to be transmitted by two transmitters identical at all points but working on different frequencies, such that the equivalent echoing areas presented by the target at these two frequencies are completely independent.

We also have two receivers which deliver at their outputs:

— a signal s_1, corresponding to $R/2$ submerged in a gaussian noise of standard deviation 1;

— a signal s_2, corresponding to $R/2$ submerged in a gaussian noise of standard deviation 1.

The target fluctuates in such a way that the probability distributions of s_1 and s_2 are identical to the distribution considered above, i.e. that s_1 and s_2 each have independently:

1 chance in 3 to be zero,

1 chance in 3 to be equal to $\sqrt{R_0/2}$,

1 chance in 3 to be equal to $\sqrt{R_0}$.

Trace the curve giving the detection probability as a function of R_0 for a false alarm probability of $5 \cdot 10^{-5}$, knowing that the noises delivered at the outputs of the receivers are independent and that the two signals s_1 and s_2 are added before the threshold.

4. What would be the probability of detection $P_d(R_0)$ for the same false alarm probability and with the same hypothesis over the fluctuation of the target if we use a very large number n of transmitter-target-receiver channels, the total transmitted power remaining the same and the echoing areas being independent? What are your conclusions?

A.2 PROBLEM 2

UTILISATION OF VARIOUS TYPES OF RADAR

A radar functions in the C band ($\lambda = 5 \cdot 5$ cm) with a rotating antenna of 50 dB gain. The range D_0 of the radar is considered to be at 90 per cent probability of detection and 10^{-5} of false alarm probability. The target has an equivalent echoing area of 1 m^2 and is not supposed to fluctuate.

1. It is required that at the range of D_0 the standard deviation of the error committed on the measurement of the range be less than 150 m. By assuming that the spectrum transmitted has a form of a bell, what is the minimal value that could be theoretically accepted for its 3 dB width?

2. What is the order of range discrimination?

3. The radar is intended for the surveillance of a zone of 300 km radius centred at the radar. Its pulse repetition frequency is 200 Hz, the period of antenna rotation is 6 sec. By admitting that the useful signal is composed of a single pulse, give the number of false plots delivered at every antenna rotation.

4. There is no voluntary jamming. The noise figure of the receiving system is 10 dB. We neglect the loss at the transmission, and the atmospheric losses. What is the minimal value of the energy to be transmitted during the duration of the measurement in order to obtain a range of 300 km?

5. Assuming that the useful transmitted signal is composed of a single pulse non-modulated in frequency and assuming that, in this case, the error in the range measurement is in practice ten times greater than the theoretical error, give the order of pulse duration to be transmitted in order to obtain the same precision over the range measurement. What will be the corresponding range discrimination (given the theoretical formula)? What has to be the peak power of the transmission signal? What must be the bandwidth of the I.F. amplifiers of the receiver?

6. We now assume that the target carries a jammer transmitting towards the radar a jamming power of 100 W spread uniformly in a band 500 MHz by means of an aerial of 3 dB gain. What is the value of the peak power to be transmitted with a pulse of the same length as in paragraph 5 in order to obtain the same range of 300 km? What is the value of the signal-to-noise ratio corresponding to a target at maximum range at the I.F. amplifier's output by assuming that there is a filter to eliminate the image frequency?

By how many decibels at least would this value diminish if we had forgotten to eliminate the image frequency?

7. We now assume that the radar uses a pulse compression, thus transmitting a pulse 100 times longer than that defined in paragraph 5 (linear modulation of the transmitted frequency). Trace the axis of the ambiguity diagram (in the plane range-radial speed). What is the peak power to be transmitted under the conditions of paragraphs 4 and 6? What is, for a target at a distance of 300 km, the signal-to-noise ratio before and after the compressor filter?

8. We now henceforth assume that the radar is a correlation radar utilising a transmission signal randomly phase modulated, obtained by utilising a signal of a given frequency whose phase changes at random, from 0 or π (with equal probability from 0 or π) to successive instants distant from θ. Calculate the width of the spectrum of such a signal.

For this we will determine:

(a) the autocorrelation function of a signal of constant amplitude whose sign changes or not, at random, every θ sec;

(b) we will evaluate the Fourier transform of this autocorrelation function (spectrum);

(c) we will admit that the signal transmitted by the radar has a spectrum just shifted in frequency with respect to the preceding.

What value should be given to θ in order to obtain the precision sought (150 m) in range? What is the range discrimination of this radar?

9. What must be the minimal duration of the useful signal so that the radial speed discrimination of the radar is 25 m/s? We will adopt this value as the duration of the transmitted signal.

In this condition, the ambiguity diagram is close to an ellipse whose principal axes are the coordinate axes. Trace the ellipse.

What is the peak power that should be transmitted in the presence of jamming as indicated in paragraph 6?

10. We are required to eliminate targets of radial speeds less than 25 m/s and not to eliminate targets whose radial speeds are greater than 50 m/s with the help of a correlation radar. Is there a theoretical limit to the sub-clutter visibility? If so, calculate it.

11. We assume the time of integration of the correlators to be equal to the duration of the transmitted signal. What is the signal-to-noise ratio for a target at 300 km before and after the correlator?

12. By assuming that we use the same antenna at the transmission as well as at the reception, what is the maximal value that we could admit for the duty cycle of the radar (the ratio mean power/peak power) by assuming that the time of recuperation of the duplexor is negligible? What is the corresponding value to the mean power transmitted by adopting this value?

How many decibels do we lose over a target situated at 150 km, at 75 km, at 30 km?

Trace the curve giving the error committed over the measurement with this radar, as a function of the range, when this varies between 0 and 300 km (under the conditions of jamming defined in paragraph 6).

13. We are now required to study what happens when a mobile target at 15 m/s radial speed and another at 35 m/s radial speed are at the same range. What must be the ratio of the equivalent echoing areas so that the faster target is not eliminated?

A.3 PROBLEM 3

DETERMINATION OF A COUNTRY'S COVERAGE BY RADARS

1. The problem

We assume that a country is in danger of being attacked by a certain number of enemy aircraft capable of flying at a height of between 4,000 and 20,000 m. These aircraft carry jammers which can upset the country's detection system.

To detect these aircraft, a radar infrastructure must be installed to protect the country being attacked. The radars must ensure the total coverage of the country between the altitudes of 4,000 and 20,000 m in the presence of jamming. In order to achieve this result, we could envisage different solutions; in particular, the range of the radar chosen will determine the total number of radars to be installed and hence the total cost of the operation.

We could envisage numerous radars of low power, few radars of great power, or radars of different types, i.e. classical pulse radars or pulse compression radars.

Finally the problem would be to choose the optimal infrastructure in order to assure a coverage (i.e. the solution) which would ensure the country's protection.

2. Technical and operational characteristics

2.1   *Characteristics of the enemy raids*

The enemy aircraft are estimated to be 100 in number, 20 km apart (i.e. 1 aircraft per 400 km^2). Their velocities vary between Mach 0·6 and Mach 2. Their mean equivalent echoing area is assumed to be 10 m^2.

The aircraft fly at a maximum altitude of 20,000 m. During the raid we find that the proportion of quiet targets and jamming targets is unknown.

We could find quiet targets or jamming targets in limited numbers at a low altitude.

(These two hypotheses are meant to simplify the calculations.)

2.2   *The threat of jamming*

The aircraft, flying at a high altitude, could be jamming carriers.

The mean power of the jammers is

200 W per plane.

The jammer transmits by means of a omnidirectional aerial for the radar whose gain is of 3 dB.

The jamming is assumed to be noise of constant spectral density. The frequency band jammed by each plane is matched with the frequency band of the radars.

2.3   *Information to be provided by the radars*

All the targets, jamming or silent, must be detected with a detection probability of 90 per cent and a false alarm probability of 10^{-3}.

The required range accuracy is ±1 km.

It should be possible to distinguish targets 5 km apart.

Altitude measurement is not necessary.

Renewal of information: 6 per min.

We will admit a gap in the coverage at nearly 35 km along the radius (30° in elevation).

2.4   *Technical limitations*

For the radars we will take into account the following limitations:

— two aerials as a maximum for a radar,

— maximal area of aerial: 50 m^2,

— dimensions of the aerials:

span $L < 12$ m,   height $H < 6$ m.

— in the case of multi-beam radars, we will limit these to 10 beams.

— we could introduce as a maximum two parallel tubes under each antenna.

— we will take into account a loss of at least 2 dB in transmission (in the microwave circuit) and of at least 2 dB in the signal processing in the presence of jamming (constant false alarm reception).

— we will use the tubes described in the Appendix as the power tubes.

— the side-lobes of the aerials could not be assumed to be less than 25 dB below the main lobe.

3. Remarks on the preliminary plan

In this plan we will provide the technical characteristics of the chosen solution. In particular we are required to measure precisely:

(a) the characteristics of the aerial (dimensions, number of beams and the angular width of each).

(b) the characteristic of the transmitter tube(s) utilised, method of utilisation.

(c) The radar performances (coverage without jamming, coverage in the presence of a jamming threat). In this later case, we will examine the range over jamming aircraft at high altitude, the range over aircraft at low altitude (in the presence of jamming).

Do not forget to take into consideration the jamming that penetrates through the side-lobes.

(d) The financial estimate.

It is obvious that the reason for the choice of each of these parameters must be given.

4. Complementary information

4.1 *Utilisable tubes*

We have the choice between two types of tubes:

(a)	Maximal peak power	10 MW
	Mean power	6 kW
(b)	Maximal peak power	1 MW
	Mean power	20 kW

These tubes cover the frequency band 4,500–5,000 MHz.

4.2 *Formulae for cost determination*

In order to determine the cost of the solutions adopted, we will use the following empirical formulae where:

S = total area of aerial(s) expressed in m^2,

W = total mean power of the radar expressed in kW,

N = number of beams,

P = cost in thousands of pounds.

For pulsed radars we assume

$$0{\cdot}01P = 1 + 0{\cdot}10W + (0{\cdot}015S + 0{\cdot}13N)(0{\cdot}8 + 0{\cdot}06W).$$

For pulse compression radars we assume

$$0{\cdot}01P = 1 + 0{\cdot}05W + (0{\cdot}015S + 0{\cdot}13N)(0{\cdot}8 + 0{\cdot}02W).$$

5. Indications on the method of study

Examination of the problem shows that the element to be determined as soon as possible is the radar aerial.

The aerial is determined essentially by the geometric conditions for precision and coverage to be ensured.

5.1 *Determination of the aerial*

A study of the coverage diagrams shows that, in order to ensure a coverage at 4,000 m, a radar having a range (in the presence of jamming) greater than 200 km is useless.

We could hence consider three distinct cases:

(a) radars of range 200 km,

(b) radars of range 140 km,

(c) radars of range 100 km.

In each of these cases we will study the dimensions of the antenna and the number of beams.

5.2 *Determination of the radar*

In each of the cases examined above, we could choose either a pulse radar, or a pulse compression radar (i.e. utilisation of tubes A or B).

We could determine the power necessary for each of the possibilities in each of the cases (a), (b) and (c).

In order to calculate this power, we must not forget to take into account (if necessary) the jamming over the side-lobes and we must verify the range over the silent aircraft.

5.3 *Choice of the solution*

The cost formulae enable us to estimate the financial expenditure.

In the choice of the solution we shall take into account the financial consideration and also the complexities of the proposed solutions.

APPENDIX

TABLE OF THE FUNCTION

$$\Theta(x) = \frac{2}{\sqrt{\pi}} \int_{0}^{x} \exp(-u^2) \mathrm{d}u$$

x	$\Theta(x)$		x	$\Theta(x)$
0·1	0·11		1·1	0·88
0·2	0·22		1·2	0·91
0·3	0·33		1·3	0·93
0·4	0·43		1·4	0·95
0·5	0·52		1·5	0·97
0·6	0·60		1·6	0·98
0·7	0·68		1·8	0·990
0·8	0·74		2·3	0·9990
0·9	0·80		2·75	0·99990
1·0	0·84		3·1	0·999990

BIBLIOGRAPHY

[1] P. M. WOODWARD, *Probability and Information Theory with Application to Radar*, McGraw-Hill Book Company, New York, 1953.

[2] F. PENIN, *Cours de Radar*, published by École Nationale Supérieure de l'Aéronautique, Paris.

[3] L. THOVEL, Course given at École Nationale Supérieure de l'Aéronautique, published by E.N.S.A.

[4] J. I. MARCUM, *A Statistical Theory of Target Detection by Pulsed Radar*, The Rand Corp., Dec. 1947 and July 1948.

[5] L. N. RIDENOUR, "Radar system engineering", *M.I.T.*, vol. 1.

[6] W. M. HALL, "Pulse radar performance", *P.I.R.E.*, **44**, 224, Feb. 1956.

[7] J. L. LAWSON and G. E. UHLENBERCK, "Threshold signals", *M.I.T.*, vol. 24.

[8] S. O. RICE, "Statistical properties of a sine wave plus random noise", *B.S.T.J.*, **27**, 709–757, Jan. 1948.

[9] G. L. TURIN, "An introduction to matched filters", *I.R.E. Transactions on Information Theory*, **IT.6**, 311, June 1960.

[10] J. VILLE, *Câbles et Trans.*, **1**, 61, 1948.

[11] J. R. KLAUDER, A. C. PRICE, S. DARLINGTON and W. J. ALBERSHEIM, "The theory and design of chirp radars", *B.S.T.J.*, **39**, No. 4, 745–808, July 1960.

[12] J. R. KLAUDER, "Design of high-resolution radar signals", *B.S.T.J.*, **39**, No. 4, July 1960.

[13] C. E. SHANNON, "A mathematical theory of communications", *B.S.T.J.*, July 1948.

[14] J. OSWALD, "Sur la limitation spectrale et la fréquence instantanée des signaux", *I.R.E. Transactions on Information Theory*, Sept. 1962.

[15] C. SKENDEROFF, "Rôle de la fonction d'ambiguïté dans les radars", *L'onde Électrique*, May 1965.

[16] S. DRABOVITCH, "Applications aux antennes de la théorie du signal", *L'onde Électrique*, May 1965.

BIBLIOGRAPHY

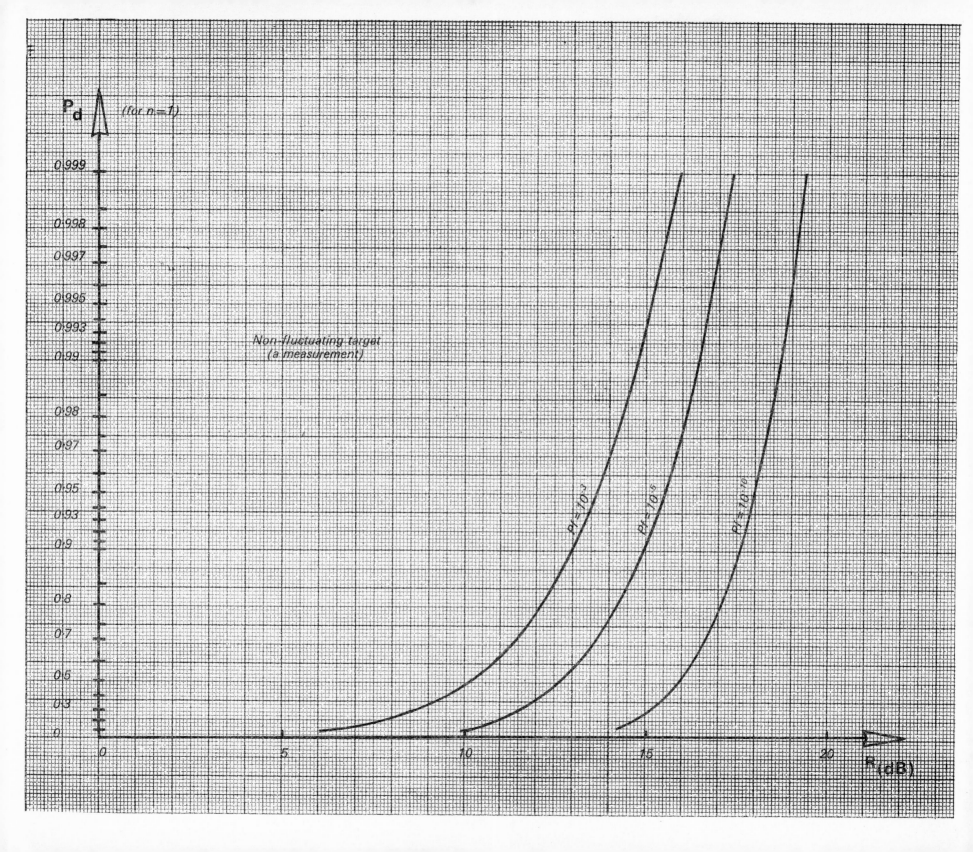

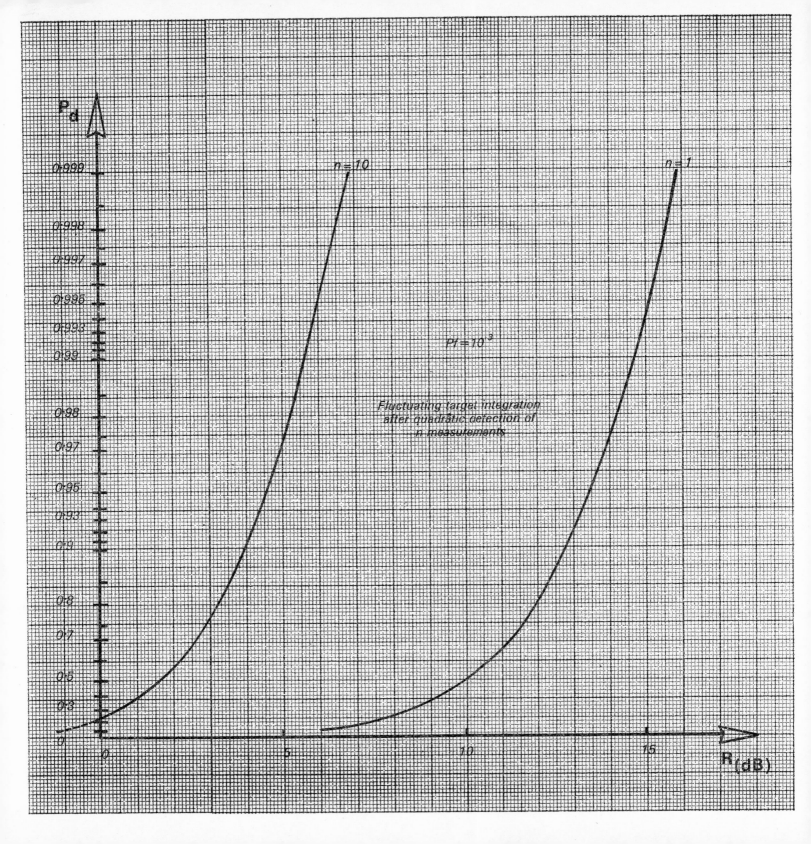